ADVANCES IN ENERGY RESEARCH

VOLUME 20

ADVANCES IN ENERGY RESEARCH

Additional books in this series can be found on Nova's website under the Series tab.

Additional e-books in this series can be found on Nova's website under the e-book tab.

ADVANCES IN ENERGY RESEARCH

VOLUME 20

MORENA J. ACOSTA
EDITOR

New York

Library of Congress Cataloging-in-Publication Data

ISSN: 2157-1562

ISBN: 978-1-63463-169-3

Published by Nova Science Publishers, Inc. † New York

CONTENTS

PREFACE

This book presents a comprehensive review of energy research studies from authors around the globe, including strategic interactions during oil exploration in the gulf of Mexico; ownership and regional economic impact; wind energy assessment and analysis; principle of low energy building design; conventional energy use, environment and sustainable development; drinking water from solar stills; and solar energy research, sustainable development and applications.

Chapter 1 – Wind power has been acclaimed as one of the most potential and techno-economically viable renewable energy sources of power generation. In addition, wind energy is a clean, plentiful and sustainable energy source with almost zero pollution during the wind energy conversion system operation. Utilization of wind energy in generation of electricity is growing at a fast rate due to the continued technological improvements that make wind turbines cheaper and more efficient resulting in reduction of the overall kWh generation cost. A large emphasis in the current research and application studies is on the developing reliable and accurate wind energy assessment and analysis. The wind assessment community is facing important challenges in their classical methodologies with the advent of more sophisticated numerical tools and experimental techniques. Besides, wind turbines are growing in size, standing well above the surface layer, and being installed in sites with complex flow topologies like complex terrain, forest or offshore. Wind is a highly intermittent phenomenon with high spatio-temporal variability, leading to difficulties in using in a continuous mode of operation. Atmospheric flows are subject to sub-hourly, hourly, diurnal, seasonal, yearly, and climate variations in addition to their dependence on height above the ground and nature of the surrounding terrain. Wind resource characteristics are critical to all aspects of wind-energy exploitation, from the identification of suitable sites and predictions of the economic viability of wind energy projects through to the wind turbine design themselves, and understanding their effects on electricity distribution networks. For a reliable assessment, wind tower measurements at hub and blade heights are required at least over an annual cycle. However, in many real situations the full-cycle elevated measurements at specific locations are not available and the assessment inputs are substituted by either the surface measurements or from 3-D meteorological models. The forecasting systems need to operate on multiple spatial scales: from an individual turbine, wind farm, mesoscale, and regional areas. Regarding the forecasting methodology, the used models can be of physical, statistical, and machine learning origins. For the future projections of the winds and wind power, regional climate models that dynamically downscale global climate models' results to higher spatial and temporal resolution have been used. Some of the simpler techniques such as statistical downscaling from the climate models to a specific location where measurements exist are also used to infer future projection of the winds and wind power. The main objective of this chapter is to provide a comprehensive review of the most common used wind energy assessment and analysis methods, as well as the new developments and approaches for the wind energy potential analysis and assessment to identify and select the proper and best suited sites for wind energy generation and other data essential in designing and operations and management of wind energy power generation systems and wind farms. The chapter also includes up-to-date references for interested readers, instructors, students, practitioners and researchers.

Chapter 2 – The move towards a de-carbonised world, driven partly by climate science and partly by the business opportunities it offers, will need the promotion of environmentally friendly alternatives, if an acceptable stabilisation level of atmospheric carbon dioxide is to be achieved. This requires the harnessing and use of natural resources that produce no air pollution or greenhouse gases and provides comfortable coexistence of human, livestock, and plants. This study reviews the energy-using technologies based on natural resources, which are available to and applicable in the farming industry. Integral concept for buildings with both excellent indoor environment control and sustainable environmental impact are reported in the present communication. Techniques considered are hybrid (controlled natural and mechanical) ventilation including night ventilation, thermo-active building mass systems with free cooling in a cooling tower, and air intake via ground heat exchangers. Special emphasis is put on ventilation concepts utilising ambient energy from air ground and other renewable energy sources, and on the interaction with heating and cooling. It has been observed that for both residential and office buildings, the electricity demand of ventilation systems is related to the overall demand of the building and the potential of photovoltaic systems and advanced co-generation units. The focus of the world's attention on environmental issues in recent years has stimulated response in many countries, which have led to a closer examination of energy conservation strategies for conventional fossil fuels. One way of reducing building energy consumption is to design buildings, which are more economical in their use of energy for heating, lighting, cooling, ventilation and hot water supply. Passive measures, particularly natural or hybrid ventilation rather than air-conditioning, can dramatically reduce primary energy consumption. However, exploitation of renewable energy in buildings and agricultural greenhouses can, also, significantly contribute towards reducing dependency on fossil fuels. This study describes various designs of low energy buildings. It also, outlines the effect of dense urban building nature on energy consumption, and its contribution to climate change. Measures, which would help to save energy in buildings, are also presented.

Chapter 3 – Globally, buildings are responsible for approximately 40% of the total world annual energy consumption. Most of this energy is for the provision of lighting, heating, cooling, and air conditioning. Increasing awareness of the environmental impact of CO_2, NO_x and CFCs emissions triggered a renewed interest in environmentally friendly cooling, and heating technologies. Under the 1997 Montreal Protocol, governments agreed to phase out chemicals used as refrigerants that have the potential to destroy stratospheric ozone. It was therefore considered desirable to reduce energy consumption and decrease the rate of depletion of world energy reserves and pollution of the environment. One way of reducing building energy consumption is to design buildings, which are more economical in their use of energy for heating, lighting, cooling, ventilation and hot water supply. Passive measures, particularly natural or hybrid ventilation rather than air-conditioning, can dramatically reduce primary energy consumption. However, exploitation of renewable energy in buildings and agricultural greenhouses can, also, significantly contribute towards reducing dependency on fossil fuels. Therefore, promoting innovative renewable applications and reinforcing the renewable energy market will contribute to preservation of the ecosystem by reducing emissions at local and global levels. This will also contribute to the amelioration of environmental conditions by replacing conventional fuels with renewable energies that produce no air pollution or greenhouse gases. The provision of good indoor environmental quality while achieving energy and cost efficient operation of the heating, ventilating and air-conditioning (HVAC) plants in buildings represents a multi variant problem. The comfort of building occupants is dependent on many environmental parameters including air speed, temperature, relative humidity and quality in addition to lighting and noise. The overall objective is to provide a high level of building performance (BP), which can be defined as indoor environmental quality (IEQ), energy efficiency (EE) and cost efficiency (CE).

Chapter 4 – The harsh climate in the Red Sea area, for example the Sudan, presents unique challenges in meeting growing demands for water and power. The international demand for water increases compared to the available water resources. Many areas, especially near the Red Sea, already experience a serious shortage of potable water and this is likely to grow. These areas enjoy, however, a high intensity of solar energy. Among the renewable energy options that have received special attention are solar stills. A solar still was built based on the principle of the packed tray array for tandem distillation and heat recovery. This chapter provides a brief overview of efforts to expand such renewable technologies in Sudan in a cost-effective and sustainable way with environmental benefits associated with displacing fossil fuels.

Chapter 5 – People rely upon oil for primary energy and this for a few more decades. Other orthodox sources may be more enduring, but are not without serious disadvantages. Power from natural resources has always had great appeal. Coal is plentiful, though there is concern about despoliation in winning it and pollution in burning it. Nuclear power has been developed with remarkable timeliness, but is not universally welcomed, construction of the plant is energy-intensive and there is concern about the disposal of its long-lived active wastes. Barrels of oil, lumps of coal, even uranium come from nature but the possibilities of almost limitless power from the atmosphere and the oceans seem to have special attraction. The wind machine provided an early way of developing motive power. The massive increases in fuel prices over the last years have however, made any scheme not requiring fuel appear to be more attractive and to be worth reinvestigation. In considering the atmosphere and the oceans as energy sources the four main contenders are wind power, wave power, tidal and power from ocean thermal gradients. The renewable energy resources are particularly suited for the provision of rural power supplies and a major advantage is that equipment such as flat plate solar driers, wind machines, etc., can be constructed using local resources and without the advantage results from the feasibility of local maintenance and the general encouragement such local manufacture gives to the build up of small-scale rural based industry. This chapter gives some examples of small-scale energy converters, nevertheless it should be noted that small conventional, i.e., engines are currently the major source of power in rural areas and will continue to be so for a long time to come. There is a need for some further development to suit local conditions, to minimise spares holdings, to maximise interchangeability both of engine parts and of the engine application. Emphasis should be placed on full local manufacture.

Chapter 6 – This chapter examines strategic interactions during oil exploration in the Gulf of Mexico. When individual petroleum-producing firms make their exploration decisions, information externalities and extraction externalities may lead them to interact strategically with their neighbors. If they do occur, strategic interactions in exploration would lead to a loss in both firm profit and government royalty revenue. Since these strategic interactions would be inefficient, changes in the government offshore leasing policy would need to be considered. The possibility of strategic interactions thus poses a concern to policy-makers and affects the optimal government policy. This chapter examines whether these inefficient strategic interactions take place in U.S. federal lands in the Gulf of Mexico. In particular, it analyzes whether a firm's exploration decisions depend on the decisions of firms owning neighboring tracts of land. Both reduced-form and structural models are employed. The results suggest that strategic interactions do not actually take place, at least not in exploration, and therefore that the current parameters of the government offshore leasing policy do not lead to inefficient petroleum exploration.

Chapter 7 – This study investigates the regional economic impact consequences of local vs. external ownership in the developing wind industry in the state of Minnesota (U.S.A.). We employ a realistic *pro forma* model of a financial "flip" structure, whereby a local equity group pairs with an outside, tax-motivated equity partner. The present value of residuals as well as the other O&M expenditures are annuitized and entered into a state-level input-output model. In order to bracket the range of possible outcomes, we run two sets of parameter assumptions ("pessimistic" and "optimistic") through the local equity group's *pro forma,* and subsequently the state-wide input-output model. According to these two scenarios we find that the impact on state-level value added is 3.1 and 4.5 times larger, respectively, compared with the impacts from the external ownership model. The impact on employment is respectively 2.5 and 3.5 times larger.

In: Advances in Energy Research. Volume 20
Editor: Morena J. Acosta

ISBN: 978-1-63463-169-3
© 2015 Nova Science Publishers, Inc.

Chapter 1

WIND ENERGY ASSESSMENT AND ANALYSIS

Radian Belu[1] and Darko Koracin[2]

[1]Drexel University, Philadelphia, PA, US
[2]Desert Research Institute, Reno, NV, US

ABSTRACT

Wind power has been acclaimed as one of the most potential and techno-economically viable renewable energy sources of power generation. In addition, wind energy is a clean, plentiful and sustainable energy source with almost zero pollution during the wind energy conversion system operation. Utilization of wind energy in generation of electricity is growing at a fast rate due to the continued technological improvements that make wind turbines cheaper and more efficient resulting in reduction of the overall kWh generation cost. A large emphasis in the current research and application studies is on the developing reliable and accurate wind energy assessment and analysis. The wind assessment community is facing important challenges in their classical methodologies with the advent of more sophisticated numerical tools and experimental techniques. Besides, wind turbines are growing in size, standing well above the surface layer, and being installed in sites with complex flow topologies like complex terrain, forest or offshore. Wind is a highly intermittent phenomenon with high spatio-temporal variability, leading to difficulties in using in a continuous mode of operation. Atmospheric flows are subject to sub-hourly, hourly, diurnal, seasonal, yearly, and climate variations in addition to their dependence on height above the ground and nature of the surrounding terrain. Wind resource characteristics are critical to all aspects of wind-energy exploitation, from the identification of suitable sites and predictions of the economic viability of wind energy projects through to the wind turbine design themselves, and understanding their effects on electricity distribution networks. For a reliable assessment, wind tower measurements at hub and blade heights are required at least over an annual cycle. However, in many real situations the full-cycle elevated measurements at specific locations are not available and the assessment inputs are substituted by either the surface measurements or from 3-D meteorological models. The main objective of this chapter is to provide a comprehensive review of the most common used wind energy assessment and analysis methods, as well as the new developments and approaches for the wind energy potential analysis and assessment to identify and select the proper and best suited sites for wind energy generation and other data essential in designing and operations and management of wind energy power generation systems and wind farms. The chapter also includes up-to-date references for interested readers, instructors, students, practitioners and researchers.

INTRODUCTION

Wind power has been utilized for thousands of years for such tasks as propelling sailing ships, grinding grain, pumping water, and powering factory machinery. Humans have been harnessing the wind ever since farmers in ancient Persia discovered how to use it to pump water. Wind power was also used during the 7th to 10th century in the area between today's Iran and Afghanistan to grind wheat. These vertical axis windmills used the drag component of wind power generation. To work properly, the part rotating in opposite direction compared to the wind had to be protected by a wall. Obviously, devices of this type can be used only in places with a dominant wind direction because they cannot follow changes in incoming wind direction [1-15]. The first windmills built in Europe, likely inspired by the ones in the Middle East, used a horizontal axis rotor thereby substituting drag force with the lift force [3-20]. During the following centuries many modifications and improvements were applied, especially in areas with high directional variability. The best examples are the Dutch windmills that were used to drain water in reclaimed lands. Wind energy technology is one of the most rapidly expanding areas among the renewable energy sources [12-20]. Worldwide development of wind energy expanded rapidly starting in the early 1990s. The average annual growth rate of world installed capacity of wind power from 1994 to 2010 has been over 31% [1-30]. Unlike the last surge in wind power development during the late 1970s and early 1980s which was mainly due to the temporary oil embargo of OPEC countries, the current wave of wind energy development is driven by many favorable forces, including its tremendous environmental, social, and economic benefits, its technological maturity, and deregulation of electricity markets throughout the world, widespread public support, and government incentives. Wind energy is expected to play an increasingly important role in the future national energy scene. In resource-ideal locations, the cost of wind-generated energy is already competitive with traditional fossil fuel generation. Experts predict wind power will capture 5% of the world energy market by the year 2020 [5-30].

The wind energy utilization has evolved in recent decades from a marginal activity motivated mainly by local concerns for a cleaner environment into a multi-billion industry. Wind energy industry directly employed over 110,000 people in Europe alone [12-20]; if indirect jobs are considered as well, this number increases to about 160,000. In the US, it has been estimated that about 90,000 jobs were directly or indirectly related to the wind energy industry [12-20]. The estimated annual turnover of the wind energy industry is over $18 billion. Wind energy investments, at a typical overall cost of $2,000 per installed kW, require quite substantial funds even for small projects, while wind parks of several hundreds of MW are becoming common in many parts of the world, particularly the US. It is clear that an accurate estimate of the expected energy production together with an approximation of the different uncertainties associated with the project is required to secure funds and hedge risks. Wind resource assessment enters the project development arena in several stages: (1) early prospecting of suitable sites, (2) wind mapping at the potential site and conceptual wind farm design, (3) micro-siting and optimization of wind turbines, (4) risk assessment and analysis,

(5) planning of certification towers, (6) post-construction performance analysis, and (7) wind pant operation. As in other engineering fields, the higher the knowledge of the system, the smaller the safety margins and, therefore, the higher the potential returns on the investment. An accurate prediction and validation of the performance of a potential wind farm is therefore vital for the project success.

Electricity generation from wind can be economically achieved only where a significant wind resource exists [31-51]. Wind power has been acclaimed as one of the most potential and techno-economically viable renewable energy sources of power generation. However, the technical know-how is not yet fully adequate to develop reliable wind energy conversion systems for all wind speed regimes. For securing maximum power output, wind energy resource assessment at any prospective site is critical. The available wind energy varies as the wind speed cube, so an understanding of the wind characteristics is essential to all wind energy exploitation aspects, from the suitable site identification and predictions of the economic viability of wind energy projects through to the design of wind turbines, and understanding their effect on electricity distribution networks. From the point of view of wind energy, the most striking characteristic of the wind is its variability. Wind is highly variable, both geographically and temporally. Furthermore, this variability persists over a very wide range of spatio-time scales. Wind data generated by meteorological services have their limitations. Because of the cubic relationship between wind velocity and output energy, sites with small percentage differences in average wind speeds can have substantial differences in available energy. Therefore, accurate and thorough monitoring of wind resource at potential sites is critical in the wind turbine siting. An accurately measured wind speed frequency spectrum at a site is another important factor. For assessment of the wind power potential, most investigators have used simple wind speed distributions that are parameterized solely by the arithmetic mean of the wind speed. However, an assessment of wind turbine power output is accurate, only if the wind speeds, as well as wind directions are measured at the turbine hub height [38-56].

Knowledge of the local wind capacity remains vital to the industry, yet commercially viable renewable-related geospatial products that meet the wind industry needs are often suspect. There are three stage involved with wind power project planning and operations during which accurate wind characterization plays a critical role: 1) *prospecting/siting*: uses historical data, retrospective forecasts, and statistical methods to identify potential sites for wind power projects; 2) *site assessment (micro-siting)*: determines the optimum placement of a wind power project; and, 3) *operations*: uses wind forecasting and prediction to determine available power output for hour-ahead and day-ahead time frames. However, the most critical of these is the first one: identifying and characterizing the wind resources. This chapter will discuss in detail the first stage, outlining the state of the art in understanding the wind resource assessment, and discussing the strengths and weaknesses of existing methods. For example, appropriate statistical and modeling methods to compute the wind speed probability density function (PDF) are described and critically examined. In addition, although there has been an increasing awareness of wind energy as a viable energy source, there has not been a concomitant increase in the awareness of the impacts that any spatial and temporal trends in the wind resource may have on long-term production, use, and implementation of renewable energy policy. Despite environmental benefits and technological maturation, penetration of wind-generated power represents a challenge for reliability and stability of the power grids due to the highly variability and intermittent nature of winds. Wind energy resources rely on the incident wind speed and direction, both of which vary in time and space due to changes in large-scale and small-scale circulations, surface energy fluxes, and topography [1-5, 30-56]. Since the wind power density is proportional to the cube of the wind speed, any small errors in forecasted wind speeds can result in significant differences between forecasted and actual wind energy output. Consequently, accurate assessment and forecasting of spatial and temporal characteristics of the winds and turbulence remains the most significant challenge in wind energy production. The wind energy production viability is governed by such factors as: the potential for large scale energy production, the predictability of the power to be supplied to the grid, and the expected return on investment. The various wind energy uncertainties impact the reliable determination of these viability factors. Currently the worldwide nameplate capacity of wind-powered generators is approximately 2.5% of the electricity consumption, with a steady annual growth [12-22]. For wind to play a more prominent role in the future energy market, improvements in the wind power generation technology are needed, while some advancement can be realized in part through appropriate uncertainties quantification and explicit consideration of their influences in the optimal design. A robust and optimal wind farm planning include: a) site optimal selection based on the quality of the local wind resources, b) maximization of the annual energy production and/or minimization of the cost of generated energy, and c) maximization of the reliability of the predicted wind farm energy output.

The most important activity in a site selection is to determine the wind resource potential, consisting in the estimated local wind probability density function. Another important activity in this context is to determine the levels of turbulence and the resulting wind loads at the concerned site, promoting better decision making, in selecting the most suitable wind turbines for that site and in optimum life cycle cost prediction; higher wind loads generally result in higher costs. Other site selection criteria include, but not limited to: 1) local topography, 2) distance to electric grid, 3) vegetation, 4) land acquisition issues, and 5) site accessibility for turbine transport and maintenance. A planning strategy that simultaneously accounts for the key engineering design factors and addresses the uncertainties in a wind energy project can offer a powerful impetus to the wind energy development.

However, the resource itself is highly uncertain, wind conditions, including *wind speed* and *direction, turbulence intensity* and *air density*, show strong temporal variations; in addition, the wind conditions varies significantly from year to year [30-80]. The resulting ill-predictability of the annual distribution of wind conditions introduces significant errors in the *estimated resource potential* or the *predicted wind farm performances*. In the last decades, new methodologies were developed to characterize the uncertainties in the annual distribution of wind conditions, and/or to model the propagation of uncertainties into the local wind power density and into farm performance evaluation. Key measures of wind power plant performance include annual energy production, cost of energy, and payback period. Both parametric and nonparametric uncertainty models are formulated, which can be leveraged in conjunction with a wide variety of wind distribution models.

FACTORS AFFECTING WIND POWER COMPUTATION

Since the effects of wind shear, turbulence intensity, and atmospheric stability on wind turbine production are not fully understood, wind resource assessment studies can have large uncertainties. The estimation of the magnitude of the uncertainty source is often related to empirical considerations rather than analytical calculations.

Some studies suggest probability models for the natural variability of wind resources that include air density, mean wind velocity and associated Weibull parameters, surface roughness exponent, and error for prediction of long-term wind velocity. Depending on atmospheric conditions, waking by upstream turbines and terrain/roughness interactions, wind turbines often operate far from the ideal conditions, and field-deployed power curves can be very different from certified ones [40-84]. Better predictions of power output or loads require more representative wind measurements and power computations over the rotor-swept area for individual wind turbines.

Wind Variability

One of the main challenges in harvesting wind energy is that wind is generally intermittent and variable in speed and direction (Justus and Mikhail, 1976). Depending on the flow properties and scales of motion, the flow can become turbulent with chaotic and stochastic properties. There are three main aspects that can reduce the intermittency problem: spatial distribution of wind facilities, accurate forecasting methods, and storage systems [57-78]. Although a single wind generation is subject to large variations of the wind, if the facilities are spatially distributed, a total output at any time becomes more uniform and reliable. For example, in Denmark, which is relatively flat and has high penetration of wind energy (20%), while output from a single wind farm may occasionally change by 100% within an hour, total power output from an entire network of wind farms are generally less than +/-3% of its initial value [24,25, 27, 38].

Air Density and Temperature

Since wind speed generally increases with height, higher elevation sites often offer greater resources than comparable lower elevation sites. However, the decrease of air density with height can make an impact on the computed power, since wind power density is directly proportional to air density. In most of the cases, it is advantageous to site turbines at higher elevations to take advantage of higher wind speeds. However, power and the power curve depend on the air density. As an example, the air density values encountered at measurement sites in western Nevada were mostly between 0.936 kg/m^3 and 1.025 kg/m3 with a multi-annual mean value of 0.982 kg/m3, significantly lower than the mean standard air density of 1.25 kg/m^3. Power curves for various values of the air density effect must be accounted for in order to improve the power output estimate accuracy. Air density is usually calculated from temperature and pressure measurements. Depending on the turbine's method of control, either the power or velocity is normalized for use in power density calculations [57-80], as here were the velocity is normalized with the reference air density ρ_0:

$$v_{norm} = \bar{v} \left(\frac{\bar{\rho}}{\rho_0} \right)^{1/3}$$

(1)

Effects of Turbulence on the Wind Turbine Power Output

At today's usual hub-heights at 80 m or so, turbine rotors encounter large vertical gradients of wind speed and boundary layer turbulence. Rotors are susceptible to fatigue damage that results from turbulence [68-84]. Understanding of the impact of turbulence on the blades can help in designing long-term operational and maintenance schedules for wind turbines. Consequently, this understanding can lead to advanced control schemes to be developed to mitigate loads such as an active control of blade pitch angle. Quantification of the effects of turbulence on wind turbine is usually done by computing an equivalent fatigue load parameter, F_e (kNm), as a function of wind fluctuation amplitudes within an averaging period, blade material properties, number of counting averaging bins, and a total number of samples. Based on experimental data, it is found that the highest blade root flap bending moment equivalent fatigue load does not correspond to the greatest wind speeds, but to the class of wind speeds that has the highest amplitude of fluctuations. Turbulent fluctuations are the main source of the blade fatigue. The turbulence intensity (TI) is a measure of the overall level of turbulence and is defined as:

$$TI = \frac{\sigma_v}{v}$$

(2)

where σ_v is the wind speed standard deviation (m/s) at the nacelle height over a specified averaging period (usually 10 min). For example, Belu and Koracin (2011) found that, from the power curves for different turbulence intensity classes and for low to moderate wind speeds (4 to 10 m/s), high TI classes yield the most power and for the higher wind speeds (10 - 15 m/s), low TI classes yield the most power, as reported elsewhere in the literature [63-65, 71-84]. There also are differences in the standard deviations of the output power. In the wind speed range 4-15 m/s the standard deviation of certain turbulence intensity classes (4 - 8% and 10 - 15%) differ up to about 50% with the standard deviation for all turbulence intensities. TI is often affected by atmospheric stability, so the performance of theoretical wind turbine power curves. Wharton and Lundquist (2011) and Vanderwende and Lundquist (2012) used wind power law coefficient and the bulk Richardson number to separate time periods by stability to generate regime-dependent wind turbine power curves. Their results indicate under-performance during stable regimes and over-performance during convective regimes at moderate wind speeds.

A correction factor for the effect of turbulence intensity [65, 79-81, 84] is given by:

$$v_{corr} = v_{norm} \left(1 + 3(TI)^2\right)^{1/3}$$

(3)

The Influence of Atmospheric Stability of the Wind Turbine Power Output

The thermal stability defines the atmosphere cycles through discrete states. In the morning, as the sun warms the ground, air close to the surface begins to be heated. Eventually, the heat flux from the ground becomes significant and the resulting temperature gradient causes turbulent mixing, leading usually to a fairly uniform afternoon wind speed profile. At night, the ground changes from a heat source to a heat sink, and the lower atmosphere tends to become stably stratified. Turbulent mixing is quite suppressed and the velocity profile is highly sheared. As the atmosphere changes from stable to unstable stratification, a transient neutral condition can be observed where no thermal effects are present and the flow can be completely modeled based on conservation of momentum i.e., no energy is lost or gain. To model the lower atmosphere's relatively complex behavior, Monin-Obukhov similarity theory was used [77-84]. The model combines the integrated Monin-Obukhov similarity function with an equation derived from the k-ε turbulence model to resolve the unknown atmospheric parameters u*, L, T*, and z_0. A special treatment has been proposed for the very stable case [57, 63, 77-84]. The system of equations is usually adopted for wind energy applications. Here H represents the turbine hub height and z_1 and z_2 define ΔT, the temperature difference near the hub height and close to the ground, K is the von Karman constant, taken here as equal to 0.40, while ζ is the ratio of height z, to L, the Obukhov length, and serves as a measure of atmospheric stability.

$$u(H) = \frac{u^*}{K} \left[\ln\left(\frac{H}{z_0}\right) - \Psi_m\left(\frac{H}{L}, \frac{z_0}{L}\right) \right]$$

(4)

$$T(z_2) - T(z_1) = \frac{T(z_1) u^{*2}}{K^2 gL} \left[\ln\left(\frac{z_2}{z_1}\right) - \Psi_h\left(\frac{z_2}{L}, \frac{z_1}{L}\right) \right] - \frac{g}{c_P}[z_2 - z_1]$$

(5)

Turbulence intensity at the hub height maybe express with the following relationship:

$$TI_{meas} = 2.39 \frac{u^*}{u(H)} \phi_{TI}^{1/4}(\xi)$$

(6)

By definition

$$\Psi = \int_{z_0}^{z} [1 - \phi] \frac{dz}{z}$$

The parameter ϕ is determined from measurements. Although limited to conditions that can be considered horizontally homogeneous and statistically stationary, it is quite powerful predicting the boundary layer flows. Atmospheric conditions with $z/L<0$ were grouped as unstable case, $z/L>0$ as stable, and remaining conditions as neutral. $z/L = 0$, and L is given by:

$$L = \frac{-u_*^3 \overline{T_0}}{gK \overline{w'T}} \tag{7}$$

where u_* is the friction velocity, $\overline{T_0}$ is the mean air temperature in Kelvin, $g = 9.816$ m/s the gravitational acceleration, $K = 0.4$ is the von Karman constant, z is the height, $\overline{w'T'}$, is the kinetic heat flux, and w' and T' are the fluctuations of vertical wind velocity component and temperature, respectively. In reality, neutral conditions are extremely rare, while near neutral conditions with a small span so that $z/L \approx 0$ for near neutral conditions are quite likely. Wind turbine power curves for stable, unstable and near-neutral atmospheric conditions can been constructed and, generally, the differences between the various power curves are not very large. For wind speeds above, say, 5 m/s the difference between the power for neutral atmospheric conditions and stable conditions and between neutral atmospheric conditions and unstable conditions is lower than 5% [63-84].

Wind Shear and Wind Profile

Vertical wind shear is important as wind turbines become larger and larger. It is therefore questionable whether the hub height wind speed is still representative. Various methods exist in the literature concerning the extrapolation of wind speed to the hub height of a wind turbine. There are several theoretical expressions used for determining the wind speed profile. The Monin–Obukhov method is usually used to determine the wind speed v at height z by:

$$v(z) = \frac{u_*}{K}\left[\ln\frac{z}{z_0} - \Psi\left(\frac{z}{L}\right)\right] \tag{8}$$

The function $\Psi(z/L)$ is determined by the solar radiation at the site under survey. This equation is valid for short periods of time, and not for monthly or annual average readings. This equation has proven satisfactory for detailed surveys at critical sites; however, such a method is difficult to use for general engineering studies. Thus the surveys must resort to simpler expressions and secure satisfactory results even when they are not theoretically accurate. Vertical wind shear is an important consideration as wind turbines are becoming larger. Obstacles can cause the displacement of the boundary layer from the ground, which is expressed by the parameter d. For widely scattered obstacles, parameter d is zero, while in other cases it is expressed as 70% of the obstacle height [57, 58, 63-84]. The roughness length (z_0) describes the height at which the wind is zero by definition, meaning that surfaces with a large roughness length have a large effect on the wind. It ranges from 0.0002 for open sea, 0.005-0.03 for open land, 0.03-0.1 for agricultural land, and 0.5-2 m for very rough terrain or urban areas. However, the increase of wind speed with height should be considered for the installation of large wind turbines. Thus the surveys must rely to simpler expressions and secure satisfactory results even when they are not theoretically accurate. For $h_0 = 10$ m and $z_0 = 0.01$ m, the parameter $\alpha = 1/7$, which is consistent with the value of 0.147 used in the wind turbine design standards (IEC standard, 61400-3, 2005) to represent the change of wind speeds in the lowest levels of the atmosphere. Wind speed is usually recorded at the standard meteorological height of 10 m, while wind turbines usually have hub heights near 80 m.

In cases which lack elevated measurements hub-height wind velocity is estimated by applying a vertical extrapolation coefficient to surface measurements. However, the vertical extrapolation coefficient may contain errors and uncertainties due to terrain complexity, atmospheric stability and turbulence. Various methods exist for the wind speed extrapolation to the wind turbine hub height. The theoretical background of the wind extrapolation methods is based on the Monin-Obukov similarity theory. However, the wind speed $v(z)$ at a height z can be calculated directly from the wind speed $v(z_{ref})$ at height z_{ref} (usually the standard measurement level) by using the logarithmic law (the Hellmann exponential law) expressed by:

$$\frac{v(z)}{v_0} = \left(\frac{z}{z_{ref}} \right)$$

(9)

where, $v(z)$ is the wind speed at height z, v_0 is the speed at z_{ref} (usually 10 m height, the standard meteorological wind measurement level), and α is the friction coefficient or power low index. This coefficient is a function of the surface roughness at a specific site and the thermal stability of the Prandtl layer. It is frequently assumed to be 1/7 for open land. However, this parameter can vary diurnally and seasonally as well as spatially. It was found that a single power law is insufficient to adequately project the power available from the wind at a given site, especially during nighttime and also in presence of the low-level jets [63-85]. Belu and Koracin (2009) found significant discrepancies of values for α for western Nevada, ranging from 0.09 to 0.120, quite smaller comparing to the standard 0.147 value. However, it must be borne in mind that this parameter can vary for one place to other, during the day and year [57, 58, 63-84]. Another formula, known as the logarithmic wind profile law and widely used across Europe, is the following:

$$\frac{v}{v_0} = \frac{\ln\left(z / z_0 \right)}{\ln\left(z_{ref} / z_0 \right)}$$

(10)

where z_0 is called the roughness coefficient length and is expressed in meters; it depends basically on the land type, spacing and height of the roughness factor (water, grass, etc.) and it ranges from 0.0002 up to 1.6 or more. These values can be found in the common literature. In addition to the land roughness, these values depend on several factors: they can vary during the day and at night, and even during the year. For instance, the reading or monitoring stations can be within farming land; it follows that the height/length of the crops will change. However, once the speeds have been calculated at other heights, the relevant equations can be used for calculating the useful energy potential via different methods [24-27, 58-84]. If the type of ground cover is known, the wind speed at other heights can be estimated.

Aside from ground level to hub height shear, wind shear over the rotor disc area can also significant. The standard procedure for power curve measurements is given by the IEC standard (IEC Standard, 6-1400-12-1, 2005) where the wind speed at hub height is considered to be representative of the wind over the whole turbine rotor area.

This assumption can lead to considerable wind power estimate inaccuracies, since inflow is often non-uniform and unsteady over the rotor-swept area. In most studies about the effect of wind shear on power performance, the wind speed shear is described by the shear exponent, obtained from the assumption of a power law profile. By integrating the wind profile over the rotor span, the corrected wind speed at the turbine nacelle can be obtained:

$$U_{avrg} = \frac{1}{2R} \int_{H-\frac{D}{2}}^{H+\frac{D}{2}} v(z)dz = v(H) \cdot \frac{1}{\alpha+1} \cdot \left(\left(\frac{3}{2}\right)^{\alpha+1} - \left(\frac{1}{2}\right)^{\alpha+1} \right)$$

(11)

where H is the nacelle height and D = 2R is the rotor diameter. From (11), it is obvious that the hub height wind speed z(H) is α corrected based on the profile it is experiencing [57-84] It is observed that both corrections have more or less the same effect. For wind speeds in the range 5 m/s to 20 m/s (the useful wind turbine speed regime) the corrected power differs in general less than 5% from the uncorrected power. However, in all cases the corrected power is larger than the uncorrected power.

Wind Gust

An additional wind property that can make the impact on wind turbine operations is wind gustiness. Proper design and operation of a wind turbine for a specific wind climate requires knowledge of wind extremes and gustiness, often defined by a wind gust factor. This is especially true in areas where wind climate is determined by inherently strong gusty winds, such as downslope windstorms [57, 59, 70, 71]. In sites with high ambient turbulent intensity and gusty winds, turbines are subject to extreme structural loading and fatigue. The gust factor (G) is defined as:

$$G = \frac{u_g}{U} - 1$$

(12)

where u_g is the gust speed and U is the mean daily wind speed. One expects higher gusts to be associated with higher mean speeds; however, one may also expect that the normalized gust speed u_g/U and, consequently, the gust factor, G, decreases with the increasing mean speed. The following equation relates the gust factor to the mean daily wind speed:

$$G = AU^n$$

(13)

where the parameters A and n are obtained by using a least-square fit of the logarithm of G vs. the logarithm of the mean daily wind speed. While gusts generally decrease as wind speed increases, in extreme cases the wind gusts can easily reach over twice the strongest wind speeds (v > 20 ms-1) and damage a wind turbine. However, wind gusts over 25 m/s, the upper wind speed limit of a large wind turbine, are quite unlikely in many areas.

Belu and Koracin (2009) used four and half years (2003-2009) of composite data sets and found that winds over 25 m s^{-1} occurred only about 2% of time. Gusts associated with stronger winds may cause considerable losses by reducing the energy production of the wind turbine which would otherwise operate at nominal output power. Another effect of wind gusts is the additional stress on the wind turbine structure, which may reduce its lifespan.

Low-Level Jet

The low-level jet is a mesoscale phenomenon associated with the nighttime very stable boundary layer that can have a width of hundreds of kilometers and a length of a thousand kilometers. They have been observed worldwide [57, 76, 80, 85]. During nighttime and over land, ground surface cools at a faster rate than the adjacent air and stable stratification forms near the surface and propagates upward. Downward mixing of the winds is reduced and winds aloft become decoupled from the surface and accelerate.

The maximum wind speeds are usually 10-20 m/s or more at elevations mainly at 100-300 m and occasionally as high as 900 m above ground. Consequently, it is not possible to accurately estimate winds aloft at hub and blade heights from routine surface measurements. Additionally, a strong wind shear and associated turbulence develop at the bottom and top of the jet layer.

INSTRUMENTATION AND MEASUREMENT TECHNIQUES, DATA COLLECTION AND VALIDATION

Wind resource assessment measurement campaigns have traditionally been conducted with mast based instrumentation consisting on cup anemometers and wind vanes. 92% of the wind analysts with experience in measurement campaigns use this type of instruments as a baseline. Additionally, 90% of them are also used to other meteorological instruments like temperature, pressure and humidity sensors. Wind monitors (propeller anemometers that measure both the wind speed and direction) are only used by 18% of them, while sonic anemometers and remote sensing instruments (lidar, sodar and satellites) are used by 35% and 50% of them respectively, of which 75% are consultants or researchers. Wind energy developers and manufacturers stick to the standard mast configuration for long-term measurement campaigns. Sonic anemometers or remote sensing instruments are still far from being standard instruments in wind assessment although they are being used more and more by consultants and researchers for detailed measurement campaigns or power performance testing. Given the limited time span of the measurement campaigns it is necessary to extrapolate to a period of at least 5 years in order to predict the long-term average energy yield. To this end, Measure-Correlate-Predict (MCP) methods are most used ones [24, 85].

Surprisingly, in spite of its primary importance for wind energy developers, only 70% of them declared in the questionnaire that they used MCP methods. This percentage is raised to 80% in the case of consultants. Numerical models are used in wind resource assessment to spatially extrapolate the wind measurements horizontally to obtain wind maps, and vertically to reach hub-height wind fields.

Additionally, numerical weather prediction models are being used to build virtual historical time series that can be used, via statistical downscaling, to extend limited periods of measurements to longer time spans in a similar way as it has been traditionally done with MCP methods.

Wind Measurement Techniques

Nowadays a series of measurement techniques is available for on-site wind resource measurement ranging from point measurements performed at different heights using cup anemometers [24-32, 85-107] or ultrasonic sensors to profiling techniques like sonic detection and ranging (SODAR) or light detection and ranging (LIDAR) systems. Until now, the overwhelming majority of measurement campaigns for commercial wind developments or even for wind energy research projects rely on cup anemometry and occasionally on ultrasonic sensors, where the latter is often preferred in research applications. Remote-sensing techniques like SODAR or LIDAR are increasingly explored as complementary techniques, providing high quality wind vertical profiles at higher sampling rates. In large wind projects the profiling instrument can be conveniently relocated within the project area for wind resource measurements at different site points, following the initial calibration period where the profiler is operating in conjunction with a conventional tower-based measurement system. Remote sensed wind speed measurements are needed to supplement and extend tall met mast measurements, on- and off-shore, and to evaluate various wind flow models for a number of purposes, including: wind resource assessments, wind energy development projects, power curve measurements, wind resource uncertainty evaluation, etc. The common denominator in most of these issues is high accuracy, and with a demand for reproducible certainty to more than 99% of what can be achieved with a corresponding calibrated cup anemometer.

A significant source for uncertainty with remote sensing instrumentation relative to a cup anemometer, and for SODARS in particular, is the remote instruments relative big measurement volumes. A SODAR measuring the wind speed from say 100 meters height probes a total sampling volume of more than 1000 m^3 whereas a cup anemometer essentially is essentially a point measurement device.

In addition the SODAR measured wind components are displaced in space and time, making the interpretation of measured turbulence by a SODAR impaired. In addition the huge sampling volumes will be putting restrictions on measurements in non-uniform flow regimes such as found near forest edges on offshore platforms, and over hilly or complex terrain. SODAR remote sensing is also in demand for direct turbine control integration, wind power optimization and turbine mounted gust warning systems, but here the demand on accuracy and reliability is correspondingly high.

Cup and Ultrasonic Anemometers

For about 150 years, the primary sensor used for wind speed measurements has been the vertical axis cup anemometer. The sensor must be positioned in the wind stream and kept free of ice and debris and the internal friction must remain constant. Because a structure is required to hold the sensor in place, a disturbance is introduced into the free-stream wind field and invariably some wind data must be "corrected" or discarded. Cup anemometers are known to be influenced by turbulence, air temperature, air density, and flow inclination.

A significant vertical component to the wind vector can cause over-speeding of cup anemometers. More recently, ultrasonic anemometers have been used to more precisely measure wind fields. These sensors detect Doppler shifts in an ultrasonic wave transmitted between near-field (~ 20 cm) transducers. Ultrasonic systems also are subject to structure flow disturbance effects, however, as the device must be mounted on a "lightning cage" structure to ground out lightning, and the sensed volume must be bracketed by transducer elements. All anemometers have operational characteristics that are subject to external conditions that may influence the wind speed measurement and introduce error. Despite these shortcomings, the error of class I 15 anemometers is extremely low – it cannot exceed 0.1 m/s at wind speeds below 16 m/s (IEC61400-12-1, ISO 16622).

A cup anemometer is a simple device relying on the different aerodynamic drag of the convex and concave surfaces of a suitably designed cup [85-87]. Typically two to four cups are mounted symmetrically on a vertical axis and allowed to rotate freely. If placed in a constant speed air stream, the anemometer will eventually spin at a frequency proportional to the wind speed. If coupled to a small electric synchronous generator, the corresponding electrical signal can be conveniently registered by data conditioning and logging. Since only the signal frequency information is of interest, a signal forming device is required for processing in data loggers, as the amplitude of the signal inconveniently varies proportionally to the frequency. A common choice is to convert the analog signal into a train of fixed amplitude pulses which can be counted by the digital device. The theory of operation can be illustrated easily in the case of a two-cup anemometer. The velocity ratio, related to the drag coefficients in the x and y direction is defined as:

$$\lambda = \frac{\omega R}{v} \tag{14}$$

And the velocity ratio can be related to the drag coefficient ration, μ through:

$$\lambda = \frac{\mu+1}{\mu-1} - \sqrt{\left(\frac{\mu+1}{\mu-1}\right)^2 - 1} \tag{15}$$

here R is the anemometer radius, ω is the anemometer angular velocity, and v is the wind speed. For typical values of the drag coefficients for the concave and convex surfaces of 1.4 and 0.4, respectively, the steady-state speed ratio is calculated to be 0.303, i.e., the cups will rotate at about a third of the wind speed.

The equations above assumed the wind speed to be uniform horizontally. If a horizontal wind shear is considered, then corrections have to be applied to the apparent wind speeds at the concave and convex surface, respectively. Sonic anemometers measure the wind speed in 2- or 3-D based on a comparison of the flight times of two anti-parallel sonic pulses.

In modern sonic anemometers each measurement path consists of a pair of transducers, both capable of transmitting and receiving. For a uniform and stationary wind field the wind velocity component in the direction of the measurement direction, v_M can then be calculated from:

$$v_M = \frac{l}{2}\left(\frac{1}{t_d} - \frac{1}{t_r}\right)$$

(16)

where l are the distance between transceivers and t_d and t_r are the direct and reverse travel times (see Figure 1 for details). Two or three orthogonal measurement paths can be combined in one instrument, in order to measure the full wind velocity vector. Sonic anemometers have a series of advantages over cup anemometers, such as the absence of moving parts, faster response to fluctuations and avoiding over-speeding.

Furthermore, the response is linear over a large frequency range, and the measurement is relatively independent of the flow properties, such as spatial and time variations, temperature, density, etc. Sonic anemometers are absolute instruments that do not require individual calibration. Some drawbacks do exist, such as the influence of the finite measurement path, path separation, and transducer shadows.

One of the other forms of mechanical velocity anemometer is the vane anemometer. It may be described as a windmill or a propeller anemometer, having the axis of rotation is vertical, the axis on the vane anemometer must be parallel to the direction of the wind and therefore horizontal. Furthermore, since the wind varies in direction and the axis has to follow its changes, a wind vane or some other contrivance to fulfill the same purpose must be employed. An vane anemometer thus combines a propeller and a tail on the same axis to obtain accurate and precise wind speed and direction measurements from the same instrument. The speed of the fan is measured by a rev counter and converted to a windspeed by an electronic chip. Hence, volumetric flowrate may be calculated if the cross-sectional area is known. In cases where the direction of the air motion is always the same, as in the ventilating shafts of mines and buildings for instance, wind vanes, known as air meters are employed, and give most satisfactory results.

Proplller(vane) and pressure anemometers

One of the other forms of mechanical velocity anemometer is the vane anemometer [85-87]. It may be described as a windmill or a propeller anemometer, having the axis of rotation is vertical, the axis on the vane anemometer must be parallel to the direction of the wind and therefore horizontal. Furthermore, since the wind varies in direction and the axis has to follow its changes, a wind vane or some other contrivance to fulfill the same purpose must be employed. An vane anemometer thus combines a propeller and a tail on the same axis to obtain accurate and precise wind speed and direction measurements from the same instrument. The speed of the fan is measured by a rev counter and converted to a windspeed by an electronic chip. Hence, volumetric flowrate may be calculated if the cross-sectional area is known. In cases where the direction of the air motion is always the same, as in the ventilating shafts of mines and buildings for instance, wind vanes, known as air meters are employed, and give most satisfactory results.

Pressure anemometers which measure the pressure in order to estimate the wind speed are divided into plate and tube types [86, 87].The first ones are the modern anemometers and simply consisted of a flat plate, either square or circular, which is kept normal to the wind by a wind. The plate is suspended from the top so that the wind can deflect the plate. The pressure of the wind on its face is balanced by a spring. The compression of the spring determines the actual force which the wind is exerting on the plate, and this is either read off on a suitable gauge, or on a recorder. Instruments of this kind do not respond to light winds, are inaccurate for high wind readings, and are slow at responding to variable winds. Plate anemometers have been used to trigger high wind alarms on bridges.They are used on these high places because they are in a plate shape; has a good measurement status on higher altitudes.

Tube anemometers are using the pressure difference between the open mouth of a straight tube facing the wind and a ring of small holes in a vertical tube which is closed at the upper end, both mounted at the same height [86, 87]. The pressure differences on which the action depends are very small, and special means are required to register them. The recorder consists of a float in a sealed chamber partially filled with water. The pipe from the straight tube is connected to the top of the sealed chamber and the pipe from the small tubes is directed into the bottom inside the float. Since the pressure difference determines the vertical position of the float this is a measured of the wind speed. The great advantage of the tube anemometer lies in the fact that the exposed part can be mounted on a high pole, and requires no oiling or attention for years; and the registering part can be placed in any convenient position. Two connecting tubes are required. It might appear at first sight as though one connection would serve, but the differences in pressure on which these instruments depend are so minute, that the pressure of the air in the room where the recording part is placed has to be considered.

Meteorological Towers

For estimating wind farm power production, the relevant wind field includes the entire rotor disk plane. Since these data are rarely obtainable, the usual alternative is to erect a tall offshore tower to mount sensors and measure the wind speeds up to hub height [85-87]. The cost to erect an onshore tall (90-100 m) meteorological mast is on the order of ~$250,000, but for offshore, it can cost in range of millions of dollar, depending on water depth, tower facilities, and other factors.

Cup and/or sonic anemometers are installed at specific levels, while temperature, pressure, humidity and solar radiation are measured at standard meteorological level. The use of conventional anemometers on a fixed met tower is thus problematic for the reasons, such as: limited spatial coverage and data that can be collected cost effectively; 2) increased cost and time required for resource assessment and project development; 3) it creates a barrier to competition among developers, limiting the pool to well capitalized firms that can risk the cost of a met tower; and 4) high potential environmental impacts, view-shed impacts, and human use conflicts.

Sonic Detection and Ranging (SODAR)

Both mechanical and sonic anemometers measure wind velocity at a specific location in space, requiring the use of several instruments for the assessment of vertical profiles, remote sensing techniques are capable of providing an almost instantaneous photograph of the complete vertical wind velocity profile up to a certain height.

One such technique, becoming increasingly popular in the wind energy industry, is SODAR [85-102]. SODAR is a remote sensing methodology for measurements of the wind speed and direction aloft at various heights in the atmosphere. SODAR's are ground-based instruments that transmit a sequence of short bursts of sound waves at audible frequencies (2000-4000 Hz) upward in three different inclined directions into the atmosphere. The SODAR measurement technology was well established and in operational use for decades by now, starting in the 1980' ties where they served environmental protection issues and has been extensively applied to atmospheric research for environmental protection air pollution prediction measures well before the present burst in wind energy research and application.

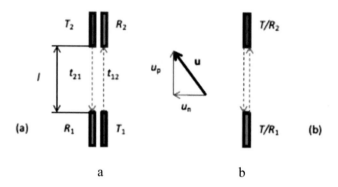

Figure 1. Geometry of ultrasonic transceiver arrangements (one measurement path). (a) Separate transmitters / receivers for each direction, (b) integrated transceiving units.

SODAR was originally developed for atmospheric research and air traffic safety but is increasingly deployed where knowledge of the wind velocity profile up to greater heights than provided by anemometer towers (generally limited to 60 m or 80 m) is required, or the assessment of different locations within a vast wind project development is desirable.

Commercially available systems tailored for wind resource assessment are capable of providing information on the atmospheric boundary layer up to heights of 200 m or 300 m, thereby covering the full range of heights swept by typical rotor blades. This type of information is particularly useful when dynamic structural analysis of the turbine rotor is performed, since both wind shear over the rotor diameter and the evolution of turbulence with height significantly impact on the prediction of rotor stress, and their precise knowledge avoids the use of sometimes oversimplifying assumptions. As the sound waves from a SODAR propagate forward a small fraction of the transmitted sound energy is scattered and reflected in all directions from temperature differences and turbulence in the atmosphere. A very small fraction of this scattered energy reaches back into the SODAR's detector, which in principle is a directional-sensitive microphone. The height at which the wind speed is measurement is usually determined by the time delay in the backscatter from the transmitted pulse. Under standard atmospheric conditions with sound propagation speed of about 340 m/s backscatter from a SODAR measurement at 170 meters height above the ground will reach back into the detector after 1 s delay time. The wind speed component in the transmitted beam direction is subsequently determined from the Doppler shift observed as frequency difference between the transmitted frequency and the frequency of the received backscattered sound wave. By combining the measured wind speed components obtained in this way from three differently inclined sound path directions, e.g. from one vertical and two inclined sound paths, the three-dimensional wind vector including wind speed and direction and tilt can be measured by SODAR from preset heights from the ground and up to the limit determined by the SODARS lowest acceptable Carrier-to-Noise (C/N) ratios. The above description is for a mono-static system, where transmitter and receivers are co-located on the ground. But alternative configurations, e.g. in the form of so-called bi-static SODAR configurations exists as well, where the transmitter and receivers are separated e.g. 100-200 meters on the ground. Bi-static configurations have significant S/N-ratio advantages over mono-static configurations for wind energy applications. Received backscatter in a bi-static configuration is not limited to direct (180 degree) backscatter from temperature (density) fluctuations only, but enables also backscatter contributions from the atmospheric turbulence.

And the higher the wind speed the more turbulence. This becomes in particular relevant during strong wind situations, where the background noise level increases with the wind speed. A particular configuration considered for wind energy applications is therefore the bi-static Continuous Wave (CW) SODAR configuration. Alternatively to the range gating in a pulsed system, the range to the wind speed measurement in a CW system can be determined by well-defined overlapping transmission and receiving antenna functions.

Light Detection and Ranging (LIDAR)

A recent adaptation of a common remote sensing technology can help provide the type of wind data required to measure the energy field on the relevant time and spatial scales. Although other remote sensing methods exist for measuring wind speeds (e.g., Sodar, Radar), using a coherent laser provides the most accurate and versatile way to provide remote measurements. Lidar has been in use for decades to accurately measure distances and generate digital elevation models for topography and mapping. In the last ten years or so it has been adapted to measure wind speed and direction, and in the last few years it has begun to appear in the offshore wind industry. Wind lidar instruments are capable of providing diverse benefits, including better resource assessment (ECN 2012) and better turbine control systems [85, 102-107]. Lidar measures reflected light just as radar measures reflected radio waves. Doppler lidar principle (the dominant technology for wind speed measurement) is the measurement of the Doppler shift of the reflected radiation from a coherent laser6. The laser beam, at frequency ω_o, hits natural aerosols carried on the wind and is reflected and scattered. Some of the light is reflected back at a frequency altered by the Doppler shift (Δf), and the Doppler-shifted frequency of the reflected light is detected by a sensor (see Figure 1 for details). Wave interference between the two signals creates a "beat" frequency proportionally to the wind speed vector component along the laser. By probing the laser along three or more radial vectors, the wind direction can be resolved, providing an accurate estimate of the average wind speed and direction at the focal distance sampled. Although the detectors may be focused at a set distance, they actually sense the backscatter from a probed volume defined by depth of the focal field. This results in a narrow Gaussian distribution of Doppler shift which must be interpreted with algorithms.

Much like SODAR, modern LIDAR devices designed for wind energy purposes rely on the detection and frequency analysis of backscattered waves [82-84]. As in SODAR, the wind velocity component along with the observation direction is obtained through a Fast Fourier Transformation of a Doppler-shifted signal. However, instead of sound waves laser beams are used and backscattering is caused by interaction with particles (aerosols) and molecules in the atmosphere instead of density fluctuations as in the case of SODAR. Scattering mechanisms include molecular processes such as Rayleigh (elastic) and Raman (inelastic) scattering, with Rayleigh scattering being by far the dominant process. Interaction with particles is also known as Mie scattering. For eye safety, commercial units use infrared laser light at a wavelength of 1.55 μm. In order to obtain the three vector components of the wind velocity, the laser beam has to be inclined at an angle θ with respect to the normal, much like in SODAR units. As opposed to SODAR, however, where beam steering relies on phase shifts between the units contained in the antenna, requiring a relatively complex electronic control scheme, laser beams can be easily rotated by means of a rotating wedge, in order to acquire redundant information by performing a full 360° scan around the vertical axis.

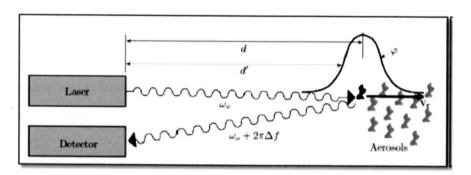

Figure 2. Doppler Shift Lidar, Beat Detection Schematic, (adapted from Pena et al. 2008).

The line-of-sight velocity component obtained from the Doppler shift of the laser frequency then becomes a function of the azimuth angle φ.

Although each Lidar system is slightly different, they are primarily characterized by their laser emission waveform, which is either continuous wave (CW) or pulsed laser (PL). This distinction is the most germane to understanding the subtleties of Lidar wind measurement. A good technical description and comparison of the strengths and weaknesses inherent in PL and CW Lidar can be found in [85, 101-107].

The summary below draws information from these three sources. Continuous Wave (CW): The CW laser emits a continuous (non-pulsed) beam and optically focuses the receiver at the target distance, resulting in a distribution of return signal gain around the focal distance, as shown in Figure 2. Due to its optical focus, the probe length of CW increases with the square of the range. This larger sample volume boosts the signal while the longer distance attenuates it, resulting in a fairly constant carrier to noise ratio (CNR) over the target range of the unit.

Although there is greater potential for range (height) error with the longer probe volume at greater heights, it may not be significant because the wind profile is generally more vertical at greater heights. Beyond several hundred meters, however, the probed volume becomes too large to render a meaningful point estimate, and clouds and other factors come into play.

Pulsed Laser (PL): The strategy used in PL is to send discrete laser pulses and set timing gates on the receiver to capture the pulse reflection from around the target range.

Thus the probe length is proportional to pulse duration (which is fixed) and the reflected signal gain exhibits a Gaussian distribution. PL can probe several different ranges near-simultaneously through the use of multiple range gates, making it valuable for capturing turbulence structures.

On the downside, the CNR of PL decreases with distance since the probed volume does not increase to offset the signal fade. This can only be overcome by increasing laser power. Also, PL must use a minimum pulse duration related to the Nyquist frequency, thus a minimum pulse length and a minimum probe length, usually the distance between targets. PL is therefore ill-suited to ranges below the minimum probe length.

There is no simple, single trade-off between the two technologies, but in general, CW is necessary at short ranges (< 30 m) and PL is necessary at long ranges (> 200 m). The transitional region lies between approximately 100 – 150 m, where various factors could drive selection either way. For example, power draw may be a factor if deployed remotely, and some CW units draw more power than PL.

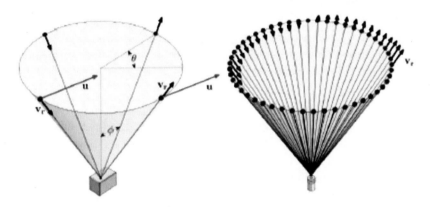

Figure 3. Laser vectors and scan configurations.

Data Validation and Editing

After the field data about the wind speed are collected and transferred to the computing environment, the next steps are to validate and process data, and generate reports. Data validation is defined as the inspection of all the collected data for completeness and reasonableness, and the elimination of erroneous values. Data validation transforms raw data into validated data. The validated data are then processed to produce the summary reports required for analysis. This step is also crucial in maintaining high rates of data completeness during the course of the monitoring program. Therefore data must be validated as soon as possible, after they are transferred. The sooner the site operator is notified of a potential measurement problem, the lower the risk of data loss. Data can be validated either manually or by using computer-based techniques. The latter is preferred to take advantage of the power and speed of computers, although some manual review will always be required. Validation software may be purchased from some data-logger vendors, created in-house using popular spreadsheet programs: e.g., Microsoft Excel, or adapted from other utility environmental monitoring projects. An advantage of using spreadsheet programs is that they can also be used to process data and generate reports. Data validation implies visual data inspection, missing data interpolation, outliers and questionable data rejection, saving data in an appropriate file format for further processing.

WIND RESOURCE ASSESSMENT

Wind resource assessment is the most important step in planning a community wind project because it is the basis for determining initial feasibility and cash flow projections, and is ultimately vital for acquiring financing. Assessment and project progress through several stages of assessment: 1) Initial Assessment; 2) Detailed site characterization; 3) Long-term validation of data; and 4) Detailed cash flow projection and acquiring financing.

Prediction of wind energy resources is crucial in the development of a commercial (large-scale) wind energy installation. The single most important characteristic to any wind development is the wind speed. The performance and power output of a wind farm is very sensitive to uncertainties and errors in estimating the wind speed.

As a result our wind resource assessment must be extremely accurate in order to procure funding and accurately estimate the project economics. Commercial wind resource assessment performed by wind developers is using both numerical and meteorological data. Wind speed and direction measurements are collected by erecting permanent or semi-permanent meteorological towers designed to measure wind speeds using a variety of wind sensors, (sonic, LIDAR, cup and vane, sonic, etc.), at different hub-heights. The most important aspect is to gain an understanding of the wind profile both spatially across the location of interest and also in elevation above terrain level. This section will discuss in brief the fundamental factors which affect wind speed and wind power. The main factors impacting the wind flows are the orography, the roughness and the atmospheric stability. The latter represents the thermal effects on the wind flow. It is rarely taken into account for the wind power assessments, since the wind statistics are averaged over the year, and the atmosphere is thus generally considered as neutral [24-27, 85, 138]. However this assumption presents some limitations:

1   on the sites where the average wind speed is low (< 6 m/s), the thermal effects are starting to be significant;
2   on offshore site, where the atmospheric stability is predominant over the orography and the roughness;
3   for simulation on short periods, by hour or by day, as it is used for short-term prediction, supervision of operation, and power curves measurement with site calibration, as defined in the norm IEC 61400-12.

Wind Energy Statistical Analysis

In a meteorological sense, winds are movements of air masses in the atmosphere due to the temperature differences generated by uneven solar heating from the sun [24, 25, 85, 108-

168]. This air circulation is also affected by the Coriolis forces associated with the rotation of the Earth. In fact, these forces deflect the upper flow towards the east and the lower flow towards the west. The effects of differential heating dwindle for latitudes greater than 30°N and 30°S, where westerly winds predominate, due to the rotation of the Earth. These large-scale, the so-called synoptic air flows that are taking place all over the atmosphere constitute the geostrophic winds. The lower layer of the atmosphere is known as surface layer and extends to a height of 100 m. In this layer, winds are delayed by frictional forces and obstacles altering not only their speed but also their direction. This is the origin of turbulent flows which cause wind speed variations over a wide range of amplitudes and frequencies. Additionally, the presence of seas and large lakes causes air masses circulation similar in nature to the geostrophic winds. All these air movements are called local winds. The wind in a given site near the surface of the Earth results from the combination of the geostrophic and local winds. Therefore, it depends on the geographic location, the climate, the height above ground level, the roughness of the terrain and the obstacles in the surroundings. These are the winds for the wind energy interests of which the wind turbines interact with.

The wind is characterized by its speed and direction which is affected by several factors, including: geographic location, climate characteristics, height above ground, vegetation and surface topography. Wind turbines interact with the wind capturing part of its kinetic energy and converting it into usable energy.

This energy conversion is the result of several phenomena that are explored briefly in this chapter. The study of geographic distribution of wind speeds, characteristic parameters of the wind, topography and local wind flow and measurement of the wind speed, are all essential in wind resource assessment and analysis for the successful wind turbine applications. A brief review of the assessment techniques is presented in this chapter. Wind availability, the influence of the turbine height installation above ground, the wind gusting effect and the wind turbine micro-sitting are the main influences of the annual energy output and are the theoretical basis for the wind energy assessment. There are two aspects of wind resource assessment: 1) determination of the general wind power potential, and 2) determination of wind power potential and predicted energy production for wind farms. The general wind power potential was determined from the wind speed data available, and then wind maps were developed. In general, the measured wind speed data that were available were at heights of 6 to 20 m, more often at 10 m height. However, some anemometers were on top of buildings or airport control towers, or at meteorological masts, which influences the accuracy of the data. Wind classes were developed for 10 m height because that was the standard for world meteorological data, and then the wind power potential at 50 m was double that at 10 m due to the assumption that the wind shear exponent was 1/7 for all locations.

Global pressure and wind patterns, upper air wind data, and boundary layer meteorology were also used to obtain a consistent estimate of the wind energy resource. The knowledge of the quasi-steady mean wind speeds that can be expected at a potential site is crucial to determine the economic viability of a wind energy project. These data are also essential in selecting the WECS in order to maximize efficiency and durability. The probability distribution of mean wind speed is predicted from measurements collected during several years. All these data are usually arranged in a histogram. Where actual wind speed frequency distribution was available, that was used. If such data was not available, wind speed probability distributions, such as Weibull or Rayleigh distributions, are used to estimate the wind power potential. The highly dependent nature of power production on wind speed necessitates accurate predictions in any proposed location. However, the wind is not highly predictable and a simple average wind speed for a location does not suffice in providing enough information for determining the annual energy production of a turbine. It is important to know both the average speed and the distribution of wind speeds for a location for an accurate energy production calculation.

Wind Speed Distribution Functions

In the following subsection we considered the most common wind speed distributions used by the wind energy community. We also consider, as we mentioned above some other closely-rated wind speed distribution probability functions (PDFs). The wind probability distribution (PDF) functions have been investigated, employed and explained by many researchers and engineers involved in the wind energy [24-27, 38-40, 85, 89-170]. In many wind power studies the features and characteristics of such distributions are used for assessment and analysis of wind resources, wind power plant operation, grid integration as well as for design purposes. Both analytical and numerical simulation methods can be carried out, although they are generally used with features of wind power and not output power in mind. However, things can be planned from a different point of view, as similar distribution functions can be described for power, if wind distribution functions are taken into account, together with WT features, on the basis of data provided by the manufacturers. Usually the time series of wind speeds and directions are rather large, differences among parameter estimation methods will not be nearly as important as differences among distributions. There are several estimators of PDF parameters, such as the Method of Moment (MOM), Maximum Likelihood Estimators (MLE), Least-Square (LS), and Percentile Estimators Methods.

These estimators are unbiased, so there is no reason to give preference to any of them. The choice of specific estimators is usually based on the existing wind speed observations, computing availability and user preference. The rule-of thumb is to select a number of estimators of the PDF parameters, while the parameters are usually computed by taking the averages of the estimates found by these methods. We preferentially use MLE, MOM and LS estimators for the large samples, and the averages are the PDF parameters [108-169]. However, when using MOM, we calculate the sample mean $\bar{v}$, standard deviation (S), and skewness (G) as:

$$\bar{v} = \frac{1}{N}\sum_{i=1}^{N} v_i$$

(17)

$$s = \sqrt{\frac{1}{N-1}\sum_{i=1}^{N}(v_i - \bar{v})^2}$$

(18)

and

$$G = \frac{1}{N} \cdot \frac{\sum_{i=1}^{N}(v_i - \bar{v})^3}{S^3} \tag{19}$$

where N is the number of observations in v, our random variable, the wind speed. The following subsection of this chapter describes each of the distribution function and some references to the parameter estimation methods usually used.

We have to notice the basis that the distribution function of the wind speed in a certain location depends just on the mean wind speed, a distribution function of the wind power can be obtained for a given WT by using its power curve. Once the wind power distribution function is obtained, the mean power available is deduced.

So as not to depend on the type of WT, this will be shown per unit of surface (mean power density). This process is performed in four different ways: 1) obtaining of the wind power; 2) Betz' law considerations; 3) consideration of realistic values, remembering that Betz' law is an upper limit; and 4) consideration of WT parameters such as Cut-In and Cut-Out wind speed, rated speed, and rated power [24-56, 108-169].

The goal of any wind energy assessment and analysis is to obtain expressions that allow us to give response to questions about the mean value of the statistical distribution of the maximum power obtainable from the wind, regardless of the WT chosen, and also taking into account its features, when the only input value is the mean wind speed.

Weibull Probability Distribution Function

The Weibull density distribution is a commonly applied statistical distribution to model wind speed distributions. The Weibull curve is a probability density function and indicates both the frequency and magnitude of a given wind speed over a period of time. The use of probability distribution functions in order to define, characterize, and fit the field data has had a long history of use. It has been established that the Weibull distribution [24-59, 109-183] can be used to characterize wind speed regimes in terms of its probability density and cumulative distribution functions, and it is commonly used to estimate and to assess wind energy potential. Although efforts have been made over the years to fit the field wind data to other distributions such as exponential distribution, Pearson type VI distribution, logistic distribution, etc., the Weibull distribution is well accepted and widely used for wind data analysis, and is given by:

$$f_{WB} = k \frac{v^{k-1}}{c^k} \exp\left(-\left(\frac{v}{c}\right)^k\right) \tag{20}$$

The Weibull distribution is a function of two parameters: k, the shape parameter, and c, the scale factor. These parameters are defining the shape or steepness of the curve and the mean value of the distribution. These coefficients are adjusted to match the wind data at a particular site. For modeling wind, typical k values range from 1 to 2.5 and can vary drastically form site to site, as well as during years and/or seasons. The scale parameter, c, corresponds to the average wind speed for the site. The main inaccuracy of the Weibull distribution is that it always has a zero probability of zero wind speed, which is not the case, since there are frequently times in which no wind is blowing. However, the fault is virtually without consequence because most turbines will not operate in speeds below 3 m/s and the distribution is more accurate, compared to measured data, within the zone most used by turbines: 8 to 14 m/s. The higher the k value, the sharper the increasing part of the curve is. The higher c values correspond to a shorter and fatter distribution, with a higher mean value. Ideally the mean value would correlate with the rated wind speed of the turbine: producing rated power for the greatest period of time annually. The cumulative probability function for Weibull distribution is given by:

$$F(v) = 1 - \exp\left[-\left(\frac{v}{c}\right)^k\right]$$

(21)

The availability of high quality wind speed distributions is crucial to accurate forecasts of annual energy production for a wind turbine. Statistical distributions suffice for early estimations, while the actual wind speed measurements are necessary for accurate predictions.

The factors k and λ featuring in Equation (20) are the shape and the scale parameters, respectively, which are determined for each measurement site. The $f_{WB}(v)$ is the probability of observing the particular wind speed, v. There are several estimators of Weibull parameters [109-183], such as the Moment, Maximum Likelihood, Least-Square, and Percentile Estimators methods.

These estimators are unbiased, although some of them, such as the Method of Moments, may have large variances, so there is no reason to prefer any of them. We select three estimators of the Weibull parameters: the standard least-square, the maximum likelihood and a variation of the maximum likelihood methods. Usually, the shape and scale parameters are determined by taking the averages of the estimates found by these methods.

Determination of Weibull Parameters

There are several estimators of Weibull parameters, such as the Moment, Maximum Likelihood, Least-Square, and Percentile Estimators Methods. These estimators are unbiased, although some of them, such as the Method of Moments, may have large variances, so there is no reason to give preference to any of them. The choice of specific estimators is usually based on the existing wind speed observations, computing availability and user preference. The rule-of thumb is to select a number of estimators of the Weibull parameters, such as: the standard least-square, maximum likelihood or variants of the maximum likelihood methods (MLE), while the shape and scale parameters are usually computed by taking the averages of the estimates found by these methods. If sufficient wind speed observations are available, one of the most used estimation method is the Method of Moments (MOM) or its variants [108-170]. It is based on the numerical iteration of the following two equations while the mean ($\bar{v}$) and standard deviation (s) of the wind speeds is available from the following observations:

$$\overline{v} = c \cdot \Gamma \left(1 + \frac{1}{k} \right)$$
(22)

$$s = c \left[\Gamma \left(1 + \frac{2}{k} \right) - \Gamma^2 \left(1 + \frac{1}{k} \right) \right]^{1/2}$$
(23)

where $\overline{v}$ is the wind speed data set (sample) mean, as defined in equation (17), s is the wind speed data set (sample) standard deviation, and $\Gamma()$ is the Gamma function expressed as:

$$\Gamma(x) = \int_0^\infty t^{x-1} \exp(-t) dt$$
(24)

A special case of the moment method is the so-called empirical method, proposed by Justus. Weibull shape parameter, k is estimated in this method by following relationship:

$$k = \left(\frac{s}{\overline{v}} \right)^{-1.086}$$
(25)

Then the scale parameter, c is computed by using the following relationship:

$$c = \frac{\overline{v}}{\Gamma(1 + 1/k)}$$
(26)

Both, the moment and empirical method require a reasonable wind speed observations data set to be available. Another Weibull parameter estimator, based on the concept of least squares, is the graphical method. In which a straight line is fitted to the wind speed data using lease squares minimization, where the time-series data must be sorted into bins. Taking a double logarithmic transformation, the equation of cumulative distribution function can be rewritten as:

$$ln\{-ln[1 - F(v)]\} = kln(v) - kln(c)$$

Plotting ln(v) against ln{-ln[1 - F(v)]}, the slope of the straight line fitted best to data pairs is the shape parameter; the scale parameter is then obtained by the intercept with y-ordinate. The application of the graphical method requires that the wind speed data be in cumulative frequency distribution format. Time-series data must therefore first be sorted into bins. The line of best fit can be drawn by hand or determined using a least-squares regression. This method is referred in literature as the "graphical method" even though the least-squares regression can be performed without producing a graph of the data [109-183]. In essence it a is a variant of the moment method, consisting of the calculation from the time series of the observations of statistical estimators, such as means of the wind speeds and of the square wind speeds. Then the Weibull parameters are calculated as follows:

$$\bar{v} = \frac{c}{k}\Gamma\left(\frac{1}{k}\right)$$

(27)

and

$$\overline{v^2} = \frac{2c^2}{k}\Gamma\left(\frac{2}{k}\right)$$

(28)

After computing the means from the observations the equations (27) and (28) are solved simultaneously and the Weibull parameters are estimated. The Weibull distribution can also be fitted to time-series wind data using the maximum likelihood method [108-183]. The shape factor k and the scale factor c are estimated using the following two equations:

$$k = \left(\frac{\sum_{i=1}^{N} v_i^k ln(v_i)}{\sum_{i=1}^{N} v_i^k} - \frac{\sum_{i=1}^{N} ln(v_i)}{N}\right)^{-1}$$

(29)

$$c = \left(\frac{1}{N}\sum_{i=1}^{N} v_i^k P(v_i)\right)^{1/k}$$

(30)

where v_i is the wind speed in the bin i and N is the number of nonzero wind speed data points (the actual wind speed observations). Equation (29) is solved numerical, usually through iterative processes, with $k = 2$ as initial guess. After which equation (30) can be solved explicitly. Care must be taken to apply equation (29) only to the nonzero wind speed observations.

When wind speed data are available in frequency distribution format, a variation of the maximum likelihood method can be applied. The Weibull parameters are estimated using the following two equations:

$$k = \left(\frac{\sum_{i=1}^{N} v_i^k ln(v_i) P(v_i)}{\sum_{i=1}^{N} v_i^k P(v_i)} - \frac{\sum_{i=1}^{N} ln(v_i) P(v_i)}{P(v \geq 0)}\right)^{-1}$$

(31)

$$c = \left(\frac{1}{P(v \geq 0)}\sum_{i=1}^{N} v_i^k P(v_i)\right)^{1/k}$$

(32)

where vi is the wind speed central to bin i, n is the number of bins, $P(vi)$ is the frequency with which the wind speed falls within bin i, $P(v \geq 0)$ is the probability that the wind speed equals or exceeds zero. Equation (31) must be solved iteratively, after which equation (32) can be solved explicitly to determine the Weibull parameters. One of the parameter estimator not very often used is the energy pattern factor method. In this approach, the energy pattern factor for a given wind speed data is defined as:

$$E_{pf} = \frac{\overline{v^3}}{\overline{v}^3} \tag{33}$$

here $\overline{v^3}$ is the mean of the cubes of the wind speed. Notice that the factors in equation (33) are related to the wind energy estimates, as we are presenting these in next section of this chapter. Weibull shape parameter can be estimated with the following equation:

$$k = 1 + \frac{3.69}{E_{pf}} \tag{34}$$

Scale parameter is estimated using equation (34). This subsection is included because it is often necessary to estimate the Weibull parameters in the absence of suitable information about the distribution of wind speeds. For example, only annual or monthly averages may be available. In such a situation, the value of k must be estimated. The value of k is usually between 1.5 and 3, depending on the variability of the wind. Smaller k values correspond to more variable (more gusty) winds. Interested readers can find more about the estimation of the Weibull parameters in the references included at the end of this chapter, such as [50-98] or elsewhere in the literature.

Goodness of the Fit

To analyze the efficiency of the aforementioned methods, the following tests are used: RMSE (root mean square error), χ^2 (chi-square), R^2 (analysis of variance or efficiency of the method) and the Kolmogorov–Smirnov test [109-183]. These tests are used to examine whether a probability density function is suitable to describe the wind speed data or not. The RMSE test is defined by:

$$RMSE = \left[\frac{1}{N} \sum_{i=1}^{N} (y_i - x_i)^2 \right]^{1/2} \tag{35}$$

where y_i are the actual values at time stage i, x_i the values computed from correlation expression for the same stage, and N is the number of data. The nest two tests are defined by:

$$\chi^2 = \frac{\sum_{i=1}^{N} (y_i - x_i)^2}{N - n} \tag{36}$$

and

$$R^2 = \frac{\sum_{i=1}^{N}(y_i - z_i)^2 - \sum_{i=1}^{N}(y_i - x_i)^2}{\sum_{i=1}^{N}(y_i - z_i)^2} \tag{37}$$

where N is the number of observations, y_i is the frequency of observations, x_i is the frequency of Weibull, z_i is the mean wind speed, and n is the number of constants used. Further criteria of fit testing can be found in. The Kolmogorov-Smirnov test is defined as the max-error between two cumulative distribution functions:

$$Q = max|F_T(v) - F_O(v)| \tag{38}$$

where $F_T(v)$ and $F_O(v)$ are the cumulative distributions functions for wind speed not exceeding v computed by using estimated Weibull parameters and by observed (or randomly generated) time-series, respectively. The critical value for the Kolmogorov–Smirnov test at 95% confident level is given by:

$$Q_{95} = \frac{1.36}{\sqrt{N}} \tag{39}$$

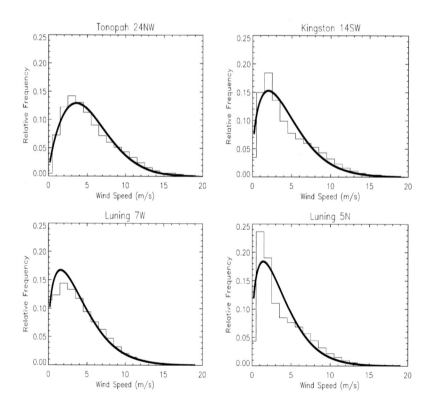

Figure 4. Experimental wind speed probability density functions, at 50 m level, using the composite 2003-2008 data sets, for the 50 m instrumented towers.

If Q value exceeds the critical value then one can say that there is significant difference between the theoretical and the time-series data under the given confident level. Figure 4 are showing the fitted Weibull probability distributions for four locations in western Nevada. The data were collected at 50-m meteorological towers for over four and half years [84, 138, 139].

The chapter's authors collected, edited and analyzed these data sets. They used several methods for determine the Weibull parameters, and the shape and scale parameters are taken as averages. Figure 4 is showing a very good agreement between fitted PDF and actual data.

The energy that a wind energy conversion system will generate depends on both its power curve (representing the nonlinear relationship between the wind speed and turbine power output) and the wind speed frequency distribution at the site. The latter is essential a graph or histogram showing the number of hours for which the wind blows at different wind speeds during a given period of time. If derived from long-term (multi-annual) wind speed data sets the histograms the shape of the probability distribution functions that characterize the wind speed at a specific site or for a region. The histogram takes into account the seasonal variation and year-by-year variations for the years covered by the statistics.

Other Probability Distribution Function Used in Wind Energy

Another used probability distribution is the Rayleigh distribution, which is a special case of the Weibull distribution where $k = 2$.

The Rayleigh distribution is simpler because it depends only on the mean wind speed, and is given by:

$$f_{RL}(v) = \frac{\pi}{2} \frac{v}{c^2} exp\left[-\frac{\pi}{4}\left(\frac{v}{c}\right)^2 \right] \qquad (40)$$

These two probability distribution functions are the most commonly used for wind energy analysis and assessment. The simpler of the two is the Rayleigh distribution which has a single parameter c. The Weibull distribution shown before has two parameters k and c. The Rayleigh distribution is actually a special case of the Weibull distribution with $k = 2$. Setting $k = 2$ in the Weibull distribution gives the Rayleigh distribution. For both distributions, $V_{min} = 0$ and $V_{max} = \infty$. Setting $k = 2$ in this result gives the cumulative Rayleigh distribution.

$$F(b) = 1 - e^{-(b/c)^2} \qquad (41)$$

Equations (31) and (32) can be used to compute the mean and variance of the Weibull distribution. Once these results are known we can set $k = 2$ to get the mean and variance of the Rayleigh distribution. For the Rayleigh distribution the single parameter, c, relates the following three properties:

$$c = V_{mp}\sqrt{2} = \frac{2\mu}{\sqrt{\pi}} = \sigma\sqrt{\frac{4}{8-\pi}} \qquad (42)$$

The Rayleigh distribution can be written using Vmp or the mean velocity, μ. The usual determination of the mean and standard deviation from experimental data for the normal distribution are well known. The minimum-least-squares-error (MLE) estimate of the mean of the normal distribution is the arithmetic mean (the sum of all values divided by the number of values). The formula for the MLE estimate of the variance is also familiar. The parameter c in the Rayleigh distribution can be evaluated from a set of N data points on wind velocity, V_i. When experimental data are used to determine parameters in probability distributions, the computed result is called an estimate of the true parameter.

Here we use the symbol to indicate that the equation below gives us only an estimate of the true distribution parameter, c.

$$\hat{c} = \sqrt{\frac{1}{2N}\sum_{i=1}^{N}V_i^2}$$

(43)

3-Paramter Weibull Distribution

The 3-parameter Weibull (W3) is a generalization of the 2-paramter Weibull distribution, where the location parameter s establishes a lower bound (which was assumed to be zero for the 2-parameter Weibull distribution). It was found that for some areas the W3 fits wind speed data better than the 2-parameter Weibull model. The W3 probability distribution and cumulative distribution functions are expressed as:

$$f(v,k,c,\tau) = \frac{kv^{k-1}}{c^k}\exp\left[-\left(\frac{v-\tau}{c}\right)^k\right]$$

(44)

and

$$F(v,k,c,\tau) = 1 - \exp\left[-\left(\frac{v-\tau}{c}\right)^k\right]$$

(45)

Respectively, for $v \geq \tau$. The authors in [113, 127, 158, 162] recommended to use MLEs for parameter estimation, as suggested in [126]:

$$\frac{\sum_{i=1}^{N}(v_i-\hat{\tau})^{\hat{k}}\ln(v-\hat{\tau})}{\sum_{i=1}^{N}(v_i-\hat{\tau})^{\hat{k}}} - \frac{1}{\hat{k}} - \frac{1}{N}\sum_{i=1}^{N}\ln(v_i-\hat{\tau}) = 0$$

(46)

and

$$\hat{c} = \left(\frac{1}{N} \sum_{i=1}^{N} (v_i - \hat{\tau})^k \right)$$

(47)

$$\hat{\tau} + \frac{\hat{c}}{N^{1/k}} \Gamma\left(1 + \frac{1}{k}\right) = U_{min}$$

(48)

where N is the number of observations in the sample v, and U_{min} indicates the minimum values in the v time series. Parameters of the W3 distributions are then found iteratively solving the equations (44) – (46).

Gamma Probability Distribution

Gamma PDF can be expressed with the following function:

$$g(v; x; \beta) = \frac{v^{x-1}}{\beta^2 \Gamma(x)} \exp\left[-\frac{v}{\beta}\right] \quad for \quad v, x, \beta > 0$$

(49)

where x and β are the shape and scale parameter, respectively, $\Gamma(x)$ is the Gamma function, as expressed in equation (24). The parameters of the Gamma distribution can be estimated using graphical, moment or maximum likelihood methods, similar to one presented above in the Weibull case [107-138]. For more information of fitting measurement data sets to Gamma distributions the reader is advised to follow [113, 132-135]. However, the Gamma PDF is usually employed in a mixture of distributions in connection with Weibull PDF.

Lognormal Probability Distribution

Another PDF used in wind energy assessment, especially in offshore applications even not quite often is the lognormal distribution. The 2-parameter lognormal PDF is given by:

$$f(v, \mu, \sigma) = \frac{1}{\sigma v \sqrt{2\pi}} \exp\left[\frac{-(\ln(v) - \mu)^2}{2\sigma^2}\right]$$

And its cumulative distribution function is expressed as:

$$F(v, \mu, \sigma) = \frac{1}{2} + \frac{1}{2} erf\left[\frac{\ln(v) - \mu}{\sigma \sqrt{2}}\right]$$

where erf() is the error function from the Normal distribution, and the parameters μ and σ are the mean and standard deviation of the natural logarithm of v [114, 115, 133, 137, 178].

As suggested in [133] the MOM method is usually employed to estimate the PDF parameters because it showed considerable better fits to the data and because it enables to handle samples with zeros. The estmators are given by:

$$\hat{\mu} = \ln\left(\frac{\bar{v}}{\sqrt{1+\frac{s^2}{\bar{v}^2}}}\right)$$

$$\hat{\sigma} = \sqrt{\ln\left(\frac{s^2}{\bar{v}^2}\right)}$$

Truncated Normal Probability Distribution

The truncated normal distribution is the probability distribution function of a normally distributed random variable whose values are either bounded bellow, above or both. Since the wind speed is only positive, the most common is the single truncated normal distribution, suitable for nonnegative case:

$$n(v,\mu,\sigma) = \frac{1}{I(\mu,\sigma)\sigma\sqrt{2\pi}}\exp\left[-\frac{(v-\mu)^2}{2\sigma^2}\right] \quad for \ \ v > 0$$

(50)

where μ and σ the date mean and standard deviation, and $I(\mu, \sigma)$ is the normalized factor that leads the integration of the truncated normal distribution to one, which can the cumulative distribution evaluated in its domain de definition. The normalized factor is given by:

$$I(\mu,\sigma) = \frac{1}{\sigma\sqrt{2\pi}}\int_0^\infty \exp\left[-\frac{(v-\mu)^2}{2\sigma^2}\right]dv$$

The distribution function parameters can be determine using graphical, moment or maximum likelihood methods or a combination of them.

Pearson Type III

The Pearson type III (P3) distribution is a Gamma type distribution with a third parameter for location, whose use for wind speed was initially advocated by. Its probability distribution and cumulative distribution functions are:

$$f(v,\tau,k,c) = (v-\tau)^{k-1}\frac{\exp\left(-\frac{v-\tau}{c}\right)}{c^k\Gamma(k)}$$

$$F(v,\tau,k,c) = \frac{\gamma\left(k, \frac{v-\tau}{c}\right)}{\Gamma(k)}$$

here $\gamma()$ is the incomplete gamma function. The PDF parameters are determined by using MOM, because the MLEs require the removal of null wind speeds.

Log Pearson Type III Distribution

The log Pearson type III (LP3) distribution describes a random variable whose logarithms follow a P3 distribution. Usually we are fitting the LP3 distribution to the wind speed sample v by transforming v by the natural logarithm and fitting the P3 distribution. The LP3 distribution is one of the most flexible 3-parameter distributions that are used in data and statistical analysis [133, 144]. However, on the authors' knowledge there are no evaluations its performance for wind speeds

Maximum Entropy Principle (MEP) Distribution

The maximum entropy concept has commonly been applied in many engineering and science areas. The entropy of PDF, f(x) is defined as [144, 160, 180-183]:

$$S(x) = -\int f(x) \ln\left(f(x)\right) dx$$

Maximizing the entropy subject to specific constrains enables to find the most likely probability distribution function if the information available is provided by moment functions. The classical MEP solution applied to wind distribution case is given by:

$$f(v) = \exp\left[-\sum_{k=0}^{N} a_k v^k\right]$$

$$(51)$$

and solution, Lagrange multipliers are given by the following nonlinear system of equations:

$$Z_n(a) = \int v^n \exp\left[-\sum_{k=0}^{n} a_k v^k\right] dv = \lambda_n \quad for \ n = 1, 2, \ldots, N$$

The λ_n, n = 0,1, ..., N, with $\lambda_0 = 1$, are the moments of the distribution representing the mean values of n powers of wind speed, calculated from the wind observation data. Usually, the MEP probability density functions are ones of third or fourth order, having three or four moment constrains.

Mixture of Distribution Functions

In recent years, in order to improve the accuracy of wind statistics, mixtures of PDFs were employed [144, 169, 177-179]. Distribution function mixed with Gamma, Weibull, or Normal distribution functions can be used to describe the wind statistics. For example, Gamma and Weibull mixture applied to wind energy assessment is given by:

$$h(v; w; x, \beta, k, c) = wg\left(v, x, \beta\right) + (1-w)f\left(v, k, c\right)$$

(52)

where $0 \leq w \leq 1$ is the weight parameter indicating the mixed proportion of each distribution included in the mixture. Again, the five parameters, in the equation (42) can be estimated using graphical, moment, maximum likelihood methods or combination them, as discussed in the Weibull case.

Wind Direction

To ensure the most effective use of a wind turbine it should be exposed to the most energetic wind. Though the wind may blow more frequently from the west more wind energy may come from a different direction if those winds are stronger. It is very important to find out which directions have the best winds for electricity production. The distribution of wind direction is crucially important for the evaluation of the possibilities of utilizing wind power. The distributions of wind speed and direction are conventionally given by wind roses. A wind rose chart, which is generated from your wind resource assessment, is a helpful tool to determine wind direction and distribution. Traditionally, wind direction changes are illustrated by a graph, which indicates percent of winds from that direction, or the wind rose diagram [139, 169, 174]. The wind rose diagrams and wind direction frequency histograms provide useful information on the prevailing wind direction and availability in different wind speed bin. Notice that a wind vane points toward the source of the wind. Wind direction is reported as the direction from which the wind blows, not the direction toward which the wind moves. A north wind blows from the north toward the south. The wind direction varies from station to station due to differential local features (topography, altitude, orientation, distance from the shore, vegetation, etc.). Notice that there can also be changes in the wind directions on diurnal, seasonal or annual basis. The wind direction can also be analyzed using continuous variable probability models to represent distributions of directional wind speeds, such as von Mises circular statistics [139, 169, 174]. The model usually comprised of a finite mixture of the von Mises distributions. The presentation of the wind circular statistics and probability distribution is beyond the scope of this chapter however interested readers are directed to use the end-of-chapter references. While obtaining the average wind speed at a given location is useful, it does not accurately portray the power of the wind resource.

The statistical distribution of wind speeds vary depending on climate conditions, landscape, and surface roughness. Strong gale force winds are rare while consistent low speed velocities are most common. The Weibull distribution is a statistical tool which is a measure of the variation, skewness and frequency of observed winds speeds.

Further use of the Weibull distribution is detailed in the wind speed validation process to provide a tool for calculating the power density of the wind resource.

Wind Direction Statistics

The wind rose diagrams and wind direction frequency histograms provide useful information on the prevailing wind direction and availability of directional wind speed in different wind speed bins. The wind roses were constructed using the composite data sets of measurements of wind velocities. The wind direction is usually analyzed using a continuous variable probability model to represent distributions of directional wind speeds. The model is comprised of a finite mixture of the von Mises distributions (vM – PDF), following the approaches given in [85, 139, 169, 174]. The parameters of the models are estimated using the least square method. The range of integration to compute the mean angle and standard deviation of the wind direction is adjusted to minimum variance requirements. The proposed probability model $mvM(\theta)$ is comprised of a sum of N von Mises probability density functions, $vM_j(\theta)$, as:

$$mvM(\theta) = \sum_{j=1}^{N} w_j vM_j(\theta)$$

(53)

where w_j are nonnegative weighting factors that sum to one [163-168]:

$$0 \leq w_j \leq 1 \; (j = 1, ..., N \; and \; \sum_{j=1}^{N} w_j = 1$$

A random variable function has a von Mises distribution vM-PDF if its probability is defined by the equation:

$$vM_j(\theta; k_j, \mu_j) = \frac{1}{2\pi I_0(k_j)} \exp[k_j \cos(\theta - \mu_j)],$$

$$0 \leq \theta \leq 2\pi$$

(54)

where $k_j \geq 0$ and $0 \leq \mu_j \leq 2\pi$ are the concentration and mean direction parameters, respectively. In this paper, the angle corresponding to the northerly direction is taken as 0°. Note that in meteorology, the angle is measured clockwise from north. Here, $I_0(k_j)$ is a modified Bessel function of the first kind and order zero and is given by:

$$I_0(k_j) = \frac{1}{2\sqrt{\pi}} \int_0^{2\pi} \exp[k_j \cos\theta] d\theta \approx \sum_{p=0}^{\infty} \frac{1}{(p!)^2} \left(\frac{k_j}{2}\right)^{2p}$$

(55)

The distribution law $mvM(\theta)$, given by Equation (37), can be numerically integrated between two given values of θ to obtain the probability that the wind direction is found within a particular angle sector. Various methods are employed to compute the 3N parameters on which the mixture of von Mises distribution depends.

In papers [137], the authors employed the least squares (LS) method. Figure 5 is showing fitted von Mise distributions to the wind direction time series collected at two locations in western Nevada, 2003 to 2008 [84, 138].

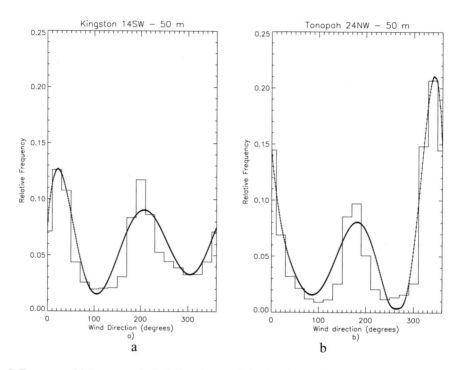

Figure 5. Frequency histograms of wind directions and the fitted von Mises distribution functions at a) Kingston 14SW tower and 50 m level, and b) Tonopah 24NW and 50 m level using the composite 2003-2008 data sets [138, 139].

Long-Term Assessment and MCP (Measure-Correlate-Predict) Methods

Measure-correlate-predict (MCP) algorithms are used to predict the wind resource at target sites for wind power development. MCP methods model the relationship between wind data (speed and direction) measured at the target site, usually over a period of up to a year, and concurrent data at a nearby reference site.

The model is then used with long-term data from the reference site to predict the long-term wind speed and direction distributions at the target site. In order to be most useful for wind power development, the uncertainties in the predictions need to be understood. Since typical wind farm assessments last anywhere from one to three years, with important decisions to be taken often only after several months, there is an obvious need for a prediction of the performance of a planned wind farm during its expected life time (20 years or more). Such an assessment is an important part of the wind power financing process.

While the measurement campaign may correspond to an untypically high or low period, correlations with nearby reference stations should help detect such trends and provide a corrected long-term estimate of the wind speed at the development site and its inter-annual variations. Moreover, since the power output of wind turbine depends on the wind speed in a non-linear way, the distribution of the wind speed values should also be predicted correctly. The methods which are reviewed here comprise a family of generic "measure-correlate-predict" (MCP) methodologies. These methods proceed by "measuring" the winds at a target site, "correlating" them with winds from a nearby reference site, and then by applying these correlations to historical data from the reference site, to "predict" the long term wind resource of the target site.

Various MCP algorithms have been studied using wind data from a number of potential wind farm sites. Some of the algorithms and methods have been improved using probabilistic methods, and have then been implemented into software packages, such as the WindPRO or WAsP for planing and projecting of wind power plants. The general methodology of the MCP process proceeds as follows: 1) collect wind data at the predictor site for an extended period; 2) identify a reference site, for which high quality, long term records exist, in the vicinity of the predictor site, and which has a similar exposure, the so-called "reference" site; 3) obtain wind data from the reference site for the same time period as for the predictor site, the so-called "concurrent period"; 4) establish a relationship between the data from the reference and predictor sites for the concurrent period; 5) obtain wind data from the reference site for a historic period of over 10 years duration or the longest possible one, the so-called "historic" period; 6) apply the relationship determined in step 4) to the historic data from the reference site to "predict" what the winds would have been at the predictor site over that period. Note that this is a prediction of the winds that would have been observed had measurements been made at the predictor site for the same period as the historic data, rather than a prediction of winds that will be observed in future. The key factor to any MCP technique is the algorithm used in step 4). Most MCP techniques use direction sectored regression analysis to establish a relationship between wind speed and direction at the reference site and the wind speed at the potential wind farm site. The long term wind data may be taken from nearby meteorological stations as well as data from the NCEP/NCAR reanalysis dataset. The general approach is to look for a relationship between the wind speed variables v_{site} and v_{met} of the site under development and a suitable reference station, respectively [24, 25, 170, 183-189]:

$$v_{site} = f\left(v_{met}\right) \tag{56}$$

Often, it may be suitable to consider several reference stations with concurrent data sets for a given development site; equation (49) has then to be generalized to:

$$v_{site} = g\left(v_{met}^1, v_{met}^2, \ldots, v_{met}^N\right) \tag{57}$$

Currently different MCP methods currently implemented in the WindPRO, WAsP software packages or other wind software applications. However, many researchers designed and developed their own MCP applications [170, 183-189].

Wind speed time series can be analyzed irrespective of wind direction; generally, however, wind direction is binned into a certain number of sectors and the wind speed subsets for each direction bin are analyzed separately for their correlation. Since wind direction readings may not always coincide, binning may be based either on the wind direction measured at the reference station(s) or the development site. If the differences between the wind direction readings at the reference and the measurement sites are too substantial, then different approaches may be taken. When a systematic veer occurs (e.g., in response to a bend in topography), the relationship between the site and the met direction may be fitted to a polynomial and the fit curve may be used to predict the long-term site wind direction.

A deeper objective, which requires a more insightful analysis of the underlying statistical behavior of the process, is to achieve an estimation of the probability density function $f_{Y,long}$ (v_{sim}, v_{met}, α), which best describes the long-term wind speed distribution at a given location and height above ground level based on the knowledge of the density in the reference site. Here α is a vector of parameters for each one of the distributions; the number and type of parameters here depend on the particular distributions. The knowledge of $f_{Y,long}$ (v_{sim}, v_{met}, α) allows to calculate the average wind speed and power density and, most importantly, the average energy yield of a given wind turbine.

Additionally, intra- or inter-annual fluctuations of the wind resource at the prospective site need to be studied, although the present study does not consider such variations. The models employed in practical applications fall into two classes, linear and non-linear and can be described mathematically, adapting previous equations, as:

$$v_{pred} = f\left(v_{ref}, \theta_{ref}\right)$$

$$\theta_{pred} = g\left(v_{ref}, \theta_{ref}\right)$$

where f, g represent the functional relationships between the concurrent data for the two sites.

Subscripts denote the data set: for example, reference as ref, or predictor as pred. There are several adaptions and variants of the these models, with their advantages and disadvantages [170, 183-189]. In the following we are discussing the most used briefly, interested readers are directed to references or elsewhere in the literature.

Linear and Regression Models

The regression MCP method holds the traditional linear regression MCP analysis as a specialized subset of other regression models using polynomials of other orders. Specializations of the polynomial-fitting methods are also included, provided in order to comply with methods used or suggested by other authors. In the simplest linear models the wind speed and direction at the target/predictor site is expressed as:

$$v_{h,pred} = f\left(v_{h,ref}\right)$$

$$\tag{58}$$

and

$$f\left(v_{h,ref}\right) = \frac{\overline{v}_{c,pred}}{\overline{v}_{c,pred}} v_{h,ref}$$

here the over bar refers to average of the concurrent data, while c and h to the concurrent and historic One of the most common used algorithm is an MCP method forcing the regression line through the origin (0,0). However, this option should be used only with caution as it typically provides a significantly poorer fit to the data than the methods where a non-zero intersection with the y-axis is allowed. Regression modelling, where only one independent (x) and one dependent (Y) variable is present, is based on the following equation:

$$Y = f(x) + e \qquad\qquad\qquad (59)$$

where Y is the dependent variable, x is the independent variable, f(x) is the regression model, and e is a random error (residual).

The regression model could be polynomials of any order or other models, but traditionally a linear model is assumed, as this model has been found to give reasonable fits for wind energy estimation. In the case of a regression MCP analysis, the independent variable could be the wind speed measured at the reference position. The dependent variable (Y) is then the wind speed at the local WTG site position. The regression parameters are estimated through a least squares algorithm. The distributions of the random errors may, reasonably be assumed to follow a zero mean Gaussian distribution, $e \sim N(0,\sigma)$.

However, the distribution of the residuals should be visually checked, so that the assumption is verified as reasonable. This is needed, as the random variable model for the residuals is included in the MCP-modelling in order to give the right energy levels in the new MCP-corrected time series. Please note, that currently the distribution of residuals is conditioned on the reference wind direction only. Thus, conditioned on the reference wind direction, the residuals should be independent on the reference wind speed.

Matrix Method

The matrix method models the changes in wind speed (speed-up) and wind direction (wind veer) through joint distributions fitted on the 'matrix' of wind speed bins and wind direction bins. The parallel period of measured wind data is used to calculate the set of non-linear transfer functions, used for transferring wind speeds and wind directions from the reference site to the site position. Since real measurements will suffer from data missing in bins in the dataset, this method needs a way to substitute the missing input bins. In WindPRO, polynomials are fitted to the statistics of the sample data enabling this interpolation/ extrapolation.

The user may choose to either use polynomials fitted to the data statistics or, where appropriate, to use the measured raw samples directly when doing the matrix MCP. A basic assumption of the matrix method is that the long-term site data (wind speed and direction) can be expressed through the simultaneous measurements of on-site data and reference site data. Actually this relationship is basically modelled through a joint distribution between the two variables wind speed-up and wind veer.

How this joint distribution is modelled should actually depend on the data in question, suggesting that a combination of binned sample distributions and modelled joint Gaussian distributions seem to work quite well. The transfer model, given as a conditional distribution, is actually the key distribution in the generalized matrix method.

The distribution gives the relationship between the site wind climate and the reference wind climate. When applying the matrix method this conditional distribution is stipulated to hold regardless of the time frame considered. The model is based on the joint distribution of the measured wind speed-ups and wind veers. Thus, for each measured sample it is necessary to calculate/measure pairs of the two quantities (a pair is data with identical timestamps):

$$\Delta v = v_{site} - v_{ref}$$

(60)

$$\Delta \theta = \theta_{site} - \theta_{ref}$$

(61)

The parameters in these equations refer to the wind speeds and directions at the wind project site and the meteorological site, respectively. The joint distribution of $f(\Delta u, \Delta \theta)$ is usually modelled conditioned on the wind speed and the wind direction on the reference site. These joint distributions are represented as either through the samples (bootstrap model) or through a joint Gaussian distribution most often.

When the data has been measured and a match between the short-term site data and the short-term reference data has been established, then the samples are sorted into bins with specific resolutions, such as 1 m/s and 10 degrees. The result from this binning is a set of joint sample distributions of wind veer and wind speed-up.

Since the data is binned with wind speed and wind direction, these sample distributions are said to be conditioned on the mean wind speed at the reference position and the wind direction on the reference position. The calculated distributions are used directly in a bootstrapping technique when doing the Matrix MCP calculation. Based on the sample distributions, the following sample statistics are calculated for the wind veer and the wind speed: mean value, standard deviation, skewness, kurtosis, correlation coefficients, etc.

In order to enable interpolations and extrapolations into bins where no data is present, we choose to parameterize a model fitted to the sample distribution statistics. This parametric distribution is represented by the two first statistical moments and the correlation, and it is assumed that a joint Gaussian distribution is a reasonable distribution assumption. Note, that even if the Gaussian distribution assumption may seem a bit crude, then the parametric model will only be applied in cases where limited or no sample data is available.

Thus, the influence of this assumption is limited, as most long-term corrected samples are typically based on the resampling approach. The mean, standard deviation and correlation are now modelled as 'slices' of polynomial surfaces:

$$P(v,\theta) = \sum_{i=0}^{N} a_i(v_i,\theta_i) v_{ref}^1$$

(62)

where P denotes the sample statistical moment (or correlation) considered, N is the order of the polynomial a_i is the polynomial coefficients, depending on the wind speeds and directions. As (partly) in the case of regression MCP, the long-term corrected meteorological data is calculated using Bootstrap and Monte-Carlo simulation techniques, i.e. probabilistic methods enabling generation of the long-term corrected wind distribution through an 'artificial' time series.

Hybrid MCP Method

The hybrid MCP method developed by Zhang et al., 2012 correlates the wind data at the targeted wind plant site with that at multiple reference stations. The strategy accounts for the local climate and the topography information. In the original hybrid MCP method, all component MCP estimations between the targeted wind plant site and each reference station use a single MCP method (e.g., linear regression, variance ratio, Weibull scale, or neural networks) [183-189]. The weight of each reference station in the hybrid strategy is determined based on: (i) the distance and (ii) the elevation differences between the target wind plant site and each reference station. The hypothesis here is that the weight of a reference station is larger when the reference station is closer (shorter distance and smaller elevation difference) to the target wind plant site. The weight of each reference station, wi, is determined by:

$$w_j = F\left(n_{ref}, \Delta d_j, \Delta h_j\right)$$

(63)

where n_{ref} is the number of reference stations; and Δd_j and Δh_j represent the distance and the elevation difference between the target plant site and jth reference station, respectively. Each wind data point is usually allocated to a bin according to the wind direction sector measurement at the target wind plant site. Within each sector, the long-term wind speed is now predicted by applying the hybrid MCP strategy based on the concurrent short-term wind speed data within that specific sector. By putting the wind speed data in each sector together, one can obtain the set of long-term wind data at the target wind plant site. The quality of the predicted long-term wind data is usually evaluated using the performance metrics [135-160].

The ANNs Method

ANNs have been used to correlate and predict wind conditions because of their ability to recognize patterns in noisy or otherwise complex data. A neural network generally contains an input layer, one or more hidden layers, and an output layer. An ANN is developed by defining the following parameters: input and output connections, number of neuron layers, the weights, and transfer functions types, the interconnection pattern between different layers of neurons, the learning process for updating the weights of the interconnections, and he activation function that converts a neuron's weighted input to its output activation. For example, the MATLAB Neural Network Toolbox can be used. The Levenberg-Marquardt algorithm is usually selected for neural network training.

Wind Index MCP

The index correlation method is a method creating the MCP analysis by means of monthly averages of the energy yield, thus disregarding the directional distribution of the winds. Even though this method may seem rather crude and primitive when comparing to other more advanced MCP methods, which takes the wind veer into account; this method has its advantages in stability and performance as it may even succeed in the cases where other MCP methods seem to fail.

This is due to the fact, that the wind indexes are related directly to WTG energy yield and that the method allows the production calculation to be completed using actual measured data before applying the correction. The Wind Index MCP method offers the opportunity to calculate the wind indexes using real power curves from the wind turbines included in the wind turbine catalogue.

Also a generic power curve based on a truncated squared wind speed approach may be chosen. When the wind indexes are calculated, the MCP correction is done on the estimated WTG energy yield, i.e. by multiplying the production estimated with a correction factor based on the difference in the wind index from the short-term site data to the long-term site data estimate. The energy level in the wind is proportional to the third power of the wind speed. However, since the power curve of a WTG is a non-linear function of the wind speed the wind index is typically modelled using well-known models [105-147].

In order for the power output (calculated for site and reference) to be comparable they must be based on a similar mean wind speed. This is done by assuming a sector uniform shear that can be applied so that both concurrent mean wind speeds are set to a fixed user-inferred wind speed, typically the expected mean wind speed at hub height. The individual wind speed measurements are thus multiplied with the relevant factor.

Both full time series wind speeds will be adjusted with the same ratio as the one applied to the respective concurrent time series. The argument for this operation is that the variations in wind speed will only be interpreted correctly in terms of wind energy if a comparable section of the power curve is considered.

WIND RESOURCES IN CLIMATE PROJECTIONS

Just as with the other aspects of climate, wind statistics are subject to natural variability on a wide range of time scales. Like other meteorological parameters, such as temperature, rainfall, or other climate variables, wind speeds and directions change on time scales of minutes, hours, months, years, and decades.

Future climate change is expected to alter the spatial and temporal distribution of surface wind speeds and directions, with associated impacts on wind-based electricity generation.

In the context of wind energy generation, even small changes in the wind speed magnitude can have major impacts on the productivity of wind power plants, as the wind power relationship (Equation 1) is directly proportional to the cube of the wind speed. However, the predictions for the direction and magnitude of these changes hinge critically on the assessment methods used. Decadal and multi-decadal variability in wind speed statistics currently introduce an element of risk into the decision process for siting new wind power generation facilities. Recent findings from the atmospheric science community suggest that climate change may introduce an added risk to this process.

Many climate change impact analyses, including those focused on wind energy, use individual climate models and/or statistical downscaling methods rooted in historical observations. Wind speed and direction vary on small scales, and respond in complex ways to changes in large-scale circulation, surface energy fluxes, and topography.

Thus, whereas multiple climate models often agree qualitatively on temperature projections, wind estimates are less robust [190-203]. The spatial variability of wind and its sensitivity to model structure suggest that higher resolution models and multi-model comparisons are particularly valuable for wind energy projections. The IPCC report by Wiser et al. (2011) emphasizes the value of growing wind energy generation in reducing current and future greenhouse gas (GHG) emissions.

Although wind power generation in 2009 accounted for only 1.8% of total power generation, it is expected to grow to 20% by 2050. US DOE (2008) recognizes that climate change has potentially significant financial consequences on wind plant facilities.

For long-term planning of wind resources, it is imperative to analyze historical datasets and establish monitoring at hub-height using meteorological towers and remote sensing. A comprehensive review of climate change impacts on wind energy is shown by Pryor and Barthelmie (2010). They discussed the main changes in the wind resources due to climate evolution. In particular, they focused on northern Europe, where there is already significant penetration of the wind energy.

According to the analysis, until the middle of the current century natural variability will exceed the effect of climate change in the wind energy resources [24, 25, 190-203]. They conclude that there is no detectable trend in the wind resources that would impact future planning and development of wind industry in northern Europe. Pryor et al. (2006) downscaled winds from ten global climate models at locations in northern Europe and found no evidence of significant changes in the 21st century compared to the 20th century. Predicted changes in the downscaled mean and 90th percentile are found to be small and comparable to the variability associated with different global climate models.

Using another approach, Ren (2010) proposed a power-law relationship between global warming and the usable wind energy. The power-law exponent was calibrated using results from eight global climate models. He found that reduction of wind power scales with the degree of warming according to method and estimated that 2-4 degrees Celsius increase in the temperatures in mid to high latitudes would result in a 4-12% decrease in wind speeds in northern latitudes. Ren (2010) suggested that an early maximized harvesting will be more beneficial and should be carried out as soon as possible while global warming is not fully developed. More studies are needed to resolve all uncertainties and errors in climate projections of wind resources under various future emission scenarios.

CONCLUSION

Many factors influence accurate assessment and prediction of wind energy production. A primary issue is adequate understanding of the effects of wind variability, atmospheric stability and turbulence on production. Non-negligible error is incurred when the effects of shear, TI, and atmospheric stability on the wind turbine power performance are ignored, as in the IEC standard, 61400-12-1 (2005). The standard procedures are valid only for ideal neutral conditions and a small wind turbine. Besides the dominant cubic dependence of the wind speed on the wind power density, there are smaller but still important corrections to the air density that are important to harvesting wind energy at high-elevation sites. Corrections that account for these factors must be included in the power output estimates, and more accurate predictions will help alleviate production-consumption imbalances. These imbalances can also be ameliorated through the use of storage devices. The field of wind resource assessment is evolving rapidly, responding to the increasingly stringent requirements of large-scale wind farm projects often involving investments of several hundred million dollars. Traditional cup anemometry is being complemented with ultrasonic sensors providing information on all three components of the wind velocity vector and enabling a better assessment of turbulence. Remote sensing devices like sodar and lidar are becoming more popular as turbine hub heights and rotor diameters increase, often placing the upper edge of the swept rotor area at heights of 130 m or more. While the traditional approach of measuring the wind speed at a few heights below hub height and extrapolating based on a logarithmic profile is still very common, the use of both vertical profiling devices and more accurate modeling tools considering the full terrain complexity and atmospheric stability is quickly moving into the mainstream. Measure-correlate-predict (MCP) methods are used to estimate wind speeds and directions at a target site where wind power is assessed for development. These methods use two sets of in-data. To begin with a series of measured wind speeds and directions from the target site during a period of time (usually one year) is needed. In addition to this, a reference series from a much longer period needs to be obtained. The target site data is usually retrieved from an anemometer that is erected at the site that needs investigating. On the other hand, the advanced hybrid MCP method uses the recorded data of multiple reference stations to estimate the long-term wind condition at a target plant site. Two scenarios were analyzed using the hybrid MCP methodology, and interesting results were observed and discussed. Because each reference station has the flexibility to use any of the available MCP techniques, the multiple reference weather stations were combined into the hybrid MCP strategy with the best suitable MCP algorithm for each reference station. In the first scenario, each reference weather station used one of the following MCP algorithms: (i) linear regression; (ii) variance ratio; (iii) neural network; and (iv) support vector regression.Climate projections and trends of wind resources in changing climate are a topic of a debate in the literature and require a thorough investigation of models' uncertainties and errors and understanding the complex interaction of atmospheric dynamics and thermodynamics. This will contribute to understanding the extent to which some of the predicted trends are the result of the weather and climate variability or the result of inadequate physical parameterizations in global and regional climate models. In order to account for uncertainties and errors in inputs and model imperfections, there is a need to further develop probabilistic wind and wind power predictions on weather and climate scales.

REFERENCES

[1]   Fung, K. T., Scheffler, R. L., Stolpe, J. 1981: Wind energy - a utility perspective. *IEEE Trans. Power Appar. System*,100, 1176-1182.

[2]   Robert, R. 1996: *Wind energy in America: a history*. US, University of Oklahoma Press.

[3]   Musgrove, P., *2010: Wind power*. Cambridge University Press, 323 p.

[4]   Pasqualetti, M. J., P. Gipe and R. W. Righter, *2002: Wind Power in View*. Academic Press, San Diego.

[5]   Belu, R., 2012, Wind Energy Conversion and Analysis, *Encyclopedia of Energy Engineering and Technology* (Ed. Sohail Anwar), Taylor and Francis, 2013 (DOI: 10.1081/E-EEE-120048430/27 pages).

[6]   Jenkins, N., Walker, J., *Wind Energy Technology*. Wiley, England, 1997.

[7]   Jenkins, N., Burton, T., Sharpe, D., Bossanyi, E., *Wind Energy Handbook*, J. Wiley and Sons, 2001.

[8]   Burton, T., Sharpe, D., Jenkins, N., Bossanyi, E., *Wind Energy Handbook*. Chichester, UK: J. Wiley and Sons, 2001.

[9]   Calero, R., and Carta, J. A., 2004: Action plan for wind energy development in the Canary Islands, Energy Policy, 32(10), pp 1185-1197

[10] Ackermann, T., L. Söder, 2000: Wind energy technology and current status: a review, *Renew. Sustain. Energy Rev.*, 4(4), 315-374.

[11] Ackermann, T., L. Söder, 2002: An overview of wind energy-status 2002, *Renew. Sustain. Energy Rev.*, 6(1-2), 67-127.

[12] US Energy Information Administration, *International Energy Outlook 2001,* May 2001.

[13] US Energy Information Administration, *International Energy Annual 1999,* Jan., 2001.

[14] International Energy Agency, *Wind Annual report* 2000, May 2001.

[15] US Dept. of Energy, *Wind powering America*; September 2009. <http://www.windpoweringamerica.gov/>.

[16] Kaldellis, J. K. and Zafirakis, D. 2011. The wind energy (r)evolution: A short review of a long history. *Renewable Energy*, 36, pp.1887-1901.

[17] Ezio, S., Claudio, C. Exploitation of wind as an energy source to meet the world's electricity demand. *Wind Engineering*, 1998, 74-76, 375-387.

[18] Sphera, D. A., *Wind Turbine Technology: Fundamental Concepts of Wind Turbine Engineering,* ASME Press, New York, 1994.

[19] Gipe, P., *Wind Energy Comes of Age*, John Wiley and Sons, New York, 1995.

[20] European Wind Energy Association (EWEA), *2010: Powering Europe: wind energy and the electricity grid.* Available on http://www.ewea.org/

[21] Blanco, M. I., 2009: The Economics of Wind Energy. *Renewable and Sustainable Energy Reviews,* (13:6-7), 1372-1382.

[22] Lu, X., M. McElroy, J. Kiviluoma, 2009: Global potential for wind generated electricity. *Proc. Natl. Acad. Sci.*, 106, 10 933-10 938.

[23] Freris, L., D. G. Infield, *2008: Wind Energy in Power Systems.* John Wiley and Sons, UK, 284 pp.

[24] Petersen, E. L., Mortensen, N. G., Landberg, L., et al., Wind power meteorology. Part I: Climate and turbulence, *Wind Energy*, 1998, 1(1), 25-45.

[25] Petersen, E. L., Mortensen, N. G., Landberg, L., et al., Wind power meteorology, Part II: Siting and models, *Wind Energy*, 1998, 1(2), 55-72.

[26] Manwell, J., McGowan, J., Rogers, A. *Wind Energy Explained: Theory, Design and Application,* New York, John Wiley and Sons, 2002.

[27] Ackermann, T. (ed.), *2005: Wind Power in Power Systems*, Wiley, England, 2005.

[28] Patel, M. R., *Wind and Solar Power System,* Second Edition, CRC Press, 2005.

[29] Lund, H., 2005: Large-scale integration of wind power into different energy systems, *Energy*, 30(13), pp. 2402-2412.

[30] Joselin Herbert, G. M., Inyian, S., Sreevalsan, E., et al., 2007. A review of wind energy technology, *Renewable and Sustainable Energy Reviews*, 11, pp. 1117-1145.

[31] Bansal, R. C., Zobaa, A. F. and Saket, R. K. 2005: Some issues related to power generation using wind energy conversion systems: An overview, *Int. J. Emerging Elect. Power Syst.*, 3(2), pp. 1–19.

[32] Archer, C. L., Jacobson, M. Z., 2003: Spatial and temporal distributions of US winds and wind power at 80 m derived from measurements, *J. Geophys. Res.*, 108; doi:10. 1029/2002/D002076. 84.

[33] Sinden, G., 2007: Characteristics of the uk wind resource: Long term patterns and relationship with electricity demand, Energy Policy, 35(1), pp. 112–127.

[33] Garcia-Bustamante, E., Gonzalez-Rouco, J. F., Jimenez, P. A., Navarro, J., and Montavez, J. P. 2008: The influence of the Weibull assumption in monthly wind energy estimation. *Wind Energy* 11, pp. 483-502.

[34] Greene, J. S., Morrissey, M. L. and Johnson, S., 2010: Wind Climatology, Climate Change, and Wind Energy, *Geography Compass*, 4(11), pp. 1592-1605.

[35] Ushiyama, I., Wind energy activities in Japan, *Renewable Energy*, 1999, 16(1-4), pp. 811-816.

[36] Wright, R. M., 2001: Wind energy development in the Caribbean, *Renewable Energy*, 24(3-4), pp. 439-444.

[37] Salameh, Z. M. and Irianto, S., 1992: Optimum windmill-site matching, *IEEE Trans. Energy Convers.*, 7(4), ppp. 669-676.

[38] Landberg, L., Myllerup, L., Rathmann, O., Petersen, E. L., Jørgensen, B. H., Badger,J., and Mortensen, N. G., 2003: Review wind resource estimation - an overview, *Wind Energy*, 6, pp. 261–271.

[39] Bechrakis, D., J. and McKeogh, D., 2004: Wind resource assessment of an area using short term data correlated to a long term data set. *Solar Energy*, 76, pp. 725-732.

[40] Tieleman, H. W., 1992: Wind characteristics in the surface layer over heterogeneous terrain, *J. Wind. Eng. Ind. Aerodyn.*, 41(44), pp. 329-340.

[41] Pallabazzer, R., 1995: Evaluation of wind-generator potentiality. *Solar Energy*, 55(1), pp. 49-59.

[42] Pallabazzer, R., 2004. Previsional estimation of the energy output of wind generators, *Renewable Energy* 29(3), pp. 413-420.

[43] Gârbacea, A., Wind energy development in west of Romania, *Renewable Energy*, 1996, 9(1-4), 815-817.

[44] Linde, H. A., Wind energy in South Africa. *Renewable Energy*, 1996, 9(1-4), 880-883.

[45] Mulugetta, Y. and Drake, F., Assessment of solar and wind energy resources in Ethiopia. II. Wind energy, *Solar Energy*, 1996, 57(4), 323-334.

[46] Hanagasioglu, M., 1992: Wind energy in Turkey, *Renewable Energy*, 16(1-4), 822-827.

[47] Merzouk, N. K., Wind energy potential of Algeria, *Ren. Energy*, 2000, 21(3-4), pp. 553-562.

[48] Osta, W. E. and Kalifa, Y., 2003: Prospects of wind power plants in Libya: A case study, *Renewable Energy*, 28(3), pp. 363-371.

[49] Jiang, Q., Doyle, J. D. Haack, T., Dvorak, M. J., Archer, C. L. and Jacobson, M. Z. 2008: Exploring wind energy potential off the California coast, *Geophys. Res. Lett.*, 35, L20819, doi:10.1029/2008GL034674.

[50] Jimenez, B., Durante, F., Lange, B., Kreutzer, T., and Tambke, J., 2007: Offshore wind resource assessment with WAsP and MM5: Comparative study for the German Bight, *Wind Energy*, 10, pp. 121-134.

[51] Sen, Z., 1997: Statistical investigation of wind energy reliability and its application, *Renewable Energy*, 10, pp.71–79.

[52] Gasset, N., Landry, M., Gagnon, Y., 2012: A Comparison of Wind Flow Models for Wind Resource Assessment in Wind Energy Applications, *Energies*, 5, pp. 4288-4322; doi:10.3390/en5114288.

[53] Ouammia, A., Sacile, R., Mimet, A., 2010: Wind energy potential in Liguria region, *Renewable and Sustainable Energy Reviews*, 14, pp. 289–300.

[54] Zhou, W., Yang, H.X., and Fang, Z.H., 2006: Wind power potential and characteristic analysis of the Pearl River Delta region, China, *Renewable Energy*, 31, pp. 739–753.

[55] Ucar A, and Balo F., 2009: Evaluation of wind energy potential and electricity generation at six locations in Turkey, *Applied Energy*, 86, pp. 1864–1872.

[56] Fyrippis, I., Axaopoulos, P.J., and Panayiotou G., 2010: Wind energy potential assessment in Naxos Island, Greece, *Applied Energy*, 87, pp. 577–586.

[57] Stull, R. B. *An Introduction to Boundary Layer Meteorology;* Kluwer Academic Publishers: Dordrecht, The Netherlands, 1988.

[58] Wieringa, J. Representative roughness parameters for homogeneous terrain, Bound. *Layer Meteorol.*, 1993, 63, 323-363.

[59] Simiu, E., Heckert, N., Filliben, J., Johnson, S. Extreme wind load estimates based on the Gumbel distribution of dynamic pressures: an assessment, *Struct. Safety*, 2001, 23 (3), 221-229.

[60] Kiss, P., Janosi, I. M., Comprehensive empirical analysis of ERA-40 surface wind speed distribution over Europe, *Energy Convers. Manage.*, 2008, 49(8), 2142–2151; doi:10.1016/j.enconman.2008.02.003.

[61] IEC Standard, 6-1400-12-1, 2005: Power performance measurements of electricity producing wind turbines.

[62] IEC. *Wind turbines – part 1: design requirements. Tech. rep. 61400-1 Ed. 3*, International Electrotechnical Commission; 2005.

[63] Antoniou, I., S. Pedersen, P. D. Enevoldsen, 2009: Wind shear and uncertainties in power curve measurement and wind resources, Wind Engineering, 33, 449-468.

[64] Hoven, I. V. D., Power spectrum of horizontal wind speed in the frequency range from 0.0007 to 900 cycles per hour, *Journal of Meteorology*, 1957, 14, 160-164.

[65] Kwon, S., Uncertainty analysis of wind energy potential assessment, *Applied Energy*, 2010, 87(3), 856-865.

[66] Weisser, D., Foxon, T. J., 2003: Implications of seasonal and diurnal variations of wind velocity for power output estimate of a turbine: a case study of Grenada, Int. J. Energy Res., 27, pp. 1165-1179.

[67] Harris, R. I. 2006: Errors in gev analysis of wind epoch maxima from Weibull parents, *Wind Struct.*, 9(3), 179-191.

[68] Justus, C. G., Mikhail, A, 1976: Height variations of wind speed and wind distribution statistics, *Geophys. Res. Lett.*, 3, 261-264.

[69] Peterson, E. W., J. P. Hennessey, 1977: On the use of power laws for estimates of wind power potential, *J. Appl. Meteorol.*, 17, 390-394.

[70] Weggel, R. J. 1999: Maximum daily wind gust related to mean daily wind speed. *J. Struct. Eng.*, 465-469.

[71] Rife, D. L. and Davis C. A. 2005: Verification of temporal variations in mesoscale numerical wind forecasts, *Mon. Wea. Rev.*, 133, 3368-3381, doi:10.1175/MWR3052.1.

[72] Horvath, K., D. Koracin, R. K. Vellore, J. Jiang, and R. Belu, 2012: Sub-kilometer dynamical downscaling of near-surface winds in complex terrain using WRF and MM5 mesoscale models. *J. Geophys. Res.*, 117, D11111, doi:10.1029/2012JD017432.

[73] Rohatgi, J., G. Barbezier, 1999: Wind turbulence and atmospheric stability-their effects on wind turbine output, *Renew. Energy*, 16, 908-911.

[74] Gustavson, M. R. 1978: Wind power extraction limits. In: *Proceedings National Conference,* Fall '78, ed. Vaughn Nelson, p. 101.

[75] Sisterson, D. L., B. B. Hick, R. L. Coulter, M. L. Wesely, 1983: Difficulties in using power laws for wind energy assessment, *Solar Energy*, 31, 201-204.

[76] Smedman, A., U. Hogstrom, H. Bergstrom, 1996: Low level jets - a decisive factor for offshore wind energy siting in the Baltic Sea, *Wind Engineering*, 28, 137-147.

[77] Sumner, J., Masson, C., Influence of atmospheric stability on wind turbine power performance curves, *J. Sol. Energy Eng.*, 2006,128, 531-537.

[78] Wagner, R., I. Antoniou, S. M. Pedersen, M. S. Courtney, H. E. Jørgensen, 2009: The influence of the wind speed profile on wind turbine performance measurements, *Wind Energy,* 12, 348-362.

[79] Wharton, S., J. K. Lundquist, 2011: Atmospheric stability affects wind turbine power collection, *Environ. Res. Lett.*, 7, 014005 (9 pp.).

[80] US DOE, 2008: Research needs for wind resource characterization. *NREL Tech. Rep. 500-43521, 116 pp.* [Available online at www.nrel.gov/docs/fy08osti/43521.pdf].

[81] Vanderwende, B. J. and Lundquist, J. K. 2012: The modification of wind turbine performance by statistically distinct atmospheric regimes. *Environ. Res. Lett.*,7 03403 5.

[82] Banta, R. M., Y. L. Pichugina, W. A. Brewer, 2006: Turbulent velocity-variance profiles in the stable boundary layer generated by a nocturnal low-level jet. *J. Atmos. Sci.,* 63, 2700-2719.

[83] Barthelmie, R. J., S. C. Pryor, S. T. Frandsen, K. S. Hansen, J. G. Schepers, K. Rados, W. Schlez, A. Neubert, L. E. Jensen, and S. Neckelmann, 2010: Quantifying the impact of wind turbine wakes on power output at offshore wind farms. *J. Atmos. Oceanic Technol.,* 27, 1302-1317, doi:10.1175/2010JTECHA1398.1.

[84] Belu, R. G., Koracin, D., 2012: Effects of the Complex Wind Regimes and Meteorological Parameters on Wind Turbine Performances, *IEEE Energy Tech. 2012 Conference* Cleveland, Ohio (CD Proceedings).

[85] Probst, O., Cárdenas, D., 2010: State of the Art and Trends in Wind Resource Assessment, *Energies*, 3, pp. 1087-1141; doi:10.3390/en3061087.

[86] Knowles Middleton, W.E., and Spilhaus, A. F. Meteorological Instruments, Third Edition revised, University of Toronto Press, Toronto, Canada, *1953*

[87] Knowles Middleton, W.E., Invention of the Meteorological Instruments, Johns Hopkins Press, Baltimore, 1969

[88] Kristensen, L., Hansen, O. F. *Distance Constant of the Risø Cup Anemometer; Report Number Risø–R–1320 (EN),* RISØ: Roskilde, Denmark, 2002.

[89] Kristensen, L. 1999: The perennial cup anemometer, *Wind Energy*, 2, pp. 59-75

[90] Wyngaard, J. C. 1981: Cup, propeller, vane, and sonic anemometers in turbulence research. *Ann. Rev. Fluid Mecha*nics, 13, pp. 399-423.

[91] Kaimal, J. C., Gaynor, J. E., Zimmerman, H. A., Zimmerman, G. A. 1990: Minimizing flow distortion errors in a sonic anemometer. *Bound.-Lay. Meteorol.*, 53, pp. 103-115.

[92] Wilczak, J. M., Oncley, S. P., Stage, S. A. 2001: Sonic anemometer tilt correction algorithms, *Bound.-Lay. Meteorol.*, 99, pp. 127-150.

[93] Cuerva, A., Sanz-Andrés, A. 2000: On sonic anemometer measurement theory. *J. Wind Eng. Ind. Aerodyn.*, 88, pp. 25-55.

[94] Kaimal, J. C., Wyndgaard, J. C., Haugen, D. A. 1968: Deriving power spectra from a three-component sonic anemometer, *J. Appl. Meteorol.*, 7, pp. 827-837.

[95] Crescenti, G. H. 1998: The degradation of doppler sodar performance due to noise: A review. *Atmos. Environ.*, 32, ppp. 1499-1509.

[96] Anderson, P. S., Ladkin, R. S., Renfrew, I. A. 2005: An autonomous doppler sodar wind profiling system. *J. Atmosph. Ocean. Technol.*, 22, ppp. 1310-1325.

[97] Antoniou, I., Jørgensen, H. E., Mikkelsen, T., Pedersen, T. F., Warmbier, G., Smith, D. Comparison of Wind Speed and Power Curve Measurements Using a Cup Anemometer, a LIDAR and a SODAR. In: *Proceedings of the EWEA European Wind Energy Conference*, London, UK, 22-25 November 2004.

[98] Bradley, S., von Hünerbein, S. Comparisons of New Technologies for Wind Profile Measurements Associated with Wind Energy Applications. In: *Proceedings of the EWEA European Wind Energy Conference,* Milan, Italy, 7-10 May 2007.

[99] Elliott, D. L., J. B. Cadogan, 1990: Effects of wind shear and turbulence on wind turbine power curves *1990 European Community Wind Energy Conf. and Exhibition* (Madrid, Sept. 1990).

[100] Graber, W. K. SODAR monitoring of the atmosphere-Recent developments. *Appl. Phys. B* 1993, 57, 1-2.

[101] Vogt, S., Thomas, P. SODAR-A useful remote sounder to measure wind and turbulence. *J. Wind Eng. Ind. Aerodyn.* 1995, 54-55, 163-172.

[102] Lang, S., McKeogh, M., LIDAR and SODAR Measurements of Wind Speed and Direction in Upland Terrain for Wind Energy Purposes, *Remote Sens.* 2011, 3, 1871-1901; doi:10.3390/rs3091871.

[103] Bingöl, F., Mann, J. and Larsen, G. C., 2010: Light detection and ranging measurements of wake dynamics part I: one-dimensional scanning. *Wind Energy*, 13: 51-61. doi: 10.1002/we.352.

[104] Krishnamurthy, R., Choukulkar, A., Calhoun, R., Fine, J., Oliver, A., and Barr, K. S. 2012:, Coherent Doppler lidar for wind farm characterization. *Wind Energy*. doi: 10. 1002/we.539.

[105] Iungo, G., Y. Wu and F. Porté-Agel, 2012: Field measurements of wind turbine wakes with LiDARs. *J. of Atmos. and Oceanic Tech*. doi: 10.1175/JTECH-D-12-00051.1.

[106] Peña, A., C. B. Hasager, S. Gryning, M. Courtney, I. Antoniou, and T. Mikkelsen, 2009: Offshore wind profiling using light detection and ranging instruments. *Wind Energy*, 12, 105-124. doi: 10.1002/we.283.

[107] Pichugina, Yelena L., Robert M., Banta, W. Alan Brewer, Scott P. Sandberg, R. Michael Hardesty, 2012: Doppler Lidar–Based Wind-Profile Measurement System for Offshore Wind-Energy and Other Marine Boundary Layer Applications. *J. Appl. Meteor. Climatology*, 51, 327-349.doi: doi: 10.1175/JAMC-D-11-040.1.

[108] Krishnamoorthy, K., *Handbook of statistical distributions with applications*, New York: Chapman and Hall; 2006.

[109] Stewart, D. A., 1978: Essenwanger, O. M. Frequency-distribution of wind speed near surface, *J. Appl. Meteorol.*, 17(11), pp. 1633-1642.

[110] Hennessy, J. P., 1977: Some aspects of wind power statistics, J. of Appl. Meteor., 16, pp. 119-128.

[111] Justus, C. G., Hargraves, W. R., Mikhail, A., Graber, D., 1978: Methods of estimating wind speed frequency distribution, J. of Appl. Meteorology, 17, pp. 350-353.

[112] Stevens, M. J. M., Smulders, P. T., 1979: The estimation of parameters of the Weibull wind speed distribution for wind energy utilization purposes, Wind Engineering, 3(2), pp. 132-145.

[113] Crotis, R. B., Sigl, A. B., Klein, J., 1978: Probability models of wind velocity magnitude and persistence, Solar Energy, 20, pp. 483-93.

[114] Kaminsky, F. C., 1977: Four probability densities (log-normal, gamma, Weibull, and Rayleigh) and their application to modelling average hourly wind speed. In: *Proceedings of the International Solar Energy Society*, pp. 19.6-19.10.

[115] Auwera, L., Meyer, F., Malet, L., 1980: The use of the Weibull three-parameter model for estimating mean wind power densities, *J. Applied Meteorology*, 19, pp. 819-825.

[116] Pavia, E. G., O'Brien, J. J., 1986: Weibull statistics of wind speed over the ocean, *J. Climate Appl. Meteorology*, 25, pp. 1324-1332.

[117] Sen, Z., 1997: Statistical investigation of wind energy reliability and its application. *Renewable Energy*, 10, pp. 71–79.

[118] Deaves, D. M., Lines, I. G., 1997: On the fitting of low mean wind speed data to the Weibull distribution, *J. Wind Engineering and Industrial Aerodynamics*, 65, pp. 169-178.

[119] Prasad, R. D. Bansal, R. C., and Sauturaga, M., 2009: Wind Energy Analysis for Vadravadra Site in Fiji Islands: A Case Study, *IEEE Trnas. On Energy Conservation*, 24(3), pp. 750-757

[120] Ulgen, K., Genc, A., Hepbasli, A., et al., Assessment of wind characteristics for energy generation, *Energy Sources*, 2004, 26(13), 1227-1237.

[121] Monahan, A. H., The probability of sea surface wind speeds, part I: Theory and Sea Winds Observations, *J. Climate*, 2006, 19, 497-520.

[122] Garcia, A., Torres, J. L., Prieto, E., Francisco, A. D., Fitting wind speed distributions: a case study, *Solar Energy*, 1998, 62(2), 139-44.

[123] Celik, A. N., 2003: Assessing the suitability of wind speed probability distribution functions based on wind power density. Renewable Energy, 28, pp. 1563-1574.

[124] Conradsen, K., Nielsen, L. B. and Prahm, L. P. 1984. Review of Weibull statistics for estimation of wind speed distributions. Journal of Climate and Applied Meteorology 23, pp. 1173-1183.

[125] Basumatary, H., Sreevalsan, E., Sai, K. K., 2005: Weibull parameter estimates – a comparison of different methods, *Wind Engeering*, 29, pp. 309-315.

[126] Christofferson, R. D., Gillete, D. A., 1987: A simple estimator of the shape factor of the two-parameter Weibull distribution, *J. Climate Appl. Meteor.*, 26, pp. 323-325.

[127] Zhou, J., Erdem, E., Li, G., and Shi, J., 2010: Comprehensive evaluation of wind speed distribution models: a case study for North Dakota sites, *Energy Convers Manage.*, 51, pp. 1449–1458.

[128] Kaylan, A.R., Harris, C.M., 1981: Efficient algorithms to derive maximum-likelihood estimates for finite exponential and Weibull mixtures. *Comput Oper Res.*, 3, pp. 97–104.

[129] Cohen, A. C. 1975: Multi-censored sampling in 3 parameter Weibull distribution, *Technometrics*, 17(3), pp. 347-351.

[130] Auwera, L.V., Meyer, F., and Malet, L. M., 1980: The use of the Weibull three-parameter model for estimating mean wind power densities. *J Appl Meteorol.* 19, pp. 819–825.

[131] Kundu, D., Raqab, M., 2005: Generalized Rayleigh distribution: different methods of estimations. *Comput. Stat. Data Anal.*, 49(1),pp. 187-200, doi:10.1016/j.csda.2004.05.008.

[132] Stedinger, J. R., 1980: Fitting log normal-distributions to hydrologic data, *Water Resour. Res.*, 16(3), pp. 481-490.

[133] Griffis, V. W., Stedinger, J. R., 2007: Log-Pearson type 3 distribution and its application in flood frequency analysis. II: parameter estimation methods. *J. Hydrology Eng.*, 12(5), pp. 492-500.

[134] Hirose, H., 1995: Maximum likelihood parameter estimation in the three-parameter gamma distribution, *Comput. Stat. Data Anal.*, 20(4), pp. 343-54.

[135] Stacy, E. W., Mihram, G. A., 1965: Parameter estimation for a generalized Gamma distribution. *Technometrics*, 7(3), pp. 349-358.

[136] Pryor, S. C., Barthelmie, R. J., 2002: Statistical analysis of flow characteristics in the coastal zone. *J. Wind Engineering and Industry Aerodynamics*, 90(3), pp. 201-221.

[137] Celik, A. N., Makkawi, A., Muneer, T., 2010: Critical evaluation of wind speed frequency distribution functions, *J. Renew. Sustain. Energy*, 2, pp. 93-102.

[138] Belu, R. G., Koracin, D., 2009: Wind Characteristics and Wind Energy Potential in Western Nevada, *Renewable Energy*, 34(10), pp. 2246-2251.

[139] Belu, R. G., Koracin, D., 2013: Statistical and Spectral Analysis of the Wind Characteristics in the Western Nevada, *J. of Wind Energy*, vol. 2013 (12 pages), Article ID 739162, 2013. doi:10.1155/2013/739162.

[140] Celik, A. N. 2004: A statistical analysis of wind power density based on the Weibull and Rayleigh models at the southern region of Turkey. *Renew. Energy*, 29(4), pp. 593-604.

[141] Ramirez, P., Carta, J. A.,2005: Influence of the data sampling interval in the estimation of the parameters of the Weibull wind speed probability density distribution: a case study. *Energy Convers. Manage.*, 46(15-16), pp. 2419-2438.

[142] Carta, J. A., Ramirez, P., 2007: Analysis of two-component mixture Weibull statistics 0for estimation of wind speed distributions, *Renew. Energy*, 32(3), pp. 518-531.

[143] Chang, T.-J., and Tu, Y.-L. 2007: Evaluation of monthly capacity factor of WECS using chronological and probabilistic wind speed data: a case study of Taiwan, Renew. *Energy*, 32(12), pp. 1999-2010.

[144] Chang, T. P., 2011: Performance comparison of six numerical methods in estimating Weibull parameters for wind energy application, *Applied Energy*, 88, pp. 272-282.

[145] Seguro, J. V., Lambert, T. W., 2000: Modern estimation of the parameters of the Weibull wind speed distribution for wind energy analysis, *J. Wind Engineering and Industry Aerodynamics*, 85, pp. 75- 85.

[146] Fawzi, A. L. J., 2009: Wind power analysis and site matching of wind turbine generators in Kingdom of Bahrain, *Applied Energy*, 86, pp. 538-545.

[147] Bekele, G., Palm, B., 2009: Wind energy potential assessment at four typical locations in Ethiopia, *Applied Energy*, 86, pp. 388-396.

[148] Ucar, A., Balo, F., 2009: Investigation of wind characteristics and assessment of wind-generation potentiality in Uludag-Bursa, Turkey, *Applied Energy*, 86, pp. 333-339.

[149] Fyrippis, I., Axaopoulos, I. P., Panayiotou, G., 2010: Wind energy potential assessment in Naxos Island, Greece, *Applied Energy*, 87, pp. 577-586.

[150] Beccali, M., Cirrincione, G., Marvuglia, A., Serporta, C., 2010; Estimation of wind velocity over a complex terrain using the Generalized Mapping Regressor, *Applied Energy*, 87, PP. 884-893.

[151] Akdag, S. A., Dinler, A., 2009: A new method to estimate Weibull parameters for wind energy applications. *Energy Convers. Management*, 50, pp. 1761-1766.

[152] Akdag, S. A., Bagiorgas, H. S., Mihalakakou, G., 2010: Use of two-component Weibull mixtures in the analysis of wind speed in the Eastern Mediterranean, *Applied Energy*, 87, pp. 2566-2573.

[153] Chang, T. P., 2011; Estimation of wind energy potential using different probability 2density functions, *Applied Energy*, 88, PP. 1848-1856.

[154] Ohunakin, O. S., Adaramola, M. S., Oyewola, O. M., 2011: Wind energy evaluation for electricity generation using WECS in seven selected locations in Nigeria, *Applied Energy*, 88, pp. 3197-3206.

[155] Fırtın, E., Guler, O., Akdag, S. A., 2011: Investigation of wind shear coefficients and their effect on electrical energy generation, *Applied Energy*, 88, pp. 4097-4105.

[156] Hossain, A., Zimmer, W., 2003: Comparison of estimation methods for Weibull parameters: Complete and censored samples, *Journal of Statistical Computation and Simulation*, 73(2), pp. 145-153.

[157] Kantar, Y. M., Senoglu, B., 2000: A comparative study for the location and scale parameters of the Weibull distribution with given shape parameter, *Comput. Geosci.*, 34, pp. 1900-1909.

[158] Raichle, B. W., Carson, W. R., 2009: Wind resource assessment of the Southern Appalachian Ridges in the Southeastern United States, *Renewable and Sustainable Energy Review*, 13, pp. 1104-1110.

[159] Chang, T. P., 2011: Performance comparison of six numerical methods in estimating Weibull parameters for wind energy application, *Applied Energy*, 88, pp. 272-282.

[160] Rocha, P. A. C., Coelho de Sousa, R., Freitas de Andrade, C., et al. 2012: Comparison of seven numerical methods for determining Weibull parameters for wind energy generation in the northeast region of Brazil, *Applied Energy*, 89, pp. 395-400.

[161] Suomalainen, K., Silva, C. A., Ferrão, P., et al., 2012: Synthetic wind speed scenarios including diurnal effects: Implications for wind power dimensioning, *Energy*, 37, pp. 41-50.

[162] Carta, J. A., Velázquez, S., 2011: A new probabilistic method to estimate the long-term wind speed characteristics at a potential wind energy conversion site, *Energy*, 36, pp. 2671-2685.

[163] Celik, A. N., 2004: On the Distributional Parameters Used in Assessment of the Suitability of Wind Speed Probability Density Functions, Energy Conversion and Management, 45(11-12), pp. 1735-1747. doi:10.1016/j.enconman.2003.09.027.

[164] Villanueva, D., Feijoo, A., 2010: Wind power distributions: A review of their applications, *Renewable and Sustainable Energy Reviews*, 14, pp. 1490-1495.

[165] Morgan, E. C., Lackner, M., Vogel, R. M., Baise, L. G., 2011: Probability distributions for offshore wind speeds, *Energy Conversion and Management*, 52, pp. 15-26.

[166] Li, M. and Li, X., 2005: MEP-Type Distribution Function: A Better Alternative to Weibull Function for Wind Speed Distributions, Renewable Energy, 30(8), pp. 1221-1240. doi:10.1016/j.renene.2004.10.003

[167] Akpinar, S., Akpinar, E. K., 2009: Estimation of wind energy potential using finite mixture distribution models, Energy Convers. Manage., 50(4), pp. 877-884.

[168] Carta, J. A., Ramirez, P., 2007: Analysis of two-component mixture Weibull statistics for estimation of wind speed distributions. Renew. Energy, 32(3), pp. 518-531.

[169] Carta, J. A., Ramirez, P., 2007: Use of finite mixture distribution models in the analysis of wind energy in the Canarian Archipelago. Energy Convers. Management, 48(1), pp. 281-291.

[170] Zhang, J., Chowdhury, S., Messac, A., and Castillo, L., 2012: A hybrid measure-correlate-predict method for wind resource assessment, In: ASME 2012 6th International Conference on Energy Sustainability, ASME Proceedings.

[171] Zhang, J., Chowdhury, S., Messac, A., and Castillo, L., 2013: A multivariate and multimodal wind distribution model, *Renewable Energy*, 51, pp. 436-447.

[172] Jaramillo, O. A., Borja, M. A. 2004: Wind speed analysis in La Ventosa, Mexico: a bimodal probability distribution case. Renew. Energy, 29(10), pp. 1613-1630.

[173] Carta, J. A., Ramirez, P., Velazquez, S., 2008: Influence of the level of fit of a density probability function to wind-speed data on the WECS mean power output estimation, Energy Convers. and Management, 49(10), pp. 2647-655

[174] Carta, J. A., Ramirez, P., Velazquez, S., 2009: A review of wind speed probability distributions used in wind energy analysis Case studies in the Canary Islands. Renew. Sustain. Energy Rev., 13(5), pp. 933-955.

[175] Ramirez, P., Carta, J. A., 2006: The use of wind probability distributions derived from the maximum entropy principle in the analysis of wind energy: a case study, Energy Convers. Manage., 47(15-16), pp. 2564-2577.

[176] Chang, T.-J., Tu, Y.-L., 2007: Evaluation of monthly capacity factor of WECS using chronological and probabilistic wind speed data: a case study of Taiwan, Renew. Energy, 32(12), pp. 1999-2010.

[177] Qina, Z., Li, W., Xiong, X., 2011: Estimating wind speed probability distribution using kernel density method, *Electric Power Systems Research,* 81(12),pp. 2139–2146

[178] Akdag, S. A., Dinler, A. 2009: A new method to estimate Weibull parameters for wind energy applications, *Energy Convers. Manage.*, 50, pp. 1761-6.

[179] Akdag, S. A., Bagiorgas, H. S., and Mihalakakou, G. 2010: Use of two-component Weibull mixtures in the analysis of wind speed in the Eastern Mediterranean, *Applied Energy*, 87, pp. 2566-73.

[180] Li, M., and Li, X., 2004: On the probabilistic distribution of wind speeds: theoretical development and comparison with data, *Int J Exergy*, 1, pp. 237–55.

[181] Li, M., and Li, X., 2004: MEP-type distribution function: a better alternative to Weibull function for wind speed distributions, *Renewable Energy*, 30, pp. 1221–1240.

[182] Akpinar, S., and Akpinar, E.K., 2007: Wind energy analysis based on maximum entropy principle (MEP)-type distribution function, *Energy Convers. Manage.*, 48, pp. 1140–1149.

[183] Kantar, Y.M., and Usta, I., 2008: Analysis of wind speed distributions: wind distribution function derived from minimum cross entropy principles as better alternative to Weibull function, *Energy Convers. Manage.*, 49, pp. 962–973.

[184] Andersen, M., A review of measure-correlate-predict techniques, Technical Report No. 01327R00022, Renewable Energy Systems, 2004.

[185] Rogers, A. L., Rogers, J. W., James, F., and Manwell, J. F. 2005: Comparison of the performance of four measure–correlate–predict algorithms. J. Wind Eng. Ind. Aerodyn., 93, 243-264.

[186] Velazquez, S., Carta, J. A. and Mat'ias, J. M., 2011: Comparison between anns and linear mcp algorithms in the long-term estimation of the cost per kwh produced by a wind turbine at a candidate site: A case study in the canary islands. Applied Energy, 88 (11), pp. 3689-3881.

[187] Perea, A. R., Amezcua, J. and Probst, O. 2011: Validation of three new measure-correlate-predict models for the long-term prospection of the wind resource. Journal of Renewable and Sustainable Energy, 3(2), pp. 023105.

[188] Woods, J. C., Watson, S. J. 1997: A new matrix method for predicting long-term wind roses with MCP. J. Wind Eng. Ind. Aerodyn., 66, pp. 85-94.

[189] Lackner, M. A., Rogers, A. L. and Manwell, J. F., 2008: Uncertainty analysis in mcp-based wind resource assessment and energy production estimation, *Journal of Solar Energy Engineering*, 130(3), pp. 031006.

[190] Messac, A., Chowdhury, S. and Zhang, J., 2012: Characterizing and mitigating the wind resource-based uncertainty in farm performance, *Journal of Turbulence*, 13(13), pp. 1-26.

[191] Baidya Roy, S., 2011: Simulating impacts of wind farms on local hydrometeorology. J. Wind Eng. Ind. Aerodyn. http://www.atmos.illinois.edu/~sbroy/publ/dx.doi.org/10. 1016/j.jweia.2010.12.013.

[192] Baidya Roy, S., J. J. Traiteur, 2010: Impacts of wind farms on surface temperatures. PNAS, 107, pp. 17899-17904

[193] Lu, H. and F. Porte-Agel, 2011: Large-eddy simulation of a very large wind farm in a stable atmospheric boundary layer, *Physics of Fluids*, 23 065101.

[194] Pryor, S. C., J. T. Schoof, R. J. Barthelmie, 2006: Winds of change?: Projections of near-surface winds under climate change scenarios, *Geophys. Res. Lett.*, 33, L11702, doi:10.1029/2006GL026000.

[195] Ren, D., 2010: Effects of global warming on wind energy availability. *J. Renewable Sustainable Energy* 2, 052301; doi: 10.1063/1.3486072.

[196] Smith, J., M. Milligan, E. DeMeo, B. Parsons, 2007: Utility wind integration and operating impact state of the art, *IEEE Trans. Power Syst.*, 22, 900-908.

[197] Storm, B., J. Dudhia, S. Basu, A. Swift, I. Giammanco, 2009: Evaluation of the Weather Research and Forecasting Model on Forecasting Low-level Jets: Implications for Wind Energy. *Wind Energy*, 12(1), 81-90. doi:10.1002/we.288.

[198] Yu, W., Benoit, R., Girard, C., Glazer, A., Lemarquis, D., Salmon, J. R., Pinard, J. P. 2006: Wind Energy Simulation Toolkit (WEST): A wind mapping system for use by wind energy industry. *Wind Eng.*, 30, pp. 15-33.

[199] Landberg, L., Myllerup, L., Rathmann, O., Petersen, E. L., Jørgensen, B. H., Badger, J., Mortensen, N. G., 2003: Wind resource estimation-An overview. *Wind Energy*, 6, pp. 261-271.

[200] Cook, N. J., Harris, R. I., 2003: Whiting, R. Extreme wind speeds in mixed climates revisited. *J. Wind Eng. Ind. Aerodyn.*, 91, pp. 403-422.

[201] Klink, K., 1999: Climatological mean and interannual variance of United States surface wind speed, direction and velocity, *Int. J. Climatol.*, 19, pp. 471-488.

[202] Calero, R., and Carta, J. A., 2004: Action plan for wind energy development in the Canary Islands, *Energy Policy*, 32(10), pp 1185-1197

[203] Gass, V., Strauss, F., Schmidt, J., and Schmid, E., 2011: Assessing the effect of wind power uncertainty on profitability, *Renewable and Sustainable Energy Reviews*, 15(6), pp. 2677-2683

In: Advances in Energy Research. Volume 20　　　　ISBN: 978-1-63463-169-3
Editor: Morena J. Acosta　　　　　　　　　　© 2015 Nova Science Publishers, Inc.

Chapter 2

PRINCIPLE OF LOW ENERGY BUILDING DESIGN: HEATING, VENTILATION AND AIR CONDITIONING

Abdeen Mustafa Omer
Energy Research Institute (ERI), Nottingham, UK

ABSTRACT

The move towards a de-carbonised world, driven partly by climate science and partly by the business opportunities it offers, will need the promotion of environmentally friendly alternatives, if an acceptable stabilisation level of atmospheric carbon dioxide is to be achieved. This requires the harnessing and use of natural resources that produce no air pollution or greenhouse gases and provides comfortable coexistence of human, livestock, and plants. This study reviews the energy-using technologies based on natural resources, which are available to and applicable in the farming industry. Integral concept for buildings with both excellent indoor environment control and sustainable environmental impact are reported in the present communication. Techniques considered are hybrid (controlled natural and mechanical) ventilation including night ventilation, thermo-active building mass systems with free cooling in a cooling tower, and air intake via ground heat exchangers. Special emphasis is put on ventilation concepts utilising ambient energy from air ground and other renewable energy sources, and on the interaction with heating and cooling. It has been observed that for both residential and office buildings, the electricity demand of ventilation systems is related to the overall demand of the building and the potential of photovoltaic systems and advanced co-generation units. The focus of the world's attention on environmental issues in recent years has stimulated response in many countries, which have led to a closer examination of energy conservation strategies for conventional fossil fuels. One way of reducing building energy consumption is to design buildings, which are more economical in their use of energy for heating, lighting, cooling, ventilation and hot water supply. Passive measures, particularly natural or hybrid ventilation rather than air-conditioning, can dramatically reduce primary energy consumption. However, exploitation of renewable energy in buildings and agricultural greenhouses can, also, significantly contribute towards reducing dependency on fossil fuels. This study describes various designs of low energy buildings. It also, outlines the effect of dense urban building nature on energy consumption, and its contribution to climate change. Measures, which would help to save energy in buildings, are also presented.

Keywords: Built environment; energy efficient comfort; ventilation; sustainable environmental impact.

NOMENCLATURE

A	Heat transfer area, m^2
A(s)	Temperature area over $25^{\circ}C$, degree-hour
A_{max}	Maximum temperature area, degree-hour
Cp	Specific heat at constant pressure, kJ/kg K
F	Shape factor, dimensionless
F(t)	Temperature at time t truncated over $25^{\circ}C$
Gb	Beam solar radiation, W/m^2
Gd	Diffuse solar radiation, W/m^2
GT	Total solar radiation (Gb + Gd), W/m^2
g	Acceleration of gravity, m/s^2
h	Heat transfer coefficient, W/m^2 K
I(s)	Normalised temperature index for scenario S, dimensionless
k	Thermal conductivity, W/m K
L	Representative length, m
M	Mass, kg
Na	Nusselt number, dimensionless
Q	Thermal gains, W
Ra	Rayleigh number (g β L^3 $\Delta T/L\nu$), dimensionless
Rb	Beam radiation geometric projection factor, dimensionless
T	Temperature, K
t	Time, s
U	Global heat transfer coefficient, W/m^2 K
V_1	Average indoor velocity
V_o	Outdoor wind speed
x	Ratio of window area to wall area

INDICES

c	Convection
d	Diffuse
i	Internal, instantaneous
r	Radiation
s	Building materials
j	Windowpane

Greek Symbols

α	Absorptance, dimensionless
ε	Emittance, dimensionless
ν	Kinematic viscosity, m^2/s
ρ	Reflectance, dimensionless
σ	Stefan-Boltzmann constant, $W/m^2\,K^4$

1. INTRODUCTION

Globally, buildings are responsible for approximately 40% of the total world annual energy consumption [1]. Most of this energy is for the provision of lighting, heating, cooling, and air conditioning. Increasing awareness of the environmental impact of CO_2, NO_x and CFCs emissions triggered a renewed interest in environmentally friendly cooling, and heating technologies. Under the 1997 Montreal Protocol, governments agreed to phase out chemicals used as refrigerants that have the potential to destroy stratospheric ozone. It was therefore considered desirable to reduce energy consumption and decrease the rate of depletion of world energy reserves and pollution of the environment.

One way of reducing building energy consumption is to design buildings, which are more economical in their use of energy for heating, lighting, cooling, ventilation and hot water supply. Passive measures, particularly natural or hybrid ventilation rather than air-conditioning, can dramatically reduce primary energy consumption [2]. However, exploitation of renewable energy in buildings and agricultural greenhouses can, also, significantly contribute towards reducing dependency on fossil fuels. Therefore, promoting innovative renewable applications and reinforcing the renewable energy market will contribute to preservation of the ecosystem by reducing emissions at local and global levels. This will also contribute to the amelioration of environmental conditions by replacing conventional fuels with renewable energies that produce no air pollution or greenhouse gases.

The provision of good indoor environmental quality while achieving energy and cost efficient operation of the heating, ventilating and air-conditioning (HVAC) plants in buildings represents a multi variant problem. The comfort of building occupants is dependent on many environmental parameters including air speed, temperature, relative humidity and quality in addition to lighting and noise. The overall objective is to provide a high level of building performance (BP), which can be defined as indoor environmental quality (IEQ), energy efficiency (EE) and cost efficiency (CE).

- Indoor environmental quality is the perceived condition of comfort that building occupants experience due to the physical and psychological conditions to which they are exposed by their surroundings. The main physical parameters affecting IEQ are air speed, temperature, relative humidity and quality.
- Energy efficiency is related to the provision of the desired environmental conditions while consuming the minimal quantity of energy.
- Cost efficiency is the financial expenditure on energy relative to the level of environmental comfort and productivity that the building occupants attained. The

overall cost efficiency can be improved by improving the indoor environmental quality and the energy efficiency of a building.

An approach is needed to integrate renewable energies in a way to meet high building performance. However, because renewable energy sources are stochastic and geographically diffuse, their ability to match demand is determined by adoption of one of the following two approaches [2]: the utilisation of a capture area greater than that occupied by the community to be supplied, or the reduction of the community's energy demands to a level commensurate with the locally available renewable resources.

For a northern European climate, which is characterised by an average annual solar irradiance of 150 Wm^{-2}, the mean power production from a photovoltaic component of 13% conversion efficiency is approximately 20 Wm^{-2}. For an average wind speed of 5 ms^{-1}, the power produced by a micro wind turbine will be of a similar order of magnitude, though with a different profile shape. In the UK, for example, a typical office building will have a demand in the order of 300 $kWhm^{-2}yr^{-1}$. This translates into approximately 50 Wm^{-2} of façade, which is twice as much as the available renewable energies [3]. Thus, the aim is to utilise energy efficiency measures in order to reduce the overall energy consumption and adjust the demand profiles to be met by renewable energies. For instance, this approach can be applied to greenhouses, which use solar energy to provide indoor environmental quality. The greenhouse effect is one result of the differing properties of heat radiation when it is generated at different temperatures. Objects inside the greenhouse, or any other building, such as plants, re-radiate the heat or absorb it. Because the objects inside the greenhouse are at a lower temperature than the sun, the re-radiated heat is of longer wavelengths, and cannot penetrate the glass. This re-radiated heat is trapped and causes the temperature inside the greenhouse to rise. Note that the atmosphere surrounding the earth, also, behaves as a large greenhouse around the world. Changes to the gases in the atmosphere, such as increased carbon dioxide content from the burning of fossil fuels, can act like a layer of glass and reduce the quantity of heat that the planet earth would otherwise radiate back into space. This particular greenhouse effect, therefore, contributes to global warming. The application of greenhouses for plants growth can be considered one of the measures in the success of solving this problem. Maximising the efficiency gained from a greenhouse can be achieved using various approaches, employing different techniques that could be applied at the design, construction and operational stages. The development of greenhouses could be a solution to farming industry and food security.

2. BUILT ENVIRONMENT

The heating or cooling of a space to maintain thermal comfort is a highly energy intensive process accounting for as much as 60-70% of total energy use in non-industrial buildings. Of this, approximately 30-50% is lost through ventilation and air infiltration. However, estimation of energy impact of ventilation relies on detailed knowledge about air change rate and the difference in enthalpy between the incoming and outgoing air streams. In practice, this is a difficult exercise to undertake since there is much uncertainty about the value of these parameters [4]. As a result, a suitable datum from which strategic planning for improving the energy efficiency of ventilation can be developed has proved difficult to establish [4]. Efforts to overcome these difficulties are progressing in the following two ways:

- Identifying ventilation rates in a representative cross section of buildings.
- The energy impact of air change in both commercial and domestic buildings.

In addition to conditioning energy, the fan energy needed to provide mechanical ventilation can make a significant further contribution to energy demand. Much depends on the efficiency of design, both in relation to the performance of fans themselves and to the resistance to flow arising from the associated ductwork. Figure 1 illustrates the typical fan and thermal conditioning needs for a variety of ventilation rates and climate conditions.

The building sector is an important part of the energy picture. Note that the major function of buildings is to provide an acceptable indoor environment, which allows occupants to carry out various activities. Hence, the purpose behind this energy consumption is to provide a variety of building services, which include weather protection, storage, communications, thermal comfort, facilities of daily living, aesthetics, work environment, etc. However, the three main energy-related building services are space conditioning (for thermal comfort), lighting (for visual comfort), and ventilation (for indoor air quality). Pollution-free environments are a practical impossibility. Therefore, it is often useful to differentiate between unavoidable pollutants over which little source control is possible, and avoidable pollutants for which control is possible. Unavoidable pollutants are primarily those emitted by metabolism and those arising from the essential activities of occupants. 'Whole building' ventilation usually provides an effective measure to deal with the unavoidable emissions, whereas 'source control' is the preferred and sometimes only practical, method to address avoidable pollutant sources [5]. Hence, achieving optimum indoor air quality relies on an integrated approach to the removal and control of pollutants using engineering judgment based on source control, filtration, and ventilation. Regardless of the kind of building involved, good indoor air quality requires attention to both source control and ventilation. While there are sources common to many kinds of buildings, buildings focusing on renewable energy may have some unique sources and, therefore, may require special attention [5]. In smaller (i.e., house size) buildings, renewable sources are already the primary mechanism for providing ventilation. Infiltration and natural ventilation are the predominant mechanisms for providing residential ventilation for these smaller buildings.

Ventilation is the building service most associated with controlling the indoor air quality to provide a healthy and comfortable environment. In large buildings ventilation is normally supplied through mechanical systems, but in smaller ones, such as single-family homes, it is principally supplied by leakage through the building envelope, i.e., infiltration, which is a renewable resource, albeit unintendedly so. Ventilation can be defined as the process by which clean air is provided to a space. It is needed to meet the metabolic requirements of occupants and to dilute and remove pollutants emitted within a space. Usually, ventilation air must be conditioned by heating or cooling in order to maintain thermal comfort and, hence, becomes an energy liability. Indeed, ventilation energy requirements can exceed 50% of the conditioning load in some spaces [5]. Thus, excessive or uncontrolled ventilation can be a major contributor to energy costs and global pollution. Therefore, in terms of cost, energy, and pollution, efficient ventilation is essential. On the other hand, inadequate ventilation can cause comfort or health problems for the occupants.

One way of reducing building energy consumption is to design buildings, which are more economical in their use of energy for heating, lighting, cooling, ventilation and hot water supply. Passive measures, particularly natural or hybrid ventilation rather than air-conditioning, can dramatically reduce primary energy consumption. However, exploitation of renewable energy in buildings and agricultural greenhouses can, also, significantly contribute towards reducing dependency on fossil fuels.

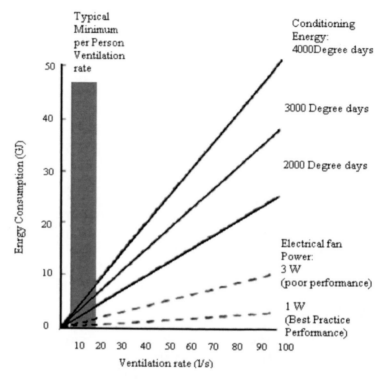

Figure 1. Energy impact of ventilation.

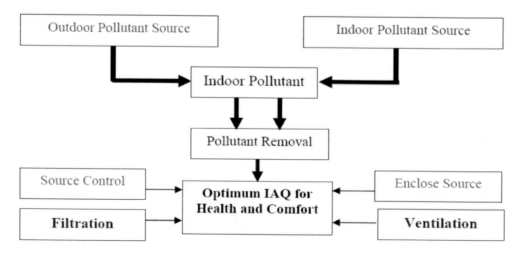

Figure 2. Strategies for controlling IAQ.

Good indoor air quality may be defined as air, which is free of pollutants that cause irritation, discomfort or ill health to occupants [6]. Since long time is spent inside buildings, considerable effort has focused on developing methods to achieve an optimum indoor environment. An almost limitless number of pollutants may be present in a space, of which many are at virtually immeasurably low concentrations and have largely unknown toxicological effects [6]. The task of identifying and assessing the risk of individual pollutants has become a major research activity [e.g., 5, 6, and 7]. In reality, a perfectly pollutants-free environment is unlikely to be attained. Some pollutants can be tolerated at low concentrations, while irritation and odour often provide an early warning of deteriorating conditions. Health related air quality standards are typically based on risk assessment and are either specified in terms of maximum-permitted concentrations or a maximum allowed dose. Higher concentrations of pollutants are normally permitted for short-term exposure than are allowed for long-term exposure [7].

Ventilation is essential for securing a good indoor air quality, but, as explained earlier, can have a dominating influence on energy consumption in buildings. Air quality problems are more likely to occur if air supply is restricted. Probably a ventilation rate averaging 7 l/s.p represents a minimum acceptable rate for normal odour and comfort requirements in office type buildings [8]. Diminishing returns are likely to be experienced at rates significantly above 10 l/s.p [8]. If air quality problems still persist, the cause is likely to be poor outdoor air quality (e.g., the entrainment of outdoor traffic fumes), and poor air distribution or the excessive release of avoidable pollutants into space. However, the energy efficiency of ventilation can be improved by introducing exhaust air heat recovery, ground pre-heating, demand controlled ventilation, displacement ventilation and passive cooling [9]. In each case, a very careful analysis is necessary to ensure that the anticipated savings are actually achievable. Also, it is essential to differentiate between avoidable and unavoidable pollutant emissions. Achieving energy efficiency and optimum Indoor Air Quality (IAQ) depends on minimising the emission of avoidable pollutants. Pollutants inside buildings are derived from both indoor and outdoor contaminant sources, as illustrated in Figure 2. Each of these tends to impose different requirements on the control strategies needed to secure good health and comfort conditions.

3. ACHIEVING ENERGY EFFICIENT VENTILATION

In addition to conditioning energy, the fan energy needed to provide mechanical ventilation can make a significant further contribution to energy demand. A recent review of the American Society of Heating, Refrigerating, and Air-conditioning Engineers (ASHRAE) [10] concludes that the thermal insulation characteristics of buildings improve; ventilation and air movement is expected to become the dominant heating and cooling loss mechanism in buildings of the next century. Poor air quality in buildings sometimes manifests itself; refer to a range of symptoms that an occupant can experience while present in the building. Typical symptoms include lethargy, headaches, lack of concentration, runny nose, dry throat and eye and skin irritation [10]. Other examples of sick building syndrome (SBS) have been associated with the presence of specific pollutants, such as outdoor fumes entering through air intakes [11]. Improved ventilation is one way of tackling the problem. Many standards are being introduced to ensure the adequacy and efficiency of ventilation. However, to be effective, standards need to address the minimum requirements of comfort, operational performance, air tightness, provision for maintenance and durability [11]. Also, various methods have been introduced to improve the energy performance of ventilation. These include:

3.1. Thermal Recovery

Recovery of thermal energy from the exhaust air stream is possible by means of air-to-air heat recovery systems or heat pumps. In theory, such methods can recover as much as 70% of the waste heat [12]. While these methods are exceedingly popular, their full potential is, often, not achieved. This is because buildings or ductwork are often excessively leaky and, hence, additional electrical energy load is needed. To be successful, the designer must integrate such ventilation design with that of the building itself and be thoroughly aware of all the energy paths [12].

3.2. Ground Pre-Conditioning

Ventilation air can be pre-conditioned by passing the supply air ducts under-ground. This can provide a good measure of winter pre-heating and summer pre-cooling [13].

3.3. Demand Control Ventilation

Demand control ventilation, DCV, systems provide a means by which the rate of ventilation is modulated in response to varying air quality conditions. This is effective if a dominant pollutant is identifiable. In transiently occupied buildings, control by metabolic carbon dioxide concentration has become popular although must be introduced with caution. For success, it is essential to ensure that no other problem pollutants are present [14].

3.4. Displacement Ventilation

Displacement ventilation involves distributing clean air at low velocity and at a temperature of approximately 2 K below the ambient air temperature of the space [15]. This dense air mass moves at floor level until it reaches a thermal source such as an occupant or electric equipment, causing the air to warm and gently rise. Polluted air is then collected and extracted above the breathing zone. This process reduces the mixing effect of classical dilution ventilation, thus reducing the amount of ventilation needed to achieve the same air quality in the vicinity of occupants [15]. For success, very careful temperature control is needed and there is a limit on potential cooling capacity [15]. Every attempt should be made to design buildings, which do not require air conditioning, because of the additional energy load is required.

4. OUTDOORS AIR POLLUTION

Clean outdoor air is essential for good indoor air quality. Although air cleaning is possible, it is costly and not effective in the many offices and dwellings that are naturally ventilated, leaky or ventilated by mechanical extract systems. Some air quality problems are global and can only be controlled by international effort. Other pollutants are much more regional and may be associated with local industry and traffic. Nature, too, presents its own problems with large volumes of dust and gaseous emissions being associated with volcanic activity. Similarly, while naturally occurring, radon can penetrate buildings from the underlying geological strata. Even rural areas are not immune to pollution, where the presence of pollen, fungal spores and agricultural chemicals can result in poor health and cause allergic reactions. There are several pollution control strategies.

Some of them are discussed below:

4.1. Filtration

Filtration is applied primarily to remove particulates from the air. Filtration of outdoor air cannot be readily applied to the many buildings that are naturally ventilated or excessively leaky. To be effective, filtration systems must be capable of trapping the smallest of particles and of handling large volumes of airflow. Activated carbon and other absorbing filters are additionally able to remove gaseous pollutants [16].

4.2. Positioning of Air Intakes

Air intakes must be located away from pollutant sources. Particular sources include street level and car parking locations [16]. Although urban air quality is normally much improved at elevations above street level, contamination from adjacent exhaust stacks and cooling towers must, also, be avoided [16]. Determining the optimum position for air intakes may require extensive wind tunnel or fluid dynamics analysis. Further information on the positioning of air intakes is reviewed by Limb 1995 [7].

4.3. Air Quality Controlled Fresh Air Dampers

Traffic pollution in urban areas is often highly transient, with peaks occurring during the morning and evening commuting periods. At these times, it may be possible to improve indoor air quality by temporarily closing fresh air intakes and windows.

4.4. Building Air Tightness

None of the above control strategies will be effective unless the building is well sealed from the outdoor environment to prevent contaminant ingress through air infiltration.

Underground parking garages must also be well sealed from occupied accommodation above. Evidence suggests that sealing is often inadequate [16].

Ventilation is the building service most associated with controlling the indoor air quality to provide a healthy and comfortable environment. In large buildings ventilation is normally supplied through mechanical systems, but in smaller ones, such as single-family homes, it is principally supplied by leakage through the building envelope, i.e., infiltration, which is a renewable resource, albeit unintendedly so.

5. INDOOR POLLUTANTS

Pollutants emitted inside buildings are derived from metabolism (odour, carbon dioxide, and bacteria), the activities of occupants (e.g., smoking, washing and cooking), emissions from materials used in construction and furnishing and emissions from machinery and processes. The preferred order of control is discussed below:

5.1. Source Control

Once a pollutant has entered a space, it can, at best, only be diluted [17]. Avoidable pollutants should, therefore, be eliminated. This means restricting or, preferably, eliminating potentially harmful pollutant emissions.

5.2. Enclosing and Ventilating at Source

Pollutants generated as part of the activity of occupants are usually highly localised. Wherever possible, source control should be applied, combined with the use of local extractors [17].

5.3. General Ventilation

General ventilation of a space is needed to dilute and remove residual pollution primarily from unavoidable contaminant sources [17].

6. VENTILATION OF SPACES IN HUMID CLIMATE

The design of windows in modern buildings in a warm, humid climate can be influenced either by their use to provide physiological and psychological comfort via providing air and daylight to interior spaces or by using them to provide aesthetically appealing fenestration. Most spaces in modern buildings are not adequately ventilated and it is recommended that effort should be directed towards the use of windows to achieve physiological comfort. Evaluation of public housing has focused on four main aspects: economics, social and physical factors, and residents' satisfaction. However, information about the physiological characteristics of spaces in a warm humid climate will aid the design of appropriate spaces with respect to the development and adequate choice of building materials and appropriate use of suitable passive energy. In this light there is a need to examine residents satisfaction with respect to these physiological issues. Proper ventilation in a space is a primary factor in determining human health, comfort and well being of the occupants. At present, getting a proper naturally ventilated space seems to be a difficult task. This is partly due to the specific environmental problems of high temperature, high humidity, low wind velocity, and variable wind direction - usually attributed to the warm humid climate, on the one hand, and the difficulty of articulating the design constraints of security, privacy and the desire of users for large spaces on the other hand. As pointed out by most researchers in the field of passive energy design, such as Givoni [18], Koenigsberger, et al. [19] Boulet [20] and Szokolay [21], the types of spaces most suited to this climate are spaces, which are cross-ventilated. This implies that these spaces must have openings at least on opposite sides of a wall, but this condition is difficult to achieve in view of the design constraints mentioned above. So in most cases, the option left to the designer is to have openings on a wall or openings on adjacent walls. The effectiveness of the above arrangement for effective ventilation of a space still depends on other parameters. Therefore, in order to optimise comfort in spaces in warm humid climate, there is a need to re-examine the factors affecting proper ventilation with respect to these design issues. In order to be thermally comfortable in interior spaces, four environmental parameters, namely air temperature, relative humidity, mean radiant temperature and air velocity, need to be present in the space in adequate proportions [21]. In a warm, humid climate, the predominance of high humidity necessitates a corresponding steady, continuous breeze of medium air speed to increase the efficiency of sweat evaporation and to avoid discomfort caused by moisture on skin and clothes. Continuous ventilation is therefore the primary requirement for comfort [18]. From the above, it is apparent that the most important of these comfort parameters in a warm, humid climate is air velocity. It should, also, be noted that indoor air velocity depends on the velocity of the air outdoors [21]. The factors affecting indoor air movement are orientation of the building with respect to wind direction, effect of the external features of the openings, the position of openings in the wall, the size of the openings and control of the openings. Cross-ventilation is the most effective method of getting appreciable air movement in interior spaces in warm, humid climates. For comfort purposes, the indoor wind velocity should be set at between 0.15 and 1.5 m/s [22]. A mathematical model based on analysis of the experimental results [23], which established the relationship between the average indoor and outdoor air velocities with the windows placed perpendicular to each other, was adapted to suit a warm, humid climate and is, usually, used to evaluate the spaces. Entropy measures the energy dispersion in a system divided by temperature. This ratio represents the tendency of energy to spread out, diffuse, and become less concentrated in one physical location or one energetic state. The formula states that:

$$V_1 = 0.45 \, (1\text{-}exp^{-3.84x}) \, V_o \tag{1}$$

where:

V_1 = average indoor velocity

x = ratio of window area to wall area

V_o = outdoor wind speed

6.1. Air Movement in Buildings

Natural ventilation is now considered to be one of the requirements for a low energy building designs. Until about three decades ago the majority of office buildings were naturally ventilated. With the availability of inexpensive fossil energy and the tendency to provide better indoor environmental control, there has been a vast increase in the use of air-conditioning in new and refurbished buildings. However, recent scientific evidence on the impact of refrigerants and air-conditioning systems on the environment has promoted the more conscious building designers to give serious considerations to natural ventilation in non-domestic buildings [24]. Two major difficulties that a designer has to resolve are the questions of airflow control and room air movement in the space. Because of the problem of scaling and the difficulty of representing natural ventilation in laboratory, most of the methods used for predicting the air movement in mechanically ventilated buildings are not very suitable for naturally ventilated spaces [25]. However, computational fluid dynamics (CFD) is now becoming increasingly used for the design of both mechanical and natural ventilation systems. Since a CFD solution is based on the fundamental flow and energy equations, the technique is equally applicable to a naturally ventilated space as well as a mechanically ventilated one, providing that a realistic representation of the boundary conditions are made in the solution.

6.2. Natural Ventilation

Generally, buildings should be designed with controllable natural ventilation. A very high range of natural ventilation rates is necessary so that the heat transfer rate between inside and outside can be selected to suit conditions [25]. The ventilation rates required to control summertime temperatures are very much higher than these required to control pollution or odour. Any natural ventilation system that can control summer temperatures can readily provide adequate ventilation to control levels of odour and carbon dioxide production in a building. Theoretically, it is not possible to achieve heat transfer without momentum transfer and loss of pressure. However, Figures 3 and 4 show some ideas for achieving heat reclaim at low velocities. Such ideas work well for small buildings.

6.3. Mechanical Ventilation

Most of the medium and large size buildings are ventilated by mechanical systems designed to bring in outside air, filter it, supply it to the occupants and then exhaust an approximately equal amount of stale air. Ideally, these systems should be based on criteria that can be established at the design stage. To return afterwards in attempts to mitigate problems may lead to considerable expense and energy waste, and may not be entirely successful [25]. The key factors that must be included in the design of ventilation systems are: code requirement and other regulations or standards (e.g., fire), ventilation strategy and systems sizing, climate and weather variations, air distribution, diffuser location and local ventilation, ease of operation and maintenance and impact of system on occupants (e.g., acoustically). These factors differ for various building types and occupancy patterns. For example, in office buildings, pollutants tend to come from sources such as occupancy, office equipment, and automobile fumes. Occupant pollutants typically include metabolic carbon dioxide emission, odours and sometimes smoking, when occupants (and not smoking) are the prime source. Carbon dioxide acts as a surrogate and can be used to cost-effectively modulate the ventilation, forming what is known as a demand controlled ventilation system. Generally, contaminant sources are varied but, often, well-defined and limiting values are often determined by occupational standards. Ventilation can be defined as the process by which clean air is provided to a space. It is needed to meet the metabolic requirements of occupants and to dilute and remove pollutants emitted within a space.

6.4. Bioclimatic Design

Bioclimatic design cannot continue to be a side issue of a technical nature to the main architectural design. In recent years started to alter course and to become much more holistic in its approach while trying to address itself to:

- The achievement of a sustainable development.
- The depletion of non-renewable sources and materials.
- The life cycle analysis of buildings.
- The total polluting effects of buildings on the environment.
- The reduction of energy consumption and
- Human health and comfort.

Hidden dimensions of architectural creation are vital to the notion of bioclimatic design. The most fundamental ones are:

TIME, which has been called the fourth dimension of architectural space, is of importance because every object cannot exist but in time. The notion of time gives life to an object and releases it to periodic (predictable) or unperiodic repetition. Times relates to seasonal and diurnal patterns and thus to climate and the way that a building behaves or should be designed to couple with and not antagonise nature. It further releases to the dynamic nature of a building in contrast to the static image that we have created for it.

AIR, is a second invisible but important element. We create space and pretend that it is empty, oblivious of the fact that it is both surrounded by and filled with air. Air in its turn, is due to air-movement, which is generated by either temperature or pressure differences, is very much there and alive. And related to the movement of air should be building shapes, sections, heights, orientations and the size and positioning of openings.

LIGHT, and in particular daylight, is a third important element. Architecture cannot exist but with light and from the time we have been able to substitute natural light with artificial lighting, many a building and a lot of architecture has become poorer so. It is not an exaggeration to say that the real form giver to architecture is not the architect himself but light and that the architect is but the forms moulder.

Vernacular architecture is beautiful to look at as well as significant to contemplate on. It is particularly interesting to realise the nature of traditional architecture where various devices to attain thermal comfort without resorting to fossil fuels can be seen. Sun shading and cross ventilation are two major concerns in house design and a south-facing façade is mandatory to harness the sun in winter as much as possible. Natural ventilation required higher ceilings to bring a cooling effect to occupants in buildings built fifty years ago, whereas modern high technology buildings have lower ceiling heights, thus making air conditioning mandatory. Admitting the human right of enjoying modern lives with a certain level of comfort and convenience, it is necessary to consider how people can live and work in an ideal environment with the least amount of energy consumption in the age of global environment problems. People in the modern age could not put up with the poor indoor environment that people in the old age used to live in. In fact, in those days people had to live with the least amount of fuels readily available and to devise various means of constructing their houses so that they would be compatible with the local climate. It is important; therefore, in designing passive and low energy architecture for the future to learn from their spirit to overcome difficulties by having their creative designs adapted to respective regional climatic conditions and to try to devise the ecotechniques in combination with a high grade of modern science. Finally, the presented theory can be used to calculate the expected effects of the reflecting wall at any particular latitude, under different weather conditions, and when the average numbers of clear days are taken into account. Thereby an assessment of the cost of a particular setup can be obtained. Under circumstances of a few clear days, it may still be worthwhile from a financial point of view to turn a classical greenhouse into one with a reflecting wall by simply covering the glass wall on the north-facing side with aluminium foil with virtually negligible expenditure.

Energy has been a vital input into the economic and social development. However, one third of the world population, living in developing and threshold countries, has no access to electricity. These people mostly live in remote and rural areas with low population density, lacking even the basic infrastructure. Accordingly, utility grid extension is not a cost-effective option and sometimes technically not feasible. Therefore, it is imperative to look for sustainable (i.e., cost-effective, environmentally benign and reliable) sources of energy for the development of these regions. Using locally available renewable energy sources (especially solar irradiation that is characterised by a sufficient availability on a daily basis), which are of high potential in most of these regions offers a strategic solution for their techno-economic development. From the point of view of technology, the design of system technology that meets electrification requirements and fulfils, if necessary, the requirements of integration into alternative current (AC) supply grids, has to be considered.

The modernisation of the system components and their power ranges which allow easy expandability of the supply structure, the standardisation of interfaces and the hybridisation by integration of different energy converters in order to increase the power availability, represent the most important measures from the point of view of system technology. Moreover, the use of renewable energy sources is essentially made easier if the existing reliable AC- technical standards of construction and extension of conventional electricity supply systems are adopted. Therefore, incompatibility cannot be taken as a reason to reduce the dissemination of renewable systems. The exploitation of the energetic potential of (solar and wind) for the production of electricity, could prove to be an adequate solution in isolated regions where the extension of the grid network would be a financial constraint. The use of wind as alternative energy source is increasing and research and development about this clean and unlimited resource is being carried out on various levels.

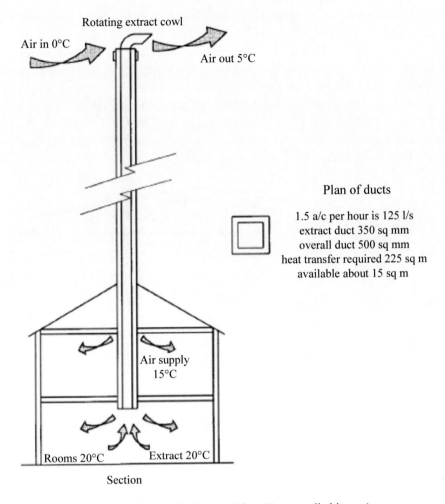

Figure 3. Small house natural ventilation with heat reclaims (A very tall chimney).

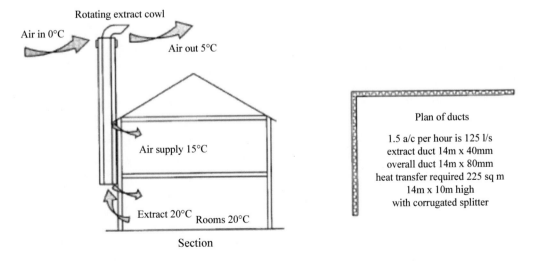

Figure 4. Ventilation duct supply and extract wraps around the building.

Heat gain in the summer is the main problem as it overheats the indoor environment of residential buildings. This forces the residents to utilise mechanical air conditioning systems to satisfy their comfort. Under today's economic crisis, energy conversation programmes and acts for respect of environment are receiving more attention. As a contribution to such efforts and in order to overcome the heat gain in houses, it is advisable to utilise passive systems, namely, producing ventilation by a solar chimney [26]. Room air is removed by ventilation produced by the metallic solar wall (MSW) as shown in Figure 5. However, this is a useful effect as further increases overall energy gain. There is also an ironing out effect expressed in terms of the ratios between peak and average insolations.

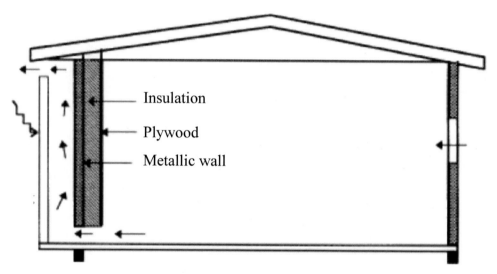

Figure 5. Schematic representations of the passive solar house and natural ventilation by metallic solar wall.

6.5. Infiltration

Infiltration is the process of air flowing in (or out) of leaks in the building envelope, thereby providing (renewable) ventilation in an uncontrolled manner [27]. All buildings are subject to infiltration, but it is more important in smaller buildings as many such buildings rely exclusively on infiltration when doors and windows are closed. In larger buildings there is less surface area to leak for a given amount of building volume, so the same leakage matters less. More importantly, the pressures in larger buildings are usually dominated by the mechanical system and the leaks in the building envelope have only a secondary impact on the ventilation rates [27]. Infiltration in larger buildings may, however, affect thermal comfort and control and systems balance. Typical minimum values of air exchange rates range from 0.5 to 1.0 h^{-1} in office buildings [27]. Buildings with higher occupant density will have higher minimum outside air exchange rates when ventilation is based on outdoor air supply per occupant, typically 7 to 10 ls^{-1} [27]. Thus, schools have minimum outdoor air ventilation rates 3 h^{-1}, while fully occupied theatres, auditoriums and meeting rooms may have minimum air exchange rates of 4 to 7 h^{-1} [27]. It is in low-rise residential buildings (most typically, single-family houses) that infiltration is a dominant force. Mechanical systems in these buildings contribute little to the ventilation rate.

6.6. Passive Ventilation Systems

Passive solar systems for space heating and cooling, as well as passive cooling techniques can significantly contribute to energy saving in the building sector when used in combination with conventional systems for heating, cooling, ventilation and lighting. The overall thermal behaviour of the building is dependent on the alternatives and interventions made on the building's shell. Passive ventilation systems share the use of renewable energy to provide ventilation with infiltration. But unlike air leakage and open windows, passive ventilation systems are designed to provide specific amounts of ventilation to minimise both energy liabilities due to excessive ventilation and periods of poor air quality due to under-ventilation [28]. However, the most common passive ventilation system is the passive stack, which is normally used to extract air from kitchen and bathrooms. In this method, prevailing wind and temperature differences are used to drive airflow through a vertical shaft. Various stack designs can be used to control or enhance the performance, based on local climate. However, careful design is required to avoid backdraughting and to insure proper mean rates. Although there is significant experience with this approach in Europe, it has been rarely used in the North America [28]. Well-designed passive ventilation systems can be used to provide whole-building ventilation as well as local exhaust. Some efforts are currently underway to develop passive ventilation systems that incorporate heat recovery to minimise the need for conditioning the ventilation air [28]. These approaches aim towards a fully renewable ventilation system in that it requires no non-renewable resources for either providing the ventilation air or conditioning it. Energy efficiency and renewable energy programmes could be more sustainable and pilot studies more effective and pulse releasing if the entire policy and implementation process was considered and redesigned from the outset. New financing and implementation processes are needed which allow reallocating financial resources and thus enabling countries themselves to achieve a sustainable energy infrastructure.

6.7. Passive Cooling

In the office environment, high heat loads are commonly developed through lighting, computers and other electrical equipment. Further heat gains are developed through solar gains, occupants and high outdoor air temperature. Passive cooling methods attempt to reduce or eliminate the need for energy intensive refrigerative cooling by minimising heat gains. This involves taking advantage of thermal mass (night cooling) and introducing high levels of air change. Night ventilation techniques seem to be the most appropriate strategy for buildings. This arises as a consequence of the large diurnal temperature range during the cooling seasons and the relatively low peak air temperatures, which occur during the day [29]. Such a combination allows the thermal mass of the building to use the cool night air to discard the heat absorbed during the day. An initial examination of the weather conditions experienced during the summer months of June to September in the UK indicates that most peak conditions of external weather fall within the ventilation and thermal mass edge of the bioclimatic chart [29, and 30]. Figure 6 shows that the summer (June to September) climatic envelope is within the heating, comfort, thermal mass and ventilation effectiveness areas of the chart. The key parameters influencing the effectiveness of night cooling are summarised into the following four categories [30]:

- Internal heat gains of 10, 25 and 40 W/m^2; representing occupancy only, occupancy plus lights, and occupancy together with lights and IT load respectively.
- Envelope gains.
- Thermal response.
- Ventilation gains/losses.

Due to the complexity resulting from all the interrelated parameters affecting the effectiveness of night ventilation, it is necessary for designers to have access to a simple user friendly and yet accurate model when assessing the viability of night ventilation during the initial design stage. The followings are the key output parameters [30]:

- Maximum dry resultant temperature during the occupied period.
- Dry resultant temperature at the start of the occupied period.
- Energy savings.

The input data required are the following:

- Thermal gains related data: solar protection is assumed good, thermal gains can be varied and the user specifies the occupancy period.
- Building fabric data: glazing ratio can be any value while thermal mass can be varied at three levels.
- Ventilation data: infiltration, day ventilation and night ventilation can be specified as necessary.
- Weather data: solar data are fixed but temperature is user specified for seven days although temperature profiles need not be the same for all days. The weather data are specified in the form of maximum and minimum temperature for each day and hourly values are calculated by sinusoidal fitting.

However, a primary strategy for cooling buildings without mechanical intervention in hot humid climates is to promote natural ventilation. To control the energy used for the cooling of buildings in hot-arid regions with ambient air temperatures during the hottest period between 42 to 47°C, passive cooling approaches should be implemented [30]. A solar chimney that employs convective currents to draw air out of the building could be used. By creating a hot zone with an exterior outlet, air can be drawn into the house, ventilating the structure as well as the occupants. Since solar energy in such a region is immense, the hot zone created with a black metal sheet on the glazing element can draw hotter air at a slightly higher speed [30]. Applications of solar chimneys in buildings were limited to external walls. Integrating a solar chimney with an evaporatively cooled cavity could result in a better cooling effect. However, this should be applied with care since water sources are limited [31]. Figure 7 shows the combined wall-roof solar chimney incorporated into that building. Average room and ambient air temperatures are 23 and 27°C respectively. Air velocity required to achieve thermal comfort in the room should reach a maximum of 0.3 m/s [31]. Figure 8 gives the cooling load versus air change per hour. This indicates that the inclined airflow by the combined wall-roof chimney is enough to overcome a high cooling load required to cool heavy residential buildings. This suggests that night ventilation could be improved, and incorporating a combined wall-roof solar chimney increases the cooling load. However, thermal mass and ventilation should be sufficient to cover cooling requirements in typical buildings. A high percentage of the cooling requirements can be met by night ventilation before another form of cooling is used. Finally, a simplified ventilation tool for assessing the applicability of night cooling in buildings, currently under development in terms of user inputs and typical outputs.

The encouragement of greater energy use is an essential component of development. In the short-term it requires mechanisms to enable the rapid increase in energy/capita, and in the long-term we should be working towards a way of life, which makes use of energy efficiency and without the impairment of the environment or of causing safety problems.

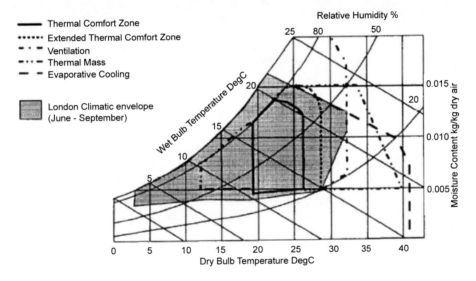

Figure 6. Bioclimatic chart with summer climatic envelope for London.

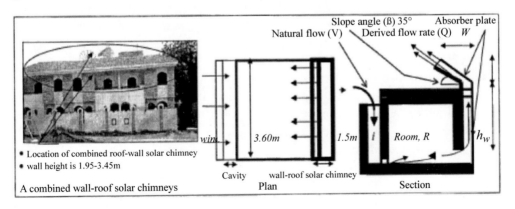

Figure 7. A combined wall-roof solar chimney incorporated into a residential building.

Night ventilation

Mean cooling load (kW)

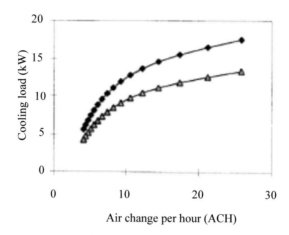

Figure 8. Cooling load by night ventilation for desired room indoor air temperatures of 23 and 25°C.

7. AIR POLLUTANTS AND TRANSMUTATION

Controlling the pollution of the present civilisation is an increasing concern. More importance is given to control global carbon dioxide, which is considered to be the main factor of green house effect. Though the complete experimental result on the fact is yet to be debated, the immense heat, temperature and turbulence of nuclear explosion oxidising the atmospheric nitrogen into nitric oxide, are considered to be similarly responsible for depletion of ozone layer [32]. At present, more importance is given for plantation to reduce the level of global carbon dioxide. The plantation over the whole earth surface may control only 50% of carbon dioxide disposed to atmosphere and its greenhouse effect. There are, also, explosions in the ozone layer time to time to add to the problem. Irrespective of the relative importance of each factor, the ozone layer protects us from harmful cosmic radiations and it is believed that the depletion of ozone layer increases the threat of outer radiations to human habitation if environmental pollution is not controlled or there is no possibility of self-sustainable stability in nature [32].

The presence of ionosphere in the outer-sphere is most probably for ionic dissociation of the gases of the outer-sphere in the presence of low pressure and cosmic radiation [32]. Moreover the ionosphere contains charged helium ions (alpha particle). Therefore, it may be concluded that the explosion in the ozone and transmission of radiations through it are the possible effects of transmutation of pollutants with exothermic reaction (emission of radiations) [32]. The existence of a black hole in the space, which is found in the photo camera of astrologist, is still unexplored. This black hole may be an effect of transmutation process with absorption of heat energy (endothermic reaction). The idea of transmutation of pollutants has been proposed for one or more of the following reasons:

- The experimental results support the transmutation of materials.
- To search the sinks of the remaining carbon dioxide not absorbed by plants or seawater.
- To find out the possible causes of explosion in the ozone layer other than the depletion of ozone layer.
- To investigate the possibilities of the self-sustaining stability of global environment.

To prove the portable of transmutation of pollutants, experimental investigations may be conducted to bombard C or CO_2 or CH_4 or other air pollutants by accelerated alpha particles in a low-pressure vacuum tube in a similar condition of ionosphere. Heating them with gamma radiation can accelerate the alpha particles. The results of such experimental investigation may prove the probable transmutation of pollutants and self-sustaining equilibrium of the global environment.

8. GREENHOUSES

Population growth and less availability of food material have become global concerns. The world population increases exponentially whereas food production has increased only arithmetically, meaning that the availability of food per capita has decreased. This is more pronounced in the cases of oils, vegetables, fruits and milk, whereas it is marginal, rather than minimum, in cereals. The increase in population has also resulted in the use of more urban areas for habitation, less land available for cultivation and, hence, more food requirements. The resultant need is, therefore, to increase productivity and year round cultivation. To maximise production and meet the global demand on food, vegetables, flowers and horticultural crops, it is necessary to increase the effective production span of crops. The sun is the source of energy for plants and animals. This energy is converted into food (i.e., carbohydrates) by plants through a process called photosynthesis. This process is accomplished at suitable atmospheric conditions. These conditions are provided by nature in different seasons and artificially by a greenhouse. The primary objective of greenhouses is to produce agricultural products outside the cultivation season. They offer a suitable microclimate for plants and make possible growth and fruiting, where it is not possible in open fields. This is why a greenhouse is also known as a "controlled environment greenhouse". Through a controlled environment, greenhouse production is advanced and can be continued for longer duration, and finally, production is increased [33]. The off-season production of flowers and vegetables is the unique feature of the controlled environment greenhouse. Hence, greenhouse technology has evolved to create the favourable environment, or maintaining the climate, in order to cultivate the desirable crop the year round. The use of "maintaining the climate" concept may be extended for crop drying, distillation, biogas plant heating and space conditioning. The use of greenhouses is widespread. During the last 10 years, the amount of greenhouses has increased considerably to cover up to several hundred hectares at present. Most of the production is commercialised locally or exported. In India, about 300 ha of land are under greenhouse cultivation. On the higher side, however, it is 98600 ha in Netherlands, 48000 ha in China and 40000 ha in Japan [34]. This shows that there is a large scope to extend greenhouse technology for various climates.

9. EFFECTS OF URBAN DENSITY

Compact development patterns can reduce infrastructure demands and the need to travel by car. As population density increases, transportation options multiply and dependence areas, per capita fuel consumption is much lower in densely populated areas because people drive so much less. Few roads and commercially viable public transport are the major merits. On the other hand, urban density is a major factor that determines the urban ventilation conditions, as well as the urban temperature. Under given circumstances, an urban area with a high density of buildings can experience poor ventilation and strong heat island effect. In warm-humid regions these features would lead to a high level of thermal stress of the inhabitants and increased use of energy in air-conditioned buildings.

Table 1. Effects of urban density on city's energy demand

Positive effects	Negative effects
Transport: Promote public transport and reduce the need for, and length of, trips by private cars.	*Transport:* Congestion in urban areas reduces fuel efficiency of vehicles.
Infrastructure: Reduce street length needed to accommodate a given number of inhabitants. Shorten the length of infrastructure facilities such as water supply and sewage lines, reducing the energy needed for pumping.	*Vertical transportation:* High-rise buildings involve lifts, thus increasing the need for electricity for the vertical transportation.
Thermal performance: Multi-story, multiunit buildings could reduce the overall area of the building's envelope and heat loss from the buildings. Shading among buildings could reduce solar exposure of buildings during the summer period.	*Ventilation:* A concentration of high-rise and large buildings may impede the urban ventilation conditions.
Energy systems: District cooling and heating system, which is usually more energy efficiency, is more feasible as density is higher.	*Urban heat island:* Heat released and trapped in the urban areas may increase the need for air conditioning. The potential for natural lighting is generally reduced in high-density areas, increasing the need for electric lighting and the load on air conditioning to remove the heat resulting from the electric lighting.
Ventilation: A desirable flow pattern around buildings may be obtained by proper arrangement of high-rise building blocks.	*Use of solar energy:* Roof and exposed areas for collection of solar energy are limited.

However, it is also possible that a high-density urban area, obtained by a mixture of high and low buildings, could have better ventilation conditions than an area with lower density but with buildings of the same height. Closely spaced or high-rise buildings are also affected by the use of natural lighting, natural ventilation and solar energy. If not properly planned, energy for electric lighting and mechanical cooling/ventilation may be increased and application of solar energy systems will be greatly limited. Table 1 gives a summary of the positive and negative effects of urban density. All in all, denser city models require more careful design in order to maximise energy efficiency and satisfy other social and development requirements. Low energy design should not be considered in isolation, and in fact, it is a measure, which should work in harmony with other environmental objectives. Hence, building energy study provides opportunities not only for identifying energy and cost savings, but also for examining the indoor and outdoor environment [35].

Greenhouse cultivation is one of the most absorbing and rewarding forms of gardening for anyone who enjoys growing plants. The enthusiastic gardener can adapt the greenhouse climate to suit a particular group of plants, or raise flowers, fruit and vegetables out of their natural season. The greenhouse can also be used as an essential garden tool, enabling the keen amateur to expand the scope of plants grown in the garden, as well as save money by raising their own plants and vegetables.

9.1. Energy Efficiency and Architectural Expression

The focus of the world's attention on environmental issues in recent years has stimulated response in many countries, which have led to a closer examination of energy conservation strategies for conventional fossil fuels. Buildings are important consumers of energy and thus important contributors to emissions of greenhouse gases into the global atmosphere. The development and adoption of suitable renewable energy technology in buildings has an important role to play. A review of options indicates benefits and some problems [36]. There are two key elements to the fulfilling of renewable energy technology potential within the field of building design; first the installation of appropriate skills and attitudes in building design professionals and second the provision of the opportunity for such people to demonstrate their skills. This second element may only be created when the population at large and clients commissioning building design in particular, become more aware of what can be achieved and what resources are required. Terms like passive cooling or passive solar use mean that the cooling of a building or the exploitation of the energy of the sun is achieved not by machines but by the building's particular morphological organisation. Hence, the passive approach to themes of energy savings is essentially based on the morphological articulations of the constructions. Passive solar design, in particular, can realise significant energy and cost savings. For a design to be successful, it is crucial for the designer to have a good understanding of the use of the building. Few of the buildings had performed as expected by their designers. To be more precise, their performance had been compromised by a variety of influences related to their design, construction and operation. However, there is no doubt that the passive energy approach is certainly the one that, being supported by the material shape of the buildings has a direct influence on architectural language and most greatly influences architectural expressiveness [37]. Furthermore, form is a main tool in architectural expression. To give form to the material things that one produces is an ineluctable necessity. In architecture, form, in fact, summarises and gives concreteness to its every value in terms of economy, aesthetics, functionality and, consequently, energy efficiency [38]. The target is to enrich the expressive message with forms producing an advantage energy-wise. Hence, form, in its geometric and material sense, conditions the energy efficiency of a building in its interaction with the environment. It is, then, very hard to extract and separate the parameters and the elements relative to this efficiency from the expressive unit to which they belong. By analysing energy issues and strategies by means of the designs, of which they are an integral part, one will, more easily, focus the attention on the relationship between these themes, their specific context and their architectural expressiveness. Many concrete examples and a whole literature have recently grown up around these subjects and the wisdom of forms and expedients that belong to millennia-old traditions has been rediscovered. Such a revisiting, however, is only, or most especially, conceptual, since it must be filtered through today's technology and needs; both being almost irreconcilable with those of the past. Two among the historical concepts are of special importance. One is rooted in the effort to establish rational and friendly strategic relations with the physical environment, while the other recognises the interactions between the psyche and physical perceptions in the creation of the feeling of comfort. The former, which may be defined as an alliance with the environment deals with the physical parameters involving a mixture of natural and artificial ingredients such as soil and vegetation, urban fabrics and pollution [39]. The most dominant outside parameter is, of course, the sun's irradiation, our planet's primary energy source. All these elements can be measured in physical terms and are therefore the subject of science. Within the second concept, however, one considers the emotional and intellectual energies, which are the prime inexhaustible source of renewable power [33]. In this case, cultural parameters, which are not exactly measurable, are involved. However, they represent the very essence of the architectural quality. Objective scientific measurement parameters tell us very little about the emotional way of perceiving, which influences the messages of human physical sensorial organs. The perceptual reality arises from a multitude of sensorial components; visual, thermal, acoustic, olfactory and kinaesthetics. It can, also, arise from the organisational quality of the space in which different parameters come together, like the sense of order or of serenity. Likewise, practical evaluations, such as usefulness, can be involved too. The evaluation is a wholly subjective matter, but can be shared by a set of experiencing persons [40]. Therefore, these cultural parameters could be different in different contexts in spite of the inexorable levelling on a planet- wide scale. However, the parameters change in the anthropological sense, not only with the cultural environment, but also in relation to function. The scientifically measurable parameters can, thus, have their meanings very profoundly altered by the non-measurable, but describable, cultural parameters.

However, the low energy target also means to eliminate any excess in the quantities of material and in the manufacturing process necessary for the construction of our built environment. This claims for a more sober, elegant and essential expression, which is not jeopardising at all, but instead enhancing, the richness and preciousness of architecture, while contributing to a better environment from an aesthetic viewpoint [34]. Arguably, the most successful designs were in fact the simplest. Paying attention to orientation, plan and form can have far greater impact on energy performance than opting for elaborate solutions [34]. However, a design strategy can fail when those responsible for specifying materials for example, do not implement the passive solar strategy correctly. Similarly, cost-cutting exercises can seriously upset the effectiveness of a design strategy. Therefore, it is imperative that a designer fully informs key personnel, such as the quantity surveyor and client, about their design and be prepared to defend it. Therefore, the designer should have an adequate understanding of how the occupants or processes, such as ventilation, would function within the building. Thinking through such processes in isolation without reference to others can lead to conflicting strategies, which can have a detrimental impact upon performance. Likewise, if the design intent of the building is not communicated to its occupants, there is a risk that they will use it inappropriately, thus, compromising its performance. Hence, the designer should communicate in simple terms the actions expected of the occupant to control the building. For example, occupants should be well informed about how to guard against summer overheating. If the designer opted for a simple, seasonally adjusted control; say, insulated sliding doors were to be used between the mass wall and the internal space. The lesson here is that designers must be prepared to defend their design such that others appreciate the importance and interrelationship of each component. A strategy will only work if each individual component is considered as part of the bigger picture. Failure to implement a component or incorrect installation, for example, can lead to failure of the strategy and consequently, in some instances, the building may not liked by its occupants due to its poor performance.

9.2. Sustainable Practices

Within the last decade sustainable development and building practices have acquired great importance due to the negative impact of various development projects on the environment. In line with a sustainable development approach, it is critical for practitioners to create a healthy, sustainable built environment [31, 32 and 33]. In Europe, 50% of material resources taken from nature are building-related, over 50% of national waste production comes from the building sector and 40% of energy consumption is building-related [30]. Therefore, more attention should be directed towards establishing sustainable guidelines for practitioners. Furthermore, the rapid growth in population has led to active construction that, in some instances, neglected the impact on the environment and human activities. At the same time, the impact on the traditional heritage, an often-neglected issue of sustainability, has not been taken into consideration, despite representing a rich resource for sustainable building practices.

Sustainability has been defined as the extent to which progress and development should meet the need of the present without compromising the ability of the future generations to meet their own needs [30]. This encompasses a variety of levels and scales ranging from economic development and agriculture, to the management of human settlements and building practices. This general definition was further developed to include sustainable building practices and management of human settlements. The following issues were addressed during the Rio Earth Summit in 1992 [30]:

- The use of local materials and indigenous building sources.
- Incentive to promote the continuation of traditional techniques, with regional resources and self-help strategies.
- Regulation of energy-efficient design principles.
- International information exchange on all aspects of construction related to the environment, among architects and contractors, particularly non-conventional resources.

- Exploration of methods to encourage and facilitate the recycling and reuse of building materials, especially those requiring intensive energy use during manufacturing, and the use of clean technologies.

The objectives of the sustainable building practices aim to:

- Develop a comprehensive definition of sustainability that includes socio-cultural, bio-climate, and technological aspects.
- Establish guidelines for future sustainable architecture.
- Predict the CO_2 emissions in buildings.
- The proper architectural measure for sustainability is efficient, energy use, waste control, population growth, carrying capacity, and resource efficiency.
- Establish methods of design that conserve energy and natural resources.

Table 2. Design, construction and environmental control description of traditional and new houses

Design characteristics	Traditional houses	New houses
Form	Courtyard (height twice its width) - open to sky	Rectangle-closed
Construction	Brick walls 50 cm thick, brick roof with no insulation in either	Brick walls 25 cm thick, concrete roof-no insulation
Environmental control	Evaporative air coolers	Evaporative air coolers
Ease of climatic control	Difficult-rooms open into the climatically uncontrolled open courtyard	Moderate-rooms open into the enclosed internal corridor
Maintenance	Well conserved and maintained	New construction
Windows	Vertical and single glazing	Horizontal-single glazing
Urban morphology	Each house attached from 3 sides	Row houses attached from 2 sides
Orientation	Varies-irregular shapes and winding alleyways	North-south (row houses)
Orientation and solar gain	Solar gains less affected by orientation due to shading provided by the deep courtyard	Solar gain determined by orientation-no obstruction (shading)
Sharing solar gain	Significant - due to long-wave exchange or convective exchange between the 4 vertical walls surrounding the courtyard	Minimal- S-wall receives much more solar radiation than the N-wall due to the absence of any interreflection and long-wave exchange
Occupant's social status	Low income families	Low and middle income families

A building inevitably consumes materials and energy resources. The technology is available to use methods and materials that reduce the environmental impacts, increase operating efficiency, and increase durability of buildings (Table 2).

Literature on green buildings reveals a number of principles that can be synthesised in the creation of the built environment that is sustainable. According to Lobo [14], these are: land development, building design and construction, occupant considerations, life cycle assessment, volunteer incentives and marketing programmes, facilitate reuse and remodelling, and final disposition of the structure. These parameters and many more are essential for analysis, making them an important element of the design decision-making process. Today, architects should prepare for this as well as dealing with existing buildings with many unfavourable urban environmental factors, such as many spaces have no choice of orientation, and, often, set in noisy streets with their windows opening into dusty and polluted air and surrounding buildings overshadowing them. The connection between technical change, economic policies and the environment is of primary importance as observed by most governments in developing countries, whose attempts to attain food self-sufficiency have led them to take the measures that provide incentives for adoption of the Green Revolution Technology.

9.3. Buildings and CO_2 Emission

To achieve carbon dioxide, CO_2, emission targets, more fundamental changes to building designs have been suggested [35]. The actual performance of buildings must also be improved to meet the emission targets. To this end, it has been suggested that the performance assessment should be introduced to ensure that the quality of construction, installation and commissioning achieve the design intent. Air-tightness and the commissioning of plant and controls are the main two elements of assessing CO_2 emission. Air-tightness is important as uncontrolled air leakage wastes energy. Uncertainties over infiltration rates are often the reason for excessive design margins that result in oversized and inefficient plants. On the other hand, commissioning to accept procedures would significantly improve energy efficiency. The slow turnover in the building stock means that improved performance of new buildings will only cut CO_2 emissions significantly in the long-term. Consequently, the performance of existing buildings must be improved. For example, improving 3% of existing buildings would be more effective in cutting emissions than, say, improving the fabric standards for new non-domestic buildings and improving the efficiency of new air conditioning and ventilation systems [27]. A reduction in emissions arising from urban activities can, however, only be achieved by a combination of energy efficiency measures and a move away from fossil fuels.

9.4. Energy Efficiency

Energy efficiency is the most cost-effective way of cutting carbon dioxide emissions and improvements to households and businesses. It can also have many other additional social, economic and health benefits, such as warmer and healthier homes, lower fuel bills and company running costs and, indirectly, jobs. Britain wastes 20 per cent of its fossil fuel and electricity use. This implies that it would be cost-effective to cut £10 billion a year off the collective fuel bill and reduce CO_2 emissions by some 120 million tonnes. Yet, due to lack of good information and advice on energy saving, along with the capital to finance energy efficiency improvements, this huge potential for reducing energy demand is not being realised. Traditionally, energy utilities have been essentially fuel providers and the industry has pursued profits from increased volume of sales. Institutional and market arrangements have favoured energy consumption rather than conservation. However, energy is at the centre of the sustainable development paradigm as few activities affect the environment as much as the continually increasing use of energy. Most of the used energy depends on finite resources, such as coal, oil, gas and uranium. In addition, more than three quarters of the world's consumption of these fuels is used, often inefficiently, by only one quarter of the world's population. Without even addressing these inequities or the precious, finite nature of these resources, the scale of environmental damage will force the reduction of the usage of these fuels long before they run out.

Throughout the energy generation process there are impacts on the environment on local, national and international levels, from opencast mining and oil exploration to emissions of the potent greenhouse gas carbon dioxide in ever increasing concentration. Recently, the world's leading climate scientists reached an agreement that human activities, such as burning fossil fuels for energy and transport, are causing the world's temperature to rise. The Intergovernmental Panel on Climate Change has concluded that "the balance of evidence suggests a discernible human influence on global climate". It predicts a rate of warming greater than any one seen in the last 10,000 years, in other words, throughout human history. The exact impact of climate change is difficult to predict and will vary regionally. It could, however, include sea level rise, disrupted agriculture and food supplies and the possibility of more freak weather events such as hurricanes and droughts. Indeed, people already are waking up to the financial and social, as well as the environmental, risks of unsustainable energy generation methods that represent the costs of the impacts of climate change, acid rain and oil spills. The insurance industry, for example, concerned about the billion dollar costs of hurricanes and floods, has joined sides with environmentalists to lobby for greenhouse gas emissions reduction. Friends of the earth are campaigning for a more sustainable energy policy, guided by the principle of environmental protection and with the objectives of sound natural resource management and long-term energy security. The key priorities of such an energy policy must be to reduce fossil fuel use, move away from nuclear power, improve the efficiency with which energy is used and increase the amount of energy obtainable from sustainable, renewable sources. Efficient energy use has never been more crucial than it is today, particularly with the prospect of the imminent introduction of the climate change levy (CCL). Establishing an energy use action plan is the essential foundation to the elimination of energy waste. A logical starting point is to carry out an energy audit that enables the assessment of the energy use and determine what actions to take. The actions are best categorised by splitting measures into the following three general groups:

1. High priority/low cost

These are normally measures, which require minimal investment and can be implemented quickly. The followings are some examples of such measures:

- Good housekeeping, monitoring energy use and targeting waste-fuel practices.
- Adjusting controls to match requirements.
- Improved greenhouse space utilisation.
- Small capital item time switches, thermostats, etc.
- Carrying out minor maintenance and repairs.
- Staff education and training.
- Ensuring that energy is being purchased through the most suitable tariff or contract arrangements.

2. Medium priority/medium cost

Measures, which, although involve little or no design, involve greater expenditure and can take longer to implement. Examples of such measures are listed below:

- New or replacement controls.
- Greenhouse component alteration, e.g., insulation, sealing glass joints, etc.
- Alternative equipment components, e.g., energy efficient lamps in light fittings, etc.

3. Long term/high cost

These measures require detailed study and design. They can be best represented by the followings:

- Replacing or upgrading of plant and equipment.
- Fundamental redesign of systems, e.g., combined heat and power CHP installations.

This process can often be a complex experience and therefore the most cost-effective approach is to employ an energy specialist to help.

9.5. Policy Recommendations for a Sustainable Energy Future

Sustainability is regarded as a major consideration for both urban and rural development. People have been exploiting the natural resources with no consideration to the effects, both short-term (environmental) and long-term (resources crunch). It is also felt that knowledge and technology have not been used effectively in utilising energy resources. Energy is the vital input for economic and social development of any country. Its sustainability is an important factor to be considered. The urban areas depend, to a large extent, on commercial energy sources. The rural areas use non-commercial sources like firewood and agricultural wastes. With the present day trends for improving the quality of life and sustenance of mankind, environmental issues are considered highly important. In this context, the term energy loss has no significant technical meaning. Instead, the exergy loss has to be considered, as destruction of exergy is possible. Hence, exergy loss minimisation will help in sustainability. In the process of developing, there are two options to manage energy resources: (1) End use matching/demand side management, which focuses on the utilities. The mode of obtaining this is decided based on economic terms. It is, therefore, a quantitative approach. (2) Supply side management, which focuses on the renewable energy resource and methods of utilising it. This is decided based on thermodynamic consideration having the resource-user temperature or exergy destruction as the objective criteria. It is, therefore, a qualitative approach. The two options are explained schematically in Figure 9. The exergy-based energy, developed with supply side perspective is shown in Figure 10.

The following policy measures had been identified:

- Clear environmental and social objectives for energy market liberalisation, including a commitment to energy efficiency and renewables.
- Economic, institutional and regulatory frameworks, which encourage the transition to total energy services.
- Economic measures to encourage utility investment in energy efficiency (e.g., levies on fuel bills).
- Incentives for demand side management, including grants for low-income households, expert advice and training, standards for appliances and buildings and tax incentives.
- Research and development funding for renewable energy technologies not yet commercially viable.
- Continued institutional support for new renewables (such as standard cost-reflective payments and obligation on utilities to buy).
- Ecological tax reform to internalise external environmental and social costs within energy prices.
- Planning for sensitive development and public acceptability for renewable energy.

Energy resources are needed for societal development. Their sustainable development requires a supply of energy resources that are sustainably available at a reasonable cost and can cause no negative societal impacts. Energy resources such as fossil fuels are finite and lack sustainability, while renewable energy sources are sustainable over a relatively longer term. Environmental concerns are also a major factor in sustainable development, as activities, which degrade the environment, are not sustainable. Hence, as much as environmental impact is associated with energy, sustainable development requires the use of energy resources, which cause as little environmental impact as possible. One way to reduce the resource depletion associated with cycling is to reduce the losses that accompany the transfer of exergy to consume resources by increasing the efficiency of exergy transfer between resources, i.e., increasing the fraction of exergy removed from one resource that is transferred to another [9].

As explained above, exergy efficiency may be thought of as a more accurate measure of energy efficiency that accounts for quantity and quality aspects of energy flows. Improved exergy efficiency leads to reduced exergy losses. Most efficiency improvements produce direct environmental benefits in two ways. First, operating energy input requirements are reduced per unit output, and pollutants generated are correspondingly reduced. Second, consideration of the entire life cycle for energy resources and technologies suggests that improved efficiency reduces environmental impact during most stages of the life cycle. Quite often, the main concept of sustainability, which often inspires local and national authorities to incorporate environmental consideration into setting up energy programmes have different meanings in different contexts though it usually embodies a long-term perspective. Future energy systems will largely be shaped by broad and powerful trends that have their roots in basic human needs. Combined with increasing world population, the need will become more apparent for successful implementation of sustainable development.

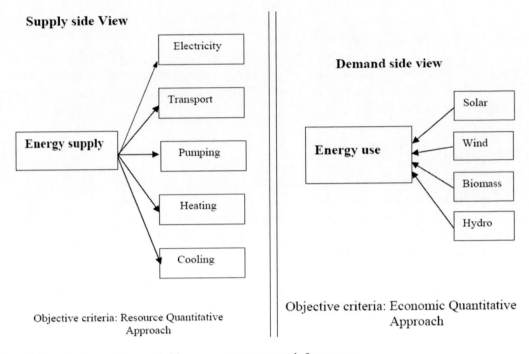

Figure 9. Supply side and demand side management approach for energy.

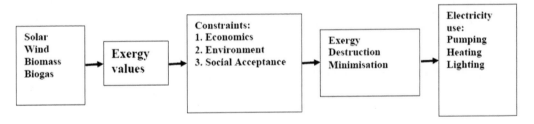

Figure 10. Exergy based optimal energy model.

Table 3. Qualities of various energy sources

Source	Energy (J)	Exergy (J)	CQF
Water at 80°C	100	16	0.16
Steam at 120°C	100	24	0.24
Natural gas	100	99	0.99
Electricity/work	100	100	1.00

Heat has a lower exergy, or quality of energy, compared with work. Therefore, heat cannot be converted into work by 100% efficiency. Some examples of the difference between energy and exergy are shown in Table 3.

The terms used in Table 3 have the following meanings:

Carnot Quality Factor (CQF) = $(1 - T_o/T_s)$ (2)

Exergy = Energy (transferred) x CQF   (3)

where T_o is the environment temperature (K) and T_s is the temperature of the stream (K).

Various parameters are essential to achieving sustainable development in a society. Some of them are as follows:

- Public awareness.
- Information.
- Environmental education and training.
- Innovative energy strategies.
- Renewable energy sources and cleaner technologies.
- Financing.
- Monitoring and evaluation tools.

The development of a renewable energy technology in a country depends on many factors. Those important to success are listed below:

(1) Motivation of the population
The population should be motivated towards awareness of high environmental issues, rational use of energy in order to reduce cost. Subsidy programme should be implemented as incentives to install renewable energy plants. In addition, image campaigns to raise awareness of renewable energy technology.

(2) Technical product development
To achieve technical development of renewable energy technologies the following should be addressed:

- Increasing the longevity and reliability of renewable energy technology.
- Adapting renewable energy technology to household technology (hot water supply).
- Integration of renewable energy technology in heating technology.
- Integration of renewable energy technology in architecture, e.g., in the roof or façade.
- Development of new applications, e.g., solar cooling.
- Cost reduction.

(3) Distribution and sales
Commercialisation of renewable energy technology requires:

- Inclusion of renewable energy technology in the product range of heating trades at all levels of the distribution process (wholesale, and retail).
- Building distribution nets for renewable energy technology.

- Training of personnel in distribution and sales.
- Training of field sales force.

(4) Consumer consultation and installation
To encourage all sectors of the population to participate in adoption of renewable energy technologies, the following has to be realised:

- Acceptance by craftspeople, and marketing by them.
- Technical training of craftspeople, initial and follow-up training programmes.
- Sales training for craftspeople.
- Information material to be made available to craftspeople for consumer consultation.

(5) Projecting and planning
Successful application of renewable energy technologies also requires:

- Acceptance by decision makers in the building sector (architects, house technology planners, etc.).
- Integration of renewable energy technology in training.
- Demonstration projects/architecture competitions.
- Renewable energy project developers should prepare to participate in the carbon market by:
- Ensuring that renewable energy projects comply with Kyoto Protocol requirements.
- Quantifying the expected avoided emissions.
- Registering the project with the required offices.
- Contractually allocating the right to this revenue stream.

Other ecological measures employed on the development include:

- Simplified building details.
- Reduced number of materials.
- Materials that can be recycled or reused.
- Materials easily maintained and repaired.
- Materials that do not have a bad influence on the indoor climate (i.e., non-toxic).
- Local cleaning of grey water.
- Collecting and use of rainwater for outdoor purposes and park elements.
- Building volumes designed to give maximum access to neighbouring park areas.
- All apartments have visual access to both backyard and park.

(6) Energy saving measures
The following energy saving measures should also be considered:
- Building integrated solar PV system.
- Day-lighting.
- Ecological insulation materials.
- Natural/hybrid ventilation.
- Passive cooling.

- Passive solar heating.
- Solar heating of domestic hot water.
- Utilisation of rainwater for flushing.

Improving access for rural and urban low-income areas in developing countries is through energy efficiency and renewable energies. Sustainable energy is a prerequisite for development. Energy-based living standards in developing countries, however, are clearly below standards in developed countries. Low levels of access to affordable and environmentally sound energy in both rural and urban low-income areas are therefore a predominant issue in developing countries. In recent years many programmes for development aid or technical assistance have been focusing on improving access to sustainable energy, many of them with impressive results.

Apart from success stories, however, experience also shows that positive appraisals of many projects evaporate after completion and vanishing of the implementation expert team. Altogether, the diffusion of sustainable technologies such as energy efficiency and renewable energies for cooking, heating, lighting, electrical appliances and building insulation in developing countries has been slow.

Energy efficiency and renewable energy programmes could be more sustainable and pilot studies more effective and pulse releasing if the entire policy and implementation process was considered and redesigned from the outset. New financing and implementation processes are needed, which allow reallocating financial resources and thus enabling countries themselves to achieve a sustainable energy infrastructure. The links between the energy policy framework, financing and implementation of renewable energy and energy efficiency projects have to be strengthened and capacity building efforts are required.

The use of renewable energy resources could play an important role in this context, especially with regard to responsible and sustainable development. It represents an excellent opportunity to offer a higher standard of living to local people and will save local and regional resources. Energy efficiency brings health, productivity, safety, comfort and savings to homeowner, as well as local and global environmental benefits.

10. LOW CARBON BUILDING FOR THE FUTURE

There was a growing awareness that cutting greenhouse gases (GHGs) is a huge business opportunity. Business can both:

- Cut its energy costs and make itself more competitive, safeguarding profits and employment.
- Grow by developing and adopting products based on the new low carbon technologies.

More than 170 countries have signed up to the Kyoto Protocol. That is a huge potential market for products based on low carbon technology. Pressure on business comes from governments, reflecting the concerns of votes, directly from consumers through green purchasing and indirectly through shareholder democracy. Non-governmental organisations

(NGOs) have done a great deal to help create the market conditions that allows business to go down the low carbon route. Many governments are investing considerable sums in low carbon technology. There is a huge amount of research and development (R&D) going on, which could help to make a reality of Kyoto. The CO_2 emissions can be cut by around 60% over the next few decades, using existing and emerging technologies, which depend on:

- Active and positive engagement from the business world.
- Governments setting a firm policy context, so those innovative companies can profit.
- A strong input from NGOs who have also played a key role.

The business and the public sectors play their full part in delivering GHG reductions and prepare the ways for a low carbon economy up to 2050 and beyond. A truly low carbon economy is impossible without business involvement and support business development and carbon reduction go hand in hand. The vision and challenges are needed. Tackling carbon emissions is good business and introducing low carbon technology is good for the bottom line.

The Kyoto Protocol to the United Nations Framework Convention on Climate Change (UNFCCC) was initially designed to reduce GHG emissions from industrialised countries by 5%. There were many debates over the controversial area of restricting the buying, selling and banking of emissions reductions, particularly with regard to carbon sinks (the temporary storage of carbon in forests, soils, etc.). The potential for renewables is vast, uncontroversial, yet under-appreciated. In the case of solar PVs, for example even in a cloudy, rainy country like UK, modern PV technology applied to all available UK roofs would generate more electricity than the nation currently consumes in a year.

Global warming is in the process of teaching us that over security is best built by making sure our neighbours are secure as well. Its beachheads are becoming clear in proliferating climate extremes like the long-running drought. Unless we cut the burning of oil, gas and coal deeply the effects of global warming would ultimately be second only to nuclear war. A new global energy-security paradigm is urgently required. Budgets and policies should be consisted with the newly convergent imperatives of environmental and global security. New technologies were credited with offering low carbon solutions with fuel cells providing primary. Fuel cell technology has yet to prove itself and consideration should be given to the many innovative devices currently available that are grossly under-utilised. There is a need to face up to the rehabilitation of nuclear power despite any additional worries. Energy efficiency meaning improvements to the performance of power conversion and energy using devices would have a crucial role to play. The electricity supply industry talked, rather altruistically, of bringing power to the 1.6 billion people in the world that do not have access to it. Conventional, centralised electricity networks are the norm in the developed world. However, the present energy infrastructure of the developed countries was mainly created during the monopolistic utility era of the past. The utilities had the power to decide what kind of capacity to construct and how to construct the grid. There was practically no competition. The main challenge for many utilities was to get construction permits for building new generation capacity- the construction itself was practically risk free as they could turn their cost structure into a solid power tariff. Capital was easily available and cost competitiveness and overall system cost optimisation were not the main concerns.

10.1. Low-Energy Device for Integrated Heating, Cooling and Humidity Control in Greenhouses

A combination of plant transpiration, wet soil, and warm temperatures leads to high humidity in greenhouse. High humidity promotes the spread of disease inside greenhouse. The growth of various types of fungi, such as downy mildew and grey mould, is greatly enhanced in a humid environment and these diseases can have a critical effect on crop quality and yield. The best way to control these fungal diseases is by humidity control. However, although ventilation is commonly used to control humidity during warm weather, the high cost of heating the inlet air during cold periods results in many greenhouse operations using fungicides rather than humidity control during cold weather. A cost effective, non-chemical method is required to replace fungicides for several reasons:

- There is growing consumer demand for pesticide-free products.
- Fungicide registrations are being cancelled.
- Botrytis cinerea and other fungi are developing resistance to fungicides.

Resistance to major groups of fungicides in botrytis has been documented in the United Kingdom, Italy, Canada and the USA. However, there are several important crops for which no fungicides effective against botrytis are registered. Thus, for several reasons, non-chemical methods of botrytis control must be exploited wherever possible. Humidity reduction is the most important, non-chemical method would offer a further advantage in controlling – calcium related disorders, which are humidity dependent and result in loss of both quality and yield.

The greenhouse effect is one result of the differing properties of heat radiation when it is generated by at different temperatures. The high temperature sun emits radiation of short wavelength, which can pass through the atmosphere and through glass. Inside the greenhouse or other building this heat is absorbed by objects, such as plants, which then re-radiate the heat. Because the objects inside the greenhouse are at a lower temperature than the sun the radiated heat is of longer wavelengths, which cannot penetrate glass. This re-radiated heat is therefore trapped and causes the temperature inside the greenhouse to rise. The atmosphere surrounding the earth also behaves as a large greenhouse around the world. Changes to the gases in the atmosphere, such as increased carbon dioxide content from the burning of fossil fuels, can act like a layer of glass and reduce the quantity of heat that the planet earth would otherwise radiate back into space. This particular greenhouse effect therefore contributes to global warming. Meeting the target of a 60% reduction in carbon dioxide (CO_2) emissions on environmental pollution is both technologically feasible and financially viable. During the past century, global surface temperatures have increased at a rate near 0.6°C/century and the average temperature of the Atlantic, Pacific and Indian oceans (covering 72% of the earth surface) have risen by 0.06°C since 1995. Global temperatures in 2001 were 0.52°C above the long-term 1880-2000 average (the 1880-2000 annually averaged combined land and ocean temperature is 13.9°C).

10.2. Bioclimatic Approach

The question of thermal comfort is increasingly generating an intensive debate. The subject is not new but the exact solution is illusive to the fact that considerable part of the thermal sensation can only be evaluated by subjective means. Consequently the thermal comfort ranges do differ and seem to be complex functions of culture, physiology and geographical location. The human body is not exempt from the effects of the second law of thermodynamics. When the body heat cannot be dissipated to the surrounding environment; a condition that occurs when the ambient temperature is higher than the body temperature, then thermal discomfort starts. The three common body index temperatures are 36.6°C (oral), 37°C (anal), and 35°C (skin temperature). While 37°C is the temperature of the internal organs, the skin temperature is the reference datum for the thermal comfort sensation.

Buildings in the tropical area of the world are constantly exposed to solar radiation almost everyday. As a result, building design should aim at minimising heat gain indoors and maximising adequate thermal cooling so that user of these spaces can have adequate thermal comfort. To achieve this objective, buildings in this part of the world should have shapes and frames which should (1) be responsive to this objective (2) be properly oriented, and (3) the fabric of the buildings should be specified to prevent and have minimal use of active energy for economic viability. In order to meet the above requirements, it implies that buildings should be bioclimatic responsive. Observation of most buildings (both traditional and contemporary) in the built environment and also of building design approaches- past and present- reveals that most of the above criteria have not been strictly adhered to. Traditional buildings have laid too much emphasis on social-cultural and economic factors. Also, contemporary buildings, especially housing, have depended on imported building materials. Various problems have emanated from the present design approaches and philosophy. First, most buildings seem to be replicas of buildings in European countries in shape and form despite marten differences in climatic conditions. Secondly, despite observed climatic differences in various cities, forms and shapes of buildings tend to look alike. Thirdly, windows of buildings have not been properly oriented to maximise air movement for space cooling indoors. Window sizes and openings have not responded to physiological comfort. Finally, material specification for buildings in the housing sector has followed the same pattern despite the difference in climate. The tropical areas of the world are generally referred to as the overheated regions. For building design purposes, overheated regions of the world are classified into three categories: (1) hot/warm, (2) arid/semi arid regions, and (3) temperate, both arid and humid regions. In order to properly access the effect of climate in any particular location and to determine appropriate climatic responsive design solution for buildings, it is necessary to evaluate the characteristics for the combined effect of thermal comfort parameters. These parameters should be carefully analysed for various areas. Two methods of climate analysis must be used so that a proper design solution for buildings can be made. The methods are: (1) the general atmospheric circulation model, and (2) the control potential technique. The general atmospheric circulation model (GACM) is based on the principle that the climate of a particular point in space and time is a result of three forces created by the earth's revolution, rotation and vertical heat transport. In other words, more characteristics of the climate of region will be considered. The vertical height is limited to the biosphere. The climatic data relevant to building design were then collected and analysed.

The maximum and minimum monthly temperatures, the relative humidity both for morning and afternoon, solar radiation, and precipitation levels were collected from past records from meteorological stations.

It is suggested that the climate of a given location should be analysed in its own terms and that this analysis should directly lead to a certain architectural response type, i.e., of the appropriate control potential strategies. For a comfortable indoor environment to be achieved, the microclimate of the locality in which design is taking place should be carried out. The analysis of climate data closely related to the design environment will lead to more adequate and precise design decisions in terms of adequate orientation, spatial organisation, prevention of heat gain into spaces and better choice of building materials.

10.3. Applications of Solar Energy

These design strategies would provide the most effective combination for heating, natural ventilation and day lighting. Passive solar systems for space heating and cooling, as well as passive cooling techniques when used in combination with conventional systems for heating, cooling, ventilation and lighting, can significantly contribute to the energy saving in the buildings sector [36-40]. The available environmentally sensitive design strategies for improving the energy performance of spaces without appropriate orientation are shown in Table 4.

Table 4. Passive solar strategies for spaces without north-facing façade

Passive solar strategies / for	Natural illumination	Heating	Cooling	Ventilation
Skylight	X	X		X
Clerestory	X	X		X
Monitor	X	X		X
Saw tooth facing south	X			X
Light shelves	X			
Light pipe systems	X			
Thermal storage mess on roofs (roof pond)		X		
Thermosiphon (roof-floor)		X		
Roof greenhouse		X		
Black attic		X		
Wind tower			X	X
Solar chimney			X	X

Design strategies that could be cost-effective and easily constructed, is the most important factor for the selection. A described by Baker, et al., [41] a skylight is an opening located on a horizontal or tilted roof. It allows the zenithal entry of daylight increase the limit level of the lower space under the skylight. It can be opened to admit ventilation. In winter, a reflector can be used to enhance solar gain, since the amount of solar energy transmitted on a horizontal surface is considerably poor. In summer, exterior shading is required to avoid excessive solar gain [42].

The clerestory roof windows are vertical or tilted openings projecting up from the roof plane. They permit zenithal penetration of daylight, redirecting it towards the spaces below. They also allow natural ventilation. They are particularly effective for heating by direct sunlight entering a space and onto an interior thermal storage wall. Roof monitors raised section of roof with north and south openings. They permit the zenithal entry of daylight towards the lower zone increasing luminic level and allowing ventilation through the apertures. They have similar attributes to the clerestory in that sunlight is directed on to an internal thermal storage wall. Spaces without northerly orientations have an impact on the energy behaviour of a building.

In this study the following are considered the envelope area, shape and tilt of the glassed area and the arrangement of the elements across the roof area. Further studies are required to measure the influence of diffuse glazing in the distribution approaches. Different approaches could be appropriate for different situations and environmental conditions depending on heating, day-lighting, ventilation requirements, or construction facilities. The more important aspects to be considered are the glazing tilt and orientation of the element. The arrangement of the zenithal strategies has little influence in the thermal performance; however, regions with heavy snowfalls in winter will have an impact on the design strategy. Snow accumulation can cause problems for large elements in terms of roof structure and insulation, and smaller elements will be a structure and insulation, and smaller elements will be a better solution. In addition, these arrangements are more expensive and have more building, and structural complications. The element and roof join is usually a weak point in the roof structure so that the use of many elements will cause problems with roof insulation water leakage. The roof monitors with their north and south-facing openings allow a better quality of illuminance giving the whole spectrum of colour. It is also important to note that roof monitors had the best-combined results in terms of lighting and thermal effects. Coupled with the possibilities of ventilation by having the two openings (north and south windows) operable, this will also allow the removal of the exhaust air in summer.

11. THEORETICAL FOUNDATIONS

The analysis of thermal exchange among building components can be performed for any number of elements. However, the basic limitation to its calculation remains the choice of pertinent heat transfer coefficients. In this communication three basic elements are considered in a lumped-parameter approach: the building materials (structure and fittings, including finishing, of floor, walls and roofs), a single window, and the inside air. The value of this last variable is taken to represent the pertinence of design.

A limiting condition to lumped parameter analyses is the definition of adducted heat transfer coefficients among the system, components, and among these and the environment. These coefficients are needed to solve the quasi-steady-state equations that describe the heat balance in each of the relevant system components. In the absence of ventilation, the windowpane heat balance equation can be written as:

$$M_v \, Cp_v \, dT_v/dt = Q_v \, A_s \, U_{sv} \, (T_v\text{-}T_s) - A_v \, U_{vi} \, (T_v\text{-}T_i) - A_v \, U_{va} \, (T_v\text{-}T_a) \tag{4}$$

In the preceding equation, the windowpane has an exposed area Av, thermal mass Mv, specific heat cp_v and its temperature T_v varies with time t as a result of solar heat Q_v received on its external face. T_s, T_a and T_i are respectively, the building, ambient and internal air temperature.

Solar gains Q_v are calculated by the following relationship:

$$Q_v = A_v \, (\alpha_v \, G_b \, R_b \, (1\text{-}\rho_i) + G_d \, (1\text{-}\rho_d) \, \alpha_v) \tag{5}$$

where the first inside the parenthesis describes direct solar gains, and the second, indirect or diffuse solar gains, as described in the nomenclature. Similarly, for the building materials,

$$M_s \, Cp_s \, dT_s/dt = Q_s - A_v \, U_{sv} \, (T_s\text{-}T_v) - A_s \, U_{si} \, (T_i\text{-}T_s) - A_s \, U_{sa} \, (T_s\text{-}T_a) \tag{6}$$

In the prior equation, the building inside temperature T_s is associated with a total thermal mass M_s, specific heat Cp_s and varies with time t as a result of solar heat Q_s received through the window. Total heat can be approximated by:

$$Q_s = A_v \, (G_b \, R_b \, (1\text{-}\alpha_b\text{-}\rho_i) + G_d \, (1\text{-}\alpha_v \text{-}\rho_d)) \tag{7}$$

where, as in the preceding case, the first term inside the parenthesis describes direct solar gains, and the second, indirect or diffuse solar gains. And finally, for the air inside the enclosure, neglecting air exchange with the ambient,

$$Mi \, Cp_i \, dT_i/dt = A_s \, U_{si} \, (T_s\text{-}T_i) - A_v \, U_{vi} - (T_i\text{-}T_v) \tag{8}$$

In this case, M_i, Cp_i and T_i refer to inside air mass, specific heat and temperature, respectively.

The universally accepted nomenclature by Duffie and Beckman [43] is retained in equations (4) through (8). Indices v, s and i refer in all cases to, respectively, the windowpane, the building mass, the inside air, and the ambient temperature. The equations are solved simultaneously by means of the variable, and non-linear internal heat transfer coefficients U_{si}, U_{vi} and U_{sv}. Coefficient that refers to thermal exchange with the external environment, U_{va} and U_{sa}, are calculated according to Watmuff, et al., [44]. In general, any U_{jk} value that depicts heat transfer between element j and element k can be approximated by:

$$U_{jk} = h_{rjk} + h_{cjk} \tag{9}$$

In eq. (9), the term with sub-index r refers to radiation and the one with c, to convection. Both are very sensitive to temperature. The radiation term is usually approximated by Duffie and Beckman [43]:

$$h_{rjk} = \sigma\varepsilon\alpha \, F \, (T_j^2 + T_k^2) \, (T_j + T_k) \tag{10}$$

where σ stands for Stefan-Boltzman constant, α is the thermal absorptance, ε is thermal emittance and F is the geometric shape factor, in such a way that radiative transfer per unit area is calculated as:

$$q_{rjk} = h_{rjk}\,(T_j\text{-}T_k) \tag{11}$$

No generally acceptable coefficients are available for this application. However, it is possible to employ adapted expressions for heat transfer by natural convection in closed cavities, such as can be found in Thomas [45], making use of the adequate aspect-ratio relationships. For the convection term,

$$h_{cjk} = N_u\,k/L\ CR\ \alpha_L{}^m\,(H/L)^n \tag{12}$$

In this case, the convective heat transfer coefficient is sensitive to the characteristic distance L, conductivity k of air at the mean temperature inside the envelope, Ray-Leigh number R_a, aspect-ratio H/L, constant C and powers m and n are adjusted to experimental results below:

For U_{vi} and U_{si}, h_r =0, and h_c values are calculated with eq. (12) using C=0.162, m=0.29, n=0, H/L=1 and L=1.2 for U_{vi} and L=1.7 for U_{si}.

Finally, the required temperature dependent air transport properties were evaluated by the following expression, which are valid between 2°C and 77°C with temperature expressed in k:

Thermal diffusivity, $\alpha = 1.534 \times 10^{-3}\,T - 0.2386\,(10^{-4}\,m^2s^{-1})$
Kinematics viscosity, $v = 0.1016\,T - 14.8\,(10^{-6}\,m^2s^{-1})$
Thermal conductivity, $k = 7.58 \times 10^{-5}\,T + 3.5 \times 10^{-3}\,(Wm^{-1}K^{-1})$, and
Thermal expansion coefficient, $\beta = T^{-1}\,(K^{-1})$

In order to depict the relative contribution of each of these techniques to inside temperature, a dimensionless index is defined as follows. When interior temperature exceeds 25°C, it will be considered as a temperature discomfort condition. This reference temperature is widely elements. Then the following expression:

$$F\,(t) = max\,(T_t - 25.25) \tag{13}$$

I_s a time function of truncated temperature and it will be able to estimate the overall discomfort by means of the integration along the day for each different scenarios S:

$$A\,(S) = \int_S F(t)\,dt \tag{14}$$

Then, for each passive technique, let:

$$A_{max} = max\,[A(S):\text{ for all scenarios S}] \tag{15}$$

Finally, the normalised temperature index (Figures 11-12) for each scenario S is:

$$I(S) = A(S)/A_{max} \tag{16}$$

Naturally, it would be preferred, for comfort reasons that this index would be small, preferably nil. It may be seen that the variable is directly related to temperature discomfort: the larger the value of the index, the farthest will inside conditions be from expected wellbeing. Also, the use of electricity operated air conditioning systems will be more expensive the higher this variable is. Hence, energy expenditure to offset discomfort will be higher when comparing two index values; the ratio of them is proportional to the expected energy savings. When the external shade blocks the windowpane completely, the excessive heat gains belong to the lowest values in the set, and the dimensionless index will be constant with orientation. For the climate conditions of the locality, it can be seen that a naked window can produce undesirable heat gains if the orientation is especially unfavourable, when the index can have an increase of up to 0.3 with respect to the totally shaded window [46].

The most favourable orientation, which is due north, results in diminished excessive solar gains through the windows. However, most buildings cannot be oriented at will. If the only possible orientation is due south, and no external shade is used, the index reveals extra heat gains of some 0.26 over the value of totally shaded window. Application of the model results from exploring the relative importance of the thermal inertia of walls, floor and ceiling. Heat stored in building materials, as proven in old, massive buildings, can be compensated during high insolation hours with thermal losses at night and early morning hours, when ambient temperatures are below 25°C.

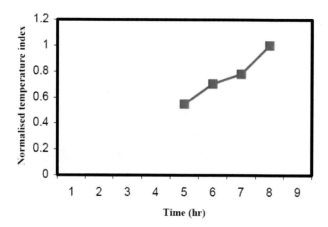

Figure 11. Effect of roof extension on normalised inside temperature.

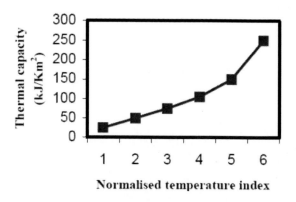

Figure 12. Effect of thermal capacity on normalised inside temperature.

Temperature variation will be lower for higher thermal capacities of building materials. However, it is known while thermal capacity increases the relative importance of individual heat flows change. For example, for lower wall temperatures, the contribution of radiative heat transfer will be reduced, and the relative importance of convective processes will increase, and thus the difficulty to calculate accurately the overall heat flows. The relevance of certain passive techniques is variable with prevailing weather. Where ambient temperature is mostly stable, thermal mass is no advantage, as Lee, et al., [46] have shown for very light housing in Korea.

Vernacular architecture, where massive buildings are common, suggests the use of some passive techniques. These are provided with thick walls and small windows and when properly shaded and ventilated, can result in very acceptable temperature levels without the need of active systems in the extreme varying weather [47]. Bioclimatic design of buildings is one strategy for sustainable development as it contributes to reducing energy consumption and therefore, ultimately, air pollution and greenhouse gas emissions (GHG) from conventional energy generation.

This temperature dependence is a direct consequence of the second law of thermodynamics and the fact that all heat transfers occur during isothermal expansion and contraction, with no temperature difference between the heat reservoir and the working fluid, so that the entropy gained by one exactly matches the entropy lost by the other, with no net change in entropy for the system as a whole.

12. Climate Change

The scientific consensus is clear-climate change is occurring. Existing renewable energy technologies could play a significant mitigating role, but the economic and political climate will have to change first. Climate change is real, it is happening now, and greenhouse gases produced by human activities are significantly contributing to it. The predicted global temperature changes of between 1.5 and 4.5 degrees C could lead to potentially catastrophic environmental impacts-including sea level rise, increased frequency of extreme weather events, floods, droughts, disease migration from various places and possible stalling of the Gulf stream. This is why scientists argue that climate change issues are not ones that politicians can afford to ignore. And policy makers tend to agree, but reaching international agreements on climate change policies is no trivial task [48].

Renewable energy is the term to describe a wide range of naturally occurring, replenishing energy sources. The use of renewable energy sources and the rational use of energy are the fundamental inputs for a responsible energy policy. The energy sector is encountering difficulties because increased production and consumption levels entail higher levels of pollution and eventually climate changes, with possibly disastrous consequences. Moreover, it is important to secure energy at acceptable cost to avoid negative impacts on economic growth. On the technological side, renewables have an obvious role to play. In general, there is no problem in terms of the technical potential of renewables to deliver energy and there are very good opportunities for renewable energy technologies to play an important role in reducing emissions of greenhouse gases into the atmosphere-certainly far more than have been exploited so far [48]. But there are still technical issues to be addressed to cope with the intermittency of some renewables, particularly wind and solar. However, the biggest problem with replying on renewables to deliver the necessary cuts in greenhouse gas emissions is more to do with politics and policy issues than with technical ones. The single most important step governments could take to promote and increase the use of renewables would be to improve access for renewables to the energy market. That access to the market would need to be under favourable conditions and possibly under favourable economic rates. One move that could help-or at least justify-better market access would be to acknowledge that there are environmental costs associated with other energy supply options, and that these costs are not currently internalised within the market price of electricity or fuels. It could make significant difference, particularly if, appropriate subsidies were applied to renewable energy in recognition of environmental benefits it offers. Cutting energy consumption through end-use efficiency is absolutely essential. And this suggests that issues of end-use consumption of energy will have to come onto the table in the foreseeable future.

CONCLUSION

Thermal comfort is an important aspect of human life. Buildings where people work require more light than buildings where people live. In buildings where people live the energy is used for maintaining both the temperature and lighting. Hence, natural ventilation is rapidly becoming a significant part in the design strategy for non-domestic buildings because of its potential to reduce the environmental impact of building operation, due to lower energy demand for cooling. A traditional, naturally ventilated building can readily provide a high ventilation rate. On the other hand, the mechanical ventilation systems are very expensive. However, a comprehensive ecological concept can be developed to achieve a reduction of electrical and heating energy consumption, optimise natural air condition and ventilation, improve the use of daylight and choose environmentally adequate building materials. Energy efficiency brings health, productivity, safety, comfort and savings to homeowner, as well as local and global environmental benefits. The use of renewable energy resources could play an important role in this context, especially with regard to responsible and sustainable development. It represents an excellent opportunity to offer a higher standard of living to local people and will save local and regional resources. Implementation of greenhouses offers a chance for maintenance and repair services. It is expected that the pace of implementation will increase and the quality of work to improve in addition to building the capacity of the private and district staff in contracting procedures. The financial accountability is important and more transparent. Various passive techniques have been put in perspective, and energy saving passive strategies can be seen to reduce interior temperature and increase thermal comfort, reducing air conditioning loads. The scheme can also be employed to analyse the marginal contribution of each specific passive measure working under realistic conditions in combination with the other housing elements. In regions where heating is important during winter months, the use of top-light solar passive strategies for spaces without an equator-facing façade can efficiently reduce energy consumption for heating, lighting and ventilation. The use of renewable energy resources could play an important role in this context, especially with regard to responsible and sustainable development. It represents an excellent opportunity to offer a higher standard of living to local people and will save local and regional resources.

Implementation of greenhouses offers a chance for maintenance and repair services. Various passive techniques have been put in perspective, and energy saving passive strategies can be seen to reduce interior temperature and increase thermal comfort, reducing air conditioning loads.

REFERENCES

[1] Jeremy, L. The energy crisis, global warming and the role of renewables. *Renewable Energy World,* 2005, 8 (2).

[2] Omer, A. Low energy building materials: an overview. In: Proceedings of the Environment 2010: Situation and Perspectives for the European Union. 16-21. Porto: Portugal. 6-10 May 2003.

[3] UNEP. Handbook for the international treaties for the protection of the ozone layer. *United Nations Environment Programme.* Nairobi: Kenya. 2003.

[4] Viktor, D. Ventilation concepts for sustainable buildings. In: Proceedings of the World Renewable Energy Congress VII, 551, Cologne: Germany. 29 June – 5 July 2002.

[5] Lam, JC. Shading effects due to nearby buildings and energy implications. *Energy Conservation and Management,* 2000, 47 (7), 647-59.

[6] Raja, J; Nichol, F; McCartney, K. Natural ventilated buildings use of controls for changing indoor climate. In: Proceedings of the 5th World Renewable Energy Congress V., 391-394. Florence: Italy. 20-25 September 1998.

[7] Limb, MJ. Air intake positioning to avoid contamination of ventilation. AIVC. 1995.

[8] Miller, G. Resource conservation and management. Wadsworth Publishers. California: USA, 51-62. 1990.

[9] Erlich, P. Forward facing up to climate change, in global climate change and life on Earth. R.C. Wyman (Ed), Chapman and Hall, London. 1991.

[10] ASHRAE. Energy efficient design of new building except new low-rise residential buildings. BSRIASHRAE proposed standards 90-2P-1993, alternative GA. American Society of Heating, Refrigerating, and Air Conditioning Engineers Inc., USA. 1993.

[11] Molla, M. Air pollutants and its probable transmutation in the ionosphere. *Renewable Energy,* 10 (2/3), 327-329. 1997.

[12] Bahadori, M. A passive cooling/heating system for hot arid regions. In: *Proceedings of the American Solar Energy Society Conference.* Cambridge. Massachusetts 364-367. 1988.

[13] Dieng, A; Wang, R. Literature review on solar absorption technologies for ice making and air conditioning purposes and recent development in solar technology. *Renewable and Sustainable Energy Review,* 2001, 5 (4), 313-42.

[14] Lobo, C. Defining a sustainable building. In: Proceedings of the 23rd National Passive Conference. *American Solar Energy Society.* (ASES'98). Albuquerque: USA. 1998.

[15] Crisp, V; Cooper, I; McKennan, G. Daylighting as a passive solar energy option: an assessment of its potential in non-domestic buildings. Report BR129-BRE. Garston. UK. 1988.

[16] Horning, M; Skeffington, R. Critical loads: concept and applications. Institute of Terrestrial Ecology. HMSO Publishers Ltd. London: UK 23-27. 1993.

[17] Humphrey's, M. Outdoor temperatures and comfort indoor. *Building Research and Practice*, 6 (2). 1978.

[18] Givoni, B. Man climate and architecture. Applied Science Publishers Ltd 289-306. London: UK. 1976.

[19] Koenigsberger, O; Ingersoll, T; Mayhew, A; Szokolay, S. Manual of tropical housing and building. Part 1: Climate design. Longmas 119-130. London: UK. 1973.

[20] Boulet, T. Controlling air movement: a manual for architects and builders. McGraw-Hill 85-138, New York: USA. 1987.

[21] Szokolay, S. Design and research issues: passive control in the tropic. *Proceedings First World Renewable Energy Congress*, 2337-2344, Reading: UK. 1990.

[22] Borda-Daiz, N; Mosconi, P; Vazquez, J. Passive cooling strategies for a building prototype design in a warm-humid tropical climate. *Solar and Wind Technology*, 6, 389-400. 1989.

[23] Givoni, B. Laboratory study of the effect of window sizes and location on indoor air motion. *Architectural Science Review*, 8, 42-46. 1965.

[24] Fanger, P. Thermal comfort: analysis and applications in environmental engineering. Danish Technical Press. 1970.

[25] Fordham, M. *Natural ventilation. Renewable Energy*, 19, 17-37. 2000.

[26] Awbi, H. *Ventilation of buildings*. Spon Publisher. London: UK. 9-13. 1991.

[27] Givoni B. Man climate and architecture. *Applied Science Publisher Ltd* 289-306. London: UK. 1976.

[28] BS 5454. Storage and exhibition archive documents. British Standard Institute. London. 1989.

[29] Lazzarin, R. D'Ascanio, A; Gaspaella, A. Utilisation of a green roof in reducing the cooling load of a new industrial building. In: *Proceedings of the 1ˢᵗ International Conference on Sustainable Energy Technologies (SET)* 32-37, Porto: Portugal. 12-14 June 2002.

[30] David, E. Sustainable energy: choices, problems and opportunities. *The Royal Society of Chemistry*, 2003, 19, 19-47.

[31] Zuatori, A. An overview on the national strategy for improving the efficiency of energy use. *Jordanian Energy Abstracts*, 2005, 9 (1), 31-32.

[32] Anne, G; Michael, S. *Building and land management*. 5ᵗʰ edition. Oxford: UK. 2005.

[33] Randal, G; Goyal, R. *Greenhouse technology*. New Delhi: Narosa Publishing House. 1998.

[34] Yadav, I; Chauadhari, M. *Progressive floriculture*. Bangalore: The house of Sarpan 1-5, 1997.

[35] EIBI (Energy in Building and Industry). Constructive thoughts on efficiency, building regulations, inside committee limited. Inside Energy: Magazine for Energy Professional. UK: KOPASS 13-14. 1999.

[36] Jermey, L. The positive solution: Solar Century. *Energy and Environmental Management*, 2002. 4-5.

[37] WEC Commission, editor. *Energy for tomorrow's world*. London: UK. St. Martin's Press, 1993.

[38] EUREC Agency, editor. *The future for renewable energy*. London: James and James, 1996.

[39] Plaz, W. Renewable energy in Europe: statistics and their problems, London: James and James, 1995.

[40] Hohmeyer, O. The social costs of electricity-renewables versus fossil and nuclear energy. *Int. J. Solar Energy,* 1992, 11, 231-50.

[41] Baker N; Fanchiotti, A; Steemers, K. Day-lighting in architecture. European Commission Directorate-General XII for Science, Research and Development, 1993.

[42] Mazria, E. *Direct gain systems: clerestories and sky-lights.* The passive solar energy book, chap. 10. Emmaus, PA: Rodale Press, 1979.

[43] Duffie, JA; Beckman, WA. *Solar engineering of thermal processes.* John Wiley and Sons, 1991.

[44] Watmuff, JH; Charters, WWS; Proctor D. Solar and wind induced external coefficients for solar collectors. *Internationale Heliotechnique,* 1997, 2, 56.

[45] Thomas LC. *Heat transfer.* Prentice Hall, 1992.

[46] Lee, K; Han, D; Lim, H. Passive design principles and techniques for folk houses in Cheju Island and Ullung Island of Korea. *Energy and Buildings,* 1996, 23, 207-16.

[47] JETFAN. Greenhouse ventilation. The thermal engineering contributes to better plant health and lower heating costs. *Devon.* 1996.

[48] John, AA; James, SD. The power of place: bringing together geographical and sociological imaginations. 1989.

In: Advances in Energy Research. Volume 20
Editor: Morena J. Acosta

ISBN: 978-1-63463-169-3
© 2015 Nova Science Publishers, Inc.

Chapter 3

CONVENTIONAL ENERGY USE, ENVIRONMENT AND SUSTAINABLE DEVELOPMENT

Abdeen Mustafa Omer
Energy Research Institute (ERI), Nottingham, UK

ABSTRACT

Globally, buildings are responsible for approximately 40% of the total world annual energy consumption. Most of this energy is for the provision of lighting, heating, cooling, and air conditioning. Increasing awareness of the environmental impact of CO_2, NO_x and CFCs emissions triggered a renewed interest in environmentally friendly cooling, and heating technologies. Under the 1997 Montreal Protocol, governments agreed to phase out chemicals used as refrigerants that have the potential to destroy stratospheric ozone. It was therefore considered desirable to reduce energy consumption and decrease the rate of depletion of world energy reserves and pollution of the environment. One way of reducing building energy consumption is to design buildings, which are more economical in their use of energy for heating, lighting, cooling, ventilation and hot water supply. Passive measures, particularly natural or hybrid ventilation rather than air-conditioning, can dramatically reduce primary energy consumption. However, exploitation of renewable energy in buildings and agricultural greenhouses can, also, significantly contribute towards reducing dependency on fossil fuels. Therefore, promoting innovative renewable applications and reinforcing the renewable energy market will contribute to preservation of the ecosystem by reducing emissions at local and global levels. This will also contribute to the amelioration of environmental conditions by replacing conventional fuels with renewable energies that produce no air pollution or greenhouse gases. The provision of good indoor environmental quality while achieving energy and cost efficient operation of the heating, ventilating and air-conditioning (HVAC) plants in buildings represents a multi variant problem. The comfort of building occupants is dependent on many environmental parameters including air speed, temperature, relative humidity and quality in addition to lighting and noise. The overall objective is to provide a high level of building performance (BP), which can be defined as indoor environmental quality (IEQ), energy efficiency (EE) and cost efficiency (CE).

Indoor environmental quality is the perceived condition of comfort that building occupants experience due to the physical and psychological conditions to which they are exposed by their surroundings. The main physical parameters affecting IEQ are air speed, temperature, relative humidity and quality.

Energy efficiency is related to the provision of the desired environmental conditions while consuming the minimal quantity of energy.

Cost efficiency is the financial expenditure on energy relative to the level of environmental comfort and productivity that the building occupants attained. The overall cost efficiency can be improved by improving the indoor environmental quality and the energy efficiency of a building.

This communication discusses the potential for such integrated systems in the stationary and portable power market in response to the critical need for a cleaner energy technology. Anticipated patterns of future energy use and consequent environmental impacts (acid precipitation, ozone depletion and the greenhouse effect or global warming) are comprehensively discussed in this study. Throughout the theme several issues relating to renewable energies, environment and sustainable development are examined from both current and future perspectives.

Keywords: Energy, environment, sustainable development, global warming, mitigations

1. INTRODUCTION

Several definitions of sustainable development have been put forth, including the following common one: development that meets the needs of the present without compromising the ability of future generations to meet their own needs. The World Energy Council (WEC) study found that without any change in our current practice, the world energy demand in 2020 would be 50-80% higher than 1990 levels. According to the USA Department of Energy (DoE) report, annual energy demand will increase from a current capacity of 363 million kilowatts to 750 million kilowatts by 2020 [1]. The world's energy consumption today is estimated to 22 billion kWh per year, 53 billion kWh by 2020 [1]. Such ever-increasing demand could place significant strain on the current energy infrastructure and potentially damage world environmental health by CO, CO_2, SO_2, NO_x effluent gas emissions and global warming. Achieving solutions to environmental problems that we face today requires long-term potential actions for sustainable development. In this regards, renewable energy resources appear to be the one of the most efficient and effective solutions since the intimate relationship between renewable energy and sustainable development. More rational use of energy is an important bridge to help transition from today's fossil fuel dominated world to a world powered by non-polluting fuels and advanced technologies such as photovoltaics (PVs) and fuel cells (FCs) [1].

An approach is needed to integrate renewable energies in a way to meet high building performance. However, because renewable energy sources are stochastic and geographically diffuse, their ability to match demand is determined by adoption of one of the following two approaches [2]: the utilisation of a capture area greater than that occupied by the community to be supplied, or the reduction of the community's energy demands to a level commensurate with the locally available renewable resources.

For a northern European climate, which is characterised by an average annual solar irradiance of 150 Wm^{-2}, the mean power production from a photovoltaic component of 13% conversion efficiency is approximately 20 Wm^{-2}. For an average wind speed of 5 ms^{-1}, the power produced by a micro wind turbine will be of a similar order of magnitude, though with a different profile shape. In the UK, for example, a typical office building will have a demand in the order of 300 kWhm^{-2}yr^{-1}. This translates into approximately 50 Wm^{-2} of façade, which is twice as much as the available renewable energies [3]. Thus, the aim is to utilise energy efficiency measures in order to reduce the overall energy consumption and adjust the demand profiles to be met by renewable energies. For instance, this approach can be applied to greenhouses, which use solar energy to provide indoor environmental quality. The greenhouse effect is one result of the differing properties of heat radiation when it is generated at different temperatures. Objects inside the greenhouse, or any other building, such as plants, re-radiate the heat or absorb it. Because the objects inside the greenhouse are at a lower temperature than the sun, the re-radiated heat is of longer wavelengths, and cannot penetrate the glass. This re-radiated heat is trapped and causes the temperature inside the greenhouse to rise. Note that the atmosphere surrounding the earth, also, behaves as a large greenhouse around the world. Changes to the gases in the atmosphere, such as increased carbon dioxide content from the burning of fossil fuels, can act like a layer of glass and reduce the quantity of heat that the planet earth would otherwise radiate back into space. This particular greenhouse effect, therefore, contributes to global warming. The application of greenhouses for plants growth can be considered one of the measures in the success of solving this problem. Maximising the efficiency gained from a greenhouse can be achieved using various approaches, employing different techniques that could be applied at the design, construction and operational stages. The development of greenhouses could be a solution to farming industry and food security.

Energy security, economic growth and environment protection are the national energy policy drivers of any country of the world. As world populations grow, many faster than the average 2%, the need for more and more energy is exacerbated (Figure 1). Enhanced lifestyle and energy demand rise together and the wealthy industrialised economics, which contain 25% of the world's population, consume 75% of the world's energy supply. The world's energy consumption today is estimated to 22 billion kWh per year. About 6.6 billion metric tonnes carbon equivalent of greenhouse gas (GHG) emission are released in the atmosphere to meet this energy demand [4]. Approximately 80% is due to carbon emissions from the combustion of energy fuels. At the current rate of usage, taking into consideration population increases and higher consumption of energy by developing countries, oil resources, natural gas and uranium will be depleted within a few decades. As for coal, it may take two centuries or so.

Technological progress has dramatically changed the world in a variety of ways. It has, however, also led to developments, e.g., environmental problems, which threaten man and nature. Build-up of carbon dioxide and other GHGs is leading to global warming with unpredictable but potentially catastrophic consequences. When fossil fuels burn, they emit toxic pollutants that damage the environment and people's health with over 700,000 deaths resulting each year, according to the World Bank review of 2000. At the current rate of usage, taking into consideration population increases and higher consumption of energy by developing countries, oil resources, natural gas and uranium will be depleted within a few decades, as shown in Figures 2, and 3. As for coal, it may take two centuries or so. One must therefore endeavour to take precautions today for a viable world for coming generations. Energy is an essential factor in development since it stimulates, and supports economic growth and development. Fossil fuels, especially oil and natural gas, are finite in extent, and should be regarded as depleting assets, and efforts are oriented to search for new sources of energy.

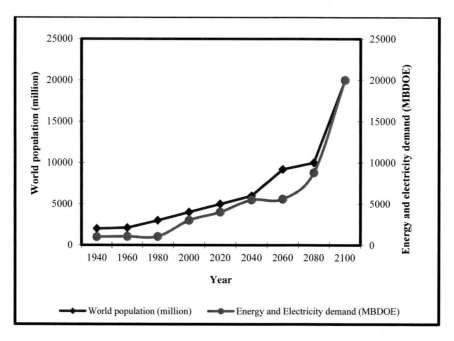

Figure 1. Annual and estimated world population and energy demand. Million of barrels per day of oil equivalent (MBDOE).

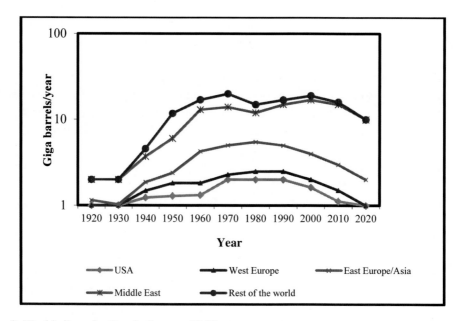

Figure 2. World oil productions in the next 10-20 years.

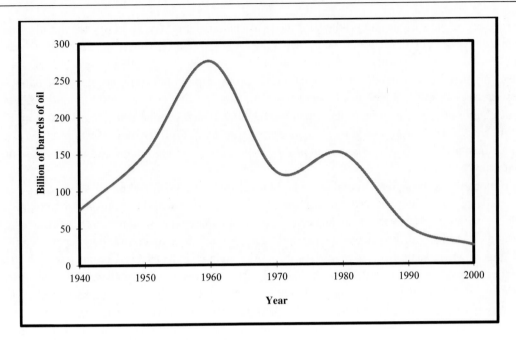

Figure 3. Volume of oil discovered worldwide.

Research into future alternatives has been and still being conducted aiming to solve the complex problems of this recent time, e.g., rising energy requirements of a rapidly and constantly growing world population and global environmental pollution. Therefore, options for a long-term and environmentally friendly energy supply have to be developed leading to the use of renewable sources (water, sun, wind, biomass, geothermal, hydrogen) and fuel cells. Renewables could shield a nation from the negative effect in the energy supply, price and related environment concerns. Hydrogen for fuel cells and the sun for PV have been considered for many years as a likely and eventual substitute for oil, gas, coal and uranium. They are the most abundant elements in the universe. The use of solar energy or PVs for the everyday electricity needs has distinct advantages: avoid consuming resources and degrading the environment through polluting emissions, oil spills and toxic by-products. A one-kilowatt PV system producing (150 kWh) each month prevents (75 kg) of fossil fuel from being mined. A (150 kg) of CO_2 is entering the atmosphere and keeps (473 litres) of water from being consumed. Electricity from fuel cells can be used in the same way as grid power: to run appliances and light bulbs and even to power cars since each gallon of gasoline produced and used in an internal combustion engine releases roughly (12 kg) of CO_2, a GHG that contributes to global warming.

2. PEOPLE, POWER AND POLLUTION

Over millions of years ago plants covered the earth, converting the energy of sunlight into living tissue, some of which was buried in the depths of the earth to produce deposits of coal, oil and natural gas. The past few decades, however, have experienced many valuable uses for these complex chemical substances, manufacturing from them plastics, textiles, fertiliser and the various end products of the petrochemical industry. Indeed, each decade sees increasing uses for these products. Renewable energy is the term used to describe a wide range of naturally occurring, replenishing energy sources. Coal, oil and gas, which will certainly be of great value to future generations, as they are to ours, are non-renewable natural resources. The rapid depletion of non-renewable fossil resources need not continue. This is particularly true now as it is, or soon will be, technically and economically feasible to supply all of man's needs from the most abundant energy source of all, the sun. The sunlight is not only inexhaustible, but, moreover, it is the only energy source, which is completely non-polluting.

Industry's use of fossil fuels has been blamed for warming the climate. When coal, gas and oil are burnt, they release harmful gases, which trap heat in the atmosphere and cause global warming. However, there has been an ongoing debate on this subject, as scientists have struggled to distinguish between changes, which are human induced, and those, which could be put down to natural climate variability. Nevertheless, industrialised countries have the highest emission levels, and must shoulder the greatest responsibility for global warming. However, action must also be taken by developing countries to avoid future increases in emission levels as their economies develop and populations grow, as clearly captured by the Kyoto Protocol [4]. Notably, human activities that emit carbon dioxide (CO_2), the most significant contributor to potential climate change, occur primarily from fossil fuel production. Consequently, efforts to control CO_2 emissions could have serious, negative consequences for economic growth, employment, investment, trade and the standard of living of individuals everywhere.

Scientifically, it is difficult to predict the relationship between global temperature and GHG concentrations. The climate system contains many processes that will change if warming occurs. Critical processes include heat transfer by winds and tides, the hydrological cycle involving evaporation, precipitation, runoff and groundwater and the formation of clouds, snow, and ice, all of which display enormous natural variability.

The equipment and infrastructure for energy supply and use are designed with long lifetimes, and the premature turnover of capital stock involves significant costs. Economic benefits occur if capital stock is replaced with more efficient equipment in step with its normal replacement cycle. Likewise, if opportunities to reduce future emissions are taken in a timely manner, they should be less costly. Such a flexible approach would allow society to take account of evolving scientific and technological knowledge, while gaining experience in designing policies to address climate change [4].

The World Summit on Sustainable Development in Johannesburg in 2002 committed itself to ''encourage and promote the development of renewable energy sources to accelerate the shift towards sustainable consumption and production''. Accordingly, it aimed at breaking the link between resource use and productivity. This can be achieved by the followings:

- Trying to ensure economic growth does not cause environmental pollution.
- Improving resource efficiency.
- Examining the whole life-cycle of a product.
- Enabling consumers to receive more information on products and services.
- Examining how taxes, voluntary agreements, subsidies, regulation and information campaigns, can best stimulate innovation and investment to provide cleaner technology.

The energy conservation scenarios include rational use of energy policies in all economy sectors and the use of combined heat and power systems, which are able to add to energy savings from the autonomous power plants. Electricity from renewable energy sources is by definition the environmental green product. Hence, a renewable energy certificate system, as recommended by the World Summit, is an essential basis for all policy systems, independent of the renewable energy support scheme. It is, therefore, important that all parties involved support the renewable energy certificate system in place if it is to work as planned. Moreover, existing renewable energy technologies (RETs) could play a significant mitigating role, but the economic and political climate will have to change first. Climate change is real. It is happening now, and GHGs produced by human activities are significantly contributing to it. The predicted global temperature increase of between 1.5 and 4.5°C could lead to potentially catastrophic environmental impacts [5]. These include sea level rise, increased frequency of extreme weather events, floods, droughts, disease migration from various places and possible stalling of the Gulf Stream. This has led scientists to argue that climate change issues are not ones that politicians can afford to ignore, and policy makers tend to agree [5]. However, reaching international agreements on climate change policies is no trivial task as the difficulty in ratifying the Kyoto Protocol has proved.

Therefore, the use of renewable energy sources and the rational use of energy, in general, are the fundamental inputs for any responsible energy policy. However, the energy sector is encountering difficulties because increased production and consumption levels entail higher levels of pollution and eventually climate change, with possibly disastrous consequences. At the same time, it is important to secure energy at an acceptable cost in order to avoid negative impacts on economic growth. To date, renewable energy contributes as much as 20% of the global energy supplies worldwide [5]. Over two thirds of this comes from biomass use, mostly in developing countries, some of it unsustainable. Yet, the potential for energy from sustainable technologies is huge. On the technological side, renewables have an obvious role to play. In general, there is no problem in terms of the technical potential of renewables to deliver energy. Moreover, there are very good opportunities for the RETs to play an important role in reducing emissions of the GHGs into the atmosphere, certainly far more than have been exploited so far. However, there are still some technical issues to address in order to cope with the intermittency of some renewables, particularly wind and solar. Yet, the biggest problem with relying on renewables to deliver the necessary cuts in the GHG emissions is more to do with politics and policy issues than with technical ones [5]. For example, the single most important step governments could take to promote and increase the use of renewables is to improve access for renewables to the energy market. This access to the market needs to be under favourable conditions and, possibly, under favourable economic rates as well. One move that could help, or at least justify, better market access would be to acknowledge that there are environmental costs associated with other energy supply options and that these costs are not currently internalised within the market price of electricity or fuels. This could make a significant difference, particularly if appropriate subsidies were applied to renewable energy in recognition of the environmental benefits it offers. Similarly, cutting energy consumption through end-use efficiency is absolutely essential. This suggests that issues of end-use consumption of energy will have to come into the discussion in the foreseeable future [6].

However, the RETs have the benefit of being environmentally benign when developed in a sensitive and appropriate way with the full involvement of local communities. In addition, they are diverse, secure, locally based and abundant. In spite of the enormous potential and the multiple benefits, the contribution from renewable energy still lags behind the ambitious claims for it due to the initially high development costs, concerns about local impacts, lack of research funding and poor institutional and economic arrangements [7].

Hence, an approach is needed to integrate renewable energies in a way that meets high building performance requirements. However, because renewable energy sources are stochastic and geographically diffuse, their ability to match demand is determined by adoption of one of the following two approaches [8]: the utilisation of a capture area greater than that occupied by the community to be supplied, or the reduction of the community's energy demands to a level commensurate with the locally available renewable resources.

2.1. Energy and Population Growth

Urban areas throughout the world have increased in size during recent decades. About 50% of the world's population and approximately 7.6% in more developed countries are urban dwellers [9]. Even though there is evidence to suggest that in many 'advanced' industrialised countries there has been a reversal in the rural-to-urban shift of populations, virtually all population growth expected between 2000 and 2030 will be concentrated in urban areas of the world. With an expected annual growth of 1.8%, the world's urban population will double in 38 years [9].

With increasing urbanisation in the world, cities are growing in number, population and complexity. At present, 2% of the world's land surface is covered by cities, yet the people living in them consume 75% of the resources consumed by mankind [10]. Indeed, the ecological footprint of cities is many times larger than the areas they physically occupy. Economic and social imperatives often dictate that cities must become more concentrated, making it necessary to increase the density to accommodate the people, to reduce the cost of public services, and to achieve required social cohesiveness. The reality of modern urbanisation inevitably leads to higher densities than in traditional settlements and this trend is particularly notable in developing countries.

Generally, the world population is rising rapidly, notably in the developing countries. Historical trends suggest that increased annual energy use per capita, which promotes a decrease in population growth rate, is a good surrogate for the standard of living factors. If these trends continue, the stabilisation of the world's population will require the increased use of all sources of energy, particularly as cheap oil and gas are depleted. The improved efficiency of energy use and renewable energy sources will, therefore, be essential in stabilising population, while providing a decent standard of living all over the world [10]. Moreover, energy is the vital input for economic and social development of any country. With an increase in industrial and agricultural activities the demand for energy is also rising. It is, however, a well-accepted fact that commercial energy use has to be minimised. This is because of the environmental effects and the availability problems. Consequently, the focus has now shifted to non-commercial energy resources, which are renewable in nature. This is bound to have less environmental effects and also the availability is guaranteed. However, even though the ideal situation will be to enthuse people to use renewable energy resources, there are many practical difficulties, which need to be tackled. The people groups who are using the non-commercial energy resources, like urban communities, are now becoming more demanding and wish to have commercial energy resources made available for their use. This is attributed to the increased awareness, improved literacy level and changing culture [10]. The quality of life practiced by people is usually represented as being proportional to the per capita energy use of that particular country. It is not surprising that people want to improve their quality of life. Consequently, it is expected that the demand for commercial energy resources will increase at a greater rate in the years to come [10]. Because of this emerging situation, the policy makers are left with two options: either to concentrate on renewable energy resources and have them as substitutes for commercial energy resources or to have a dual approach in which renewable energy resources will contribute to meet a significant portion of the demand whereas the conventional commercial energy resources would be used with caution whenever necessary. Even though the first option is the ideal one, the second approach will be more appropriate for a smooth transition [10].

2.2. Energy and Environmental Problems

Technological progress has dramatically changed the world in a variety of ways. It has, however, also led to developments of environmental problems, which threaten man and nature. During the past two decades the risk and reality of environmental degradation have become more apparent. Growing evidence of environmental problems is due to a combination of several factors since the environmental impact of human activities has grown dramatically because of the sheer increase of world population, consumption, industrial activity, etc., throughout the 1970s most environmental analysis and legal control instruments concentrated on conventional effluent gas pollutants such as SO_2, NO_x, CO_2, particulates, and CO (Table 1). Recently, environmental concerns has extended to the control of micro or hazardous air pollutants, which are usually toxic chemical substances and harmful in small doses, as well to that of globally significant pollutants such as CO_2. Aside from advances in environmental science, developments in industrial processes and structures have led to new environmental problems. For example, in the energy sector, major shifts to the road transport of industrial goods and to individual travel by cars has led to an increase in road traffic, and hence, a shift in attention paid to the effects and sources of NO_x and volatile organic compound (VOC) emissions. Environmental problems span a continuously growing range of pollutants, hazards and ecosystem degradation over wider areas. The main areas of environmental problems are major environmental accidents, water pollution, maritime pollution, land use and sitting impact, radiation and radioactivity, solid waste disposal, hazardous air pollutants, ambient air quality, acid rain, stratospheric ozone depletion and global warming (greenhouse effect, and global climatic change) (Table 2).

The four more important types of harm from man's activities are global warming gases, ozone destroying gases, gaseous pollutants and microbiological hazards (Table 3). The earth is some 30°C warmer due to the presence of gases but the global temperature is rising. This could lead to the sea level rising at the rate of 60 mm each decade with the growing risk of flooding in low-lying areas (Figure 4). At the United Nations Earth Summit at Rio in June 1992 some 153 countries agreed to pursue sustainable development [11]. A main aim was to reduce emission of carbon dioxide and other GHGs. Reduction of energy use in buildings is a major role in achieving this. Carbon dioxide targets are proposed to encourage designers to look at low energy designs and energy sources. The biomass energy sources have significant potential in the fight against climate change.

Table 1. EU criteria pollutant standards in the ambient air environment

Pollutant	EU limit
CO	30 mg/m^2; 1h
NO_2	200 $\mu g/m^2$; 1h
O_3	235 $\mu g/m^2$; 1h
SO_2	250-350 $\mu g/m^2$; 24 h
	80-120 $\mu g/m^2$; annual
PM_{10}	250 $\mu g/m^2$; 24 h
	80 $\mu g/m^2$; annual
$SO_2 + PM_{10}$	100-150 $\mu g/m^2$; 24 h
	40-60 $\mu g/m^2$; annual
Pb	2 $\mu g/m^2$; annual
Total suspended particulate (TSP)	260 $\mu g/m^2$; 24 h
HC	160 $\mu g/m^2$; 3 h

Table 2. Significant EU environmental directives in water, air and land environments

Environment	Directive name
Water	Surface water for drinking
	Sampling surface water for drinking
	Drinking water quality
	Quality of freshwater supporting fish
	Shellfish waters
	Bathing waters
	Dangerous substances in water
	Groundwater
	Urban wastewater
	Nitrates from agricultural sources
Air	Smokes in air
	Sulphur dioxide in air
	Lead in air
	Large combustion plants
	Existing municipal incineration plants
	New municipal incineration plants
	Asbestos in air
	Sulphur content of gas oil
	Lead in petrol
	Emissions from petrol engines
	Air quality standards for NO_2
	Emissions from diesel engines
Land	Protection of soil when sludge is applied

Problems with energy supply and use are related not only to global warming that is taking place, due to effluent gas emission mainly CO_2, but also to such environmental concerns as air pollution, acid precipitation, ozone depletion, forest destruction and emission of radioactive substances. These issues must be taken into consideration simultaneously if humanity is to achieve a bright energy future with minimal environmental impacts. Much evidence exists, which suggests that the future will be negatively impacted if humans keep degrading the environment (Table 4). The clamour all over the world for the need to conserve energy and the environment has intensified as traditional energy resources continue to dwindle whilst the environment becomes increasingly degraded.

Table 3. The external environment

Damage	Manifestation	Design
NO_x, SO_x	Irritant Acid rain land damage Acid rain fish damage Global warming	Low NO_x burners Low sulphur fuel Sulphur removal Thermal insulation
CO_2	Rising sea level Drought, storms Increased ultra violet	Heat recovery Heat pumps No CFC's or HCFC's
O_3 destruction	Skin cancer Crop damage Pontiac fever	Minimum air conditioning Refrigerant collection Careful maintenance
Legionnellosis	Legionnaires	Dry cooling towers

Table 4. Global emissions of the top fourteen nations by total CO_2 volume (billion of tonnes)

Rank	Nation	CO_2	Rank	Nation	CO_2	Rank	Nation	CO_2
1	USA	1.36	6	India	0.19	11	Mexico	0.09
2	Russia	0.98	7	UK	0.16	12	Poland	0.08
3	China	0.69	8	Canada	0.11	13	S. Africa	0.08
4	Japan	0.30	9	Italy	0.11	14	S. Korea	0.07

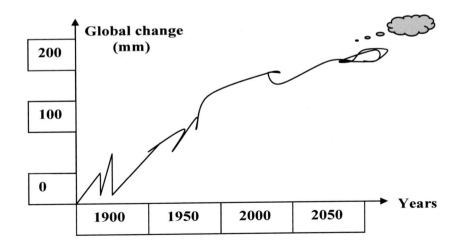

Figure 4. Change in global sea level.

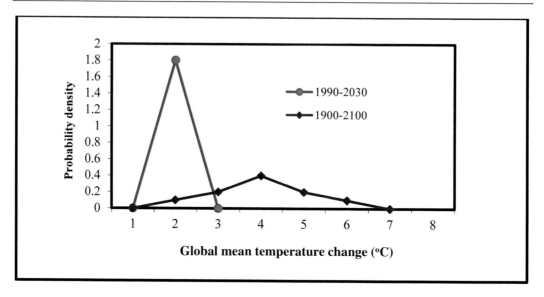

Figure 5. Global mean temperature changes over the period of 1990-2100 and 1990-2030.

During the past century, global surface temperatures have increased at a rate near 0.6°C/century and the average temperature of the Atlantic, Pacific and Indian oceans (covering 72% of the earth surface) have risen by 0.06°C since 1995. Global temperatures in 2001 were 0.52°C above the long-term 1880-2000 average (the 1880-2000 annually averaged combined land and ocean temperature is 13.9°C). Also, according to the USA Department of Energy, world emissions of carbon are expected to increase by 54% above 1990 levels by 2015 making the earth likely to warm 1.7-4.9°C over the period 1990-2100, as shown in Figure 5. Such observation and others demonstrate that interests will likely increase regarding energy related environment concerns and that energy is one of the main factors that must be considered in discussions of sustainable development.

2.3. Environmental Transformations

In recent years a number of countries have adopted policies aimed at giving a greater role to private ownership in the natural resource sector. For example, in the UK the regional water companies have been privatised and have been given a considerable degree of control over the exploitation of the nation's regional water resources. Similar policies have been followed in France and other European countries. Typically, a whole range of new regulatory instruments such as technological standards accompanies such privatisation on water treatment plants, minimum standards on drinking water quality, price controls and maximum withdrawal quotas. While some of these instruments address problems of monopolistic behaviour and other forms of imperfect competition, the bulk of regulatory measures is concerned with establishing 'good practices' aimed at maintaining the quality of the newly privatised resources as a shorthand. Society has to meet the freshwater demands of its population and its industry by extracting water from the regional water resources that are provided by the natural environment (lakes, rivers, aquifers, etc.). These water resources are renewable but potentially destructible resources. While moderate amounts of human water extractions from a given regional water system can be sustained for indefinite periods. Excessive extractions will change the geographical and climatic conditions supporting the water cycle and will diminish the regenerative capacity of the regional water system, thereby reducing the potential for future withdrawals. Typically, recovery from any such resource degradation will be very slow and difficult, if not impossible; resource degradation is partially irreversible [12].

To make sustainable water extraction economically viable, the sustainable policy has to break even (all costs are covered by revenues) while unsustainable policy has to be unprofitable (costs exceed revenues):

$$(1+r) \, vt_{-1} = 5y_t + v_t \tag{1}$$

Where: r is the interest rate, t=year, y is the revenue.

$$(1+r) \, vt_{-1} > 105y_t \tag{2}$$

$$(1+r) \, vt_{-1} < [105/(105-5)] \, v_t \tag{3}$$

The term $[105/(105-5)]$ is to define the natural productivity factor of the water resource as $(1+g) = [105/(105-5)]$; g is the natural productivity rate.

Rate g will be close to zero if the sustainable extraction level is much smaller than the unsustainable level. Using g, the equation can be as follows:

$$v_t > (1+r)/(1+g) \, v_{t-1} \tag{4}$$

Regulatory measures that prevent resource owners from adopting certain unsustainable extraction policies are a necessary pre-condition for the effective operation of a privatised natural resource sector. Unregulated water privatisation would result in an inflationary dynamics whose distributional effects would threaten the long-term viability of the economy. This inflationary dynamics is not due to any form of market imperfection but is a natural consequence of the competitive arbitrage behaviour of unregulated private resource owners.

3. SUSTAINABILITY CONCEPT

Absolute sustainability of electricity supply is a simple concept: no depletion of world resources and no ongoing accumulation of residues. Relative sustainability is a useful concept in comparing the sustainability of two or more generation technologies. Therefore, only renewables are absolutely sustainable, and nuclear is more sustainable than fossil. However, any discussion about sustainability must not neglect the ability or otherwise of the new technologies to support the satisfactory operation of the electricity supply infrastructure. The electricity supply system has been developed to have a high degree of resilience against the loss of transmission circuits and major generators, as well as unusually large and rapid load changes. It is unlikely that consumers would tolerate any reduction in the quality of the service, even if this were the result of the adoption of otherwise benign generation technologies. Renewables are generally weather-dependent and as such their likely output can be predicted but not controlled. The only control possible is to reduce the output below that available from the resource at any given time. Therefore, to safeguard system stability and security, renewables must be used in conjunction with other, controllable, generation and with large-scale energy storage. There is a substantial cost associated with this provision.

It is useful to codify all aspects of sustainability, thus ensuring that all factors are taken into account for each and every development proposal. Therefore, with the intention of promoting debate, the following considerations are proposed:

(1) Long-term availability of the energy source or fuel.
(2) Price stability of energy source or fuel.
(3) Acceptability or otherwise of by-products of the generation process.
(4) Grid services, particularly controllability of real and reactive power output.
(5) Technological stability, and likelihood of rapid technical obsolescence.
(6) Knowledge base of applying the technology.
(7) Life of the installation – a dam may last more than 100 years, but a gas turbine probably will not.
(8) Maintenance requirement of the plant.

3.1. Environmental Aspects

Environmental pollution is a major problem facing all nations of the world. People have caused air pollution since they learned to how to use fire, but man-made air pollution (anthropogenic air pollution) has rapidly increased since industrialisation began. Many volatile organic compounds and trace metals are emitted into the atmosphere by human activities. The pollutants emitted into the atmosphere do not remain confined to the area near the source of emission or to the local environment, and can be transported over long distances, and create regional and global environmental problems. The privatisation and price liberalisation in energy fields has been secured to some extent (but not fully). Availability and adequate energy supplies to the major productive sectors. The result is that, the present situation of energy supplies is for better than ten years ago (Table 5).

Table 5. Classifications of data requirements

Data	Plant data	System data
Existing data	Size Life Cost (fixed and var. O&M) Forced outage Maintenance Efficiency Fuel Emissions	Peak load Load shape Capital costs Fuel costs Depreciation Rate of return Taxes
Future data	All of above, plus Capital costs Construction trajectory Date in service	System lead growth Fuel price growth Fuel import limits Inflation

A great challenge facing the global community today is to make the industrial economy more like the biosphere, that is, to make it a more closed system. This would save energy, reduce waste and pollution, and reduce costs. In short, it would enhance sustainability. Often, it is technically feasible to recycle waste in one of several different ways. For some wastes there are powerful arguments for incineration with energy recovery, rather than material recycling. Cleaner production approach and pollution control measures are needed in the recycling sector as much as in others. The industrial sector world widely is responsible for about one third of anthropogenic emissions of carbon dioxide, the most important greenhouse gas. Industry is also an important emitter of several other greenhouse gases. And many of industry's products emit greenhouse gases as well, either during use or after they become waste. Opportunities exist for substantial reducing industrial emissions through more efficient production and use of energy. Fuel substitutions, the use of alternative energy technologies, process modification, and by revising materials strategies to make use of less energy and greenhouse gas intensive materials. Industry has an additional role to play through the design of products that use less energy and materials and produce lower greenhouse gas emissions.

Development in the environmental sense is a rather recent concern relating to the need to manage scarce natural resources in a prudent manner- because human welfare ultimately depends on ecological services. The environmental interpretation of sustainability focuses on the overall viability and health of ecological systems- defined in terms of a comprehensive, multiscale, dynamic, hierarchical measure of resilience, vigour and organisation. Natural resource degradation, pollution and loss of biodiversity are detrimental because they increase vulnerability, undermine system health, and reduce resilience. The environmental issues include:

- Global and transnational (climate change, and ozone layer depletion).
- Natural habitats (forests and other ecosystems).
- Land (agricultural zones).
- Water resources (river basin, aquifer, and water shed).
- Urban-industrial (metropolitan area, and air-shed).

Environmental sustainability depends on several factors, including:

- Climate change (magnitude and frequency of shocks).
- Systems vulnerability (extent of impact damage).
- System resilience (ability to recover from impacts).

Economic importance of environmental issue is increasing, and new technologies are expected to reduce pollution derived both from productive processes and products, with costs that are still unknown. This is due to market uncertainty, weak appropriability regime, lack of a dominant design, and difficulties in reconfiguring organisational routines. The degradation of the global environment is one of the most serious energy issues. Various options are proposed and investigated to mitigate climate change, acid rain or other environmental problems. Additionally, the following aspects play a fundamental role in developing environmental technologies, pointing out how technological trajectories depend both on exogenous market conditions and endogenous firm competencies:

(1) Regulations concerning introduction of Zero Emission Vehicles (ZEV), create market demand and business development for new technologies.

(2) Each stage of technology development requires alternative forms of division and coordination of innovative labour, upstream and downstream industries are involved in new forms of inter-firm relationships, causing a reconfiguration of product architectures and reducing effects of path dependency.

(3) Product differentiation increases firm capabilities to plan at the same time technology reduction and customer selection, while meeting requirements concerning network externalities.

(4) It is necessary to find and/or create alternative funding sources for each research, development and design stage of the new technologies.

Action areas for producers:

- Management and measurement tools- adopting environmental management systems appropriate for the business.
- Performance assessment tools- making use of benchmarking to identify scope for impact reduction and greater eco-efficiency in all aspects of the business.
- Best practice tools- making use of free help and advice from government best practice programmes (energy efficiency, environmental technology, and resource savings).
- Innovation and ecodesign- rethinking the delivery of 'value added' by the business, so that impact reduction and resource efficiency are firmly built in at the design stage.
- Cleaner, leaner production processes- pursuing improvements and savings in waste minimisation, energy and water consumption, transport and distribution, as well as reduced emissions. Tables (6-8) indicate energy conservation, sustainable development and environment.
- Supply chain management- specifying more demanding standards of sustainability from 'upstream' suppliers, while supporting smaller firms to meet those higher standards.
- Product stewardship- taking the broadest view of 'producer responsibility' and working to reduce all the 'downstream' effects of products after they have been sold on to customers.
- Openness and transparency- publicly reporting on environmental performance against meaningful targets; actively using clear labels and declarations so that customers are fully informed; building stakeholder confidence by communicating sustainability aims to the workforce, the shareholders and the local community.

Figure 6 presents the link between resources and productivity- sustainable production and consumption.

With the debate on climate change, the preference for real measured data has been changed. The analyses of climate scenarios need an hourly weather data series that allows for realistic changes in various weather parameters. By adapting parameters in a proper way, data series can be generated for the site. Weather generators should be useful for:

- Calculation of energy consumption (no extreme conditions are required).
- Design purposes (extremes are essential), and
- Predicting the effect of climate change such as increasing annually average of temperature.

This results in the following requirements:

- Relevant climate variables should be generated (solar radiation: global, diffuse, direct solar direction, temperature, humidity, wind speed and direction) according to the statistics of the real climate.
- The average behaviour should be in accordance with the real climate.
- Extremes should occur in the generated series in the way it will happen in a real warm period. This means that the generated series should be long enough to assure these extremes, and series based on average values from nearby stations.

Growing concerns about social and environmental sustainability have led to increased interest in planning for the energy utility sector because of its large resource requirements and production of emissions. A number of conflicting trends combine to make the energy sector a major concern, even though a clear definition of how to measure progress toward sustainability is lacking. These trends include imminent competition in the electricity industry, global climate change, expected long-term growth in population and pressure to balance living standards (including per capital energy consumption). Designing and implementing a sustainable energy sector will be a key element of defining and creating a sustainable society. In the electricity industry, the question of strategic planning for sustainability seems to conflict with the shorter time horizons associated with market forces as deregulation replaces vertical integration. Sustainable low-carbon energy scenarios for the new century emphasise the untapped potential of renewable resources is needed. Rural areas can benefit from this transition. The increased availability of reliable and efficient energy services stimulates new development alternatives. It is concluded that renewable environmentally friendly energy must be encouraged, promoted, implemented, and demonstrated by full-scale plant especially for use in remote rural areas.

Table 6. Classification of key variables defining facility sustainability

Criteria	Intra-system impacts	Extra-system impacts
Stakeholder satisfaction	Standard expectations met Relative importance of standard expectations	Covered by attending to extra-system resource base and ecosystem impacts
Resource base impacts	Change in intra-system resource bases Significance of change	Resource flow into/out of facility system Unit impact exerted by flow on source/sink system Significance of unit impact
Ecosystem impacts	Change in intra-system ecosystems Significance of change	Resource flows into/out of facility system Unit impact exerted by how on source/sink system Significance of unit impact

Alternatively energy sources can potentially help fulfil the acute energy demand and sustain economic growth in many regions of the world. This is the step in a long journey to encourage a progressive economy, which continues to provide us with high living standards, but at the same time helps reduce pollution, waste mountains, other environmental degradation, and environmental rationale for future policy-making and intervention to improve market mechanisms. This vision will be accomplished by:

- 'Decoupling' economic growth and environmental degradation. The basket of indicators illustrated shows the progress being made (Table 9). Decoupling air and water pollution from growth, making good headway with CO_2 emissions from energy, and transport. The environmental impact of our own individual behaviour is more closely linked to consumption expenditure than the economy as a whole.
- Focusing policy on the most important environmental impacts associated with the use of particular resources, rather than on the total level of all resource use.
- Increasing the productivity of material and energy use that are economically efficient by encouraging patterns of supply and demand, which are more efficient in the use of natural resources. The aim is to promote innovation and competitiveness. Investment in areas like energy efficiency, water efficiency and waste minimisation.
- Encouraging and enabling active and informed individual and corporate consumers

Table 7. Energy and sustainable environment

Technological criteria	Energy and environment criteria	Social and economic criteria
Primary energy saving in regional scale	Sustainability according to greenhouse gas pollutant emissions	Labour impact
Technical maturity, reliability	Sustainable according to other pollutant emissions	Market maturity
Consistence of installation and maintenance requirements with local technical known-how	Land requirement	Compatibility with political, legislative and administrative situation
Continuity and predictability of performance	Sustainability according to other environmental impacts	Cost of saved primary energy

Table 8. Positive impact of durability, adaptability and energy conservation on economic, social and environment systems

Economic system	Social system	Environmental system
Durability	Preservation of cultural values	Preservation of resources
Meeting changing needs of economic development	Meeting changing needs of individuals and society	Reuse, recycling and preservation of resources
Energy conservation and saving	Savings directed to meet other social needs	Preservation of resources, reduction of pollution and global warming

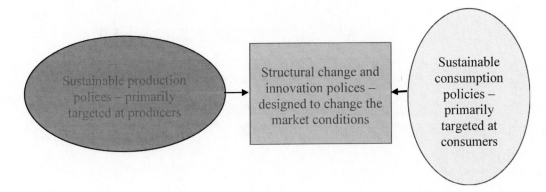

Figure 6. Link between resources and productivity.

On some climate change issues (such as global warming), there is no disagreement among the scientists. The greenhouse effect is unquestionably real; it is essential for life on earth. Water vapour is the most important GHG; next is carbon dioxide (CO_2). Without a natural greenhouse effect, scientists estimate that the earth's average temperature would be – 18°C instead of its present 14°C. There is also no scientific debate over the fact that human activity has increased the concentration of the GHGs in the atmosphere (especially CO_2 from combustion of coal, oil and gas). The greenhouse effect is also being amplified by increased concentrations of other gases, such as methane, nitrous oxide, and CFCs as a result of human emissions. Most scientists predict that rising global temperatures will raise the sea level and increase the frequency of intense rain or snowstorms. Climate change scenarios sources of uncertainty and factors influencing the future climate are:

Table 9. The basket of indicators for sustainable consumption and production

Economy-wide decoupling indicators
1.   Greenhouse gas emissions
2.   Air pollution
3.   Water pollution (river water quality)
4.   Commercial and industrial waste arisings and household waste not cycled
Resource use indicators
5.   Material use
6.   Water abstraction
7.   Homes built on land not previously developed, and number of households
Decoupling indicators for specific sectors
8.   Emissions from electricity generation
9.   Motor vehicle kilometres and related emissions
10. Agricultural output, fertiliser use, methane emissions and farmland bird populations
11. Manufacturing output, energy consumption and related emissions
12. Household consumption, expenditure energy, water consumption and waste generated

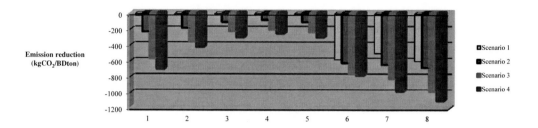

*1 Large steam power (LSP)
*2 Small steam power (SSP)
*3 Brayton cycle power (BCP)
*4 Bio-oil conversion power (B-CP)
*5 Gasification power (GP)
*6 Small steam CHP (SSCHP)
*7 Turboden cycle CHP (TCCHP)
*8 Entropic cycle CHP (ECCHP)

Figure 7. Comparison of thermal biomass usage options, CHP displacing natural gas as a heat source.

- The future emission rates of the GHGs.
- The effect of this increase in concentration on the energy balance of the atmosphere.
- The effect of these emissions on the GHGs concentrations in the atmosphere, and
- The effect of this change in energy balance on global and regional climate.

3.2. Wastes

Waste is defined as an unwanted material that is being discarded. Waste includes items being taken for further use, recycling or reclamation. Waste produced at household, commercial and industrial premises are control waste and come under the waste regulations. Waste Incineration Directive (WID) emissions limit values will favour efficient, inherently cleaner technologies that do not rely heavily on abatement. For existing plant, the requirements are likely to lead to improved control of:

- NOx emissions, by the adoption of infurnace combustion control and abatement techniques.
- Acid gases, by the adoption of abatement techniques and optimisation of their control.
- Particulate control techniques, and their optimisation, e.g., of bag filters and electrostatic precipitators.

The encouragement of greater energy use is an essential component of development. The waste and resources action programme has been working hard to reduce demand for virgin aggregates and market uptake of recycled and secondary alternatives (Figure 7). The programme targets are:

- To deliver training and information on the role of recycling and secondary aggregates in sustainable construction for influences in the supply chain, and
- To develop a promotional programme to highlight the new information on websites.

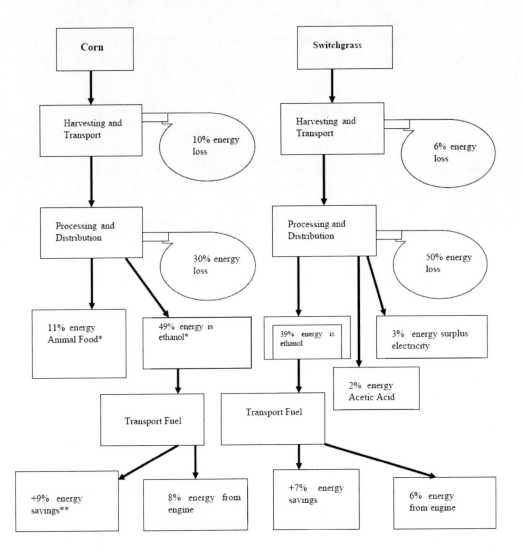

* 49% actual ethanol energy content, energy content in cattle feed by-product reflects chemical energy content, not lifecycle energy displacement.

** Energy savings in the refinery due to the higher value of ethanol compared to gasoline.

Figure 8. The lifecycle energy balance of corn and Switchgrass reveal a paradox: corn, as an ethanol feedstock requires less energy for production, i.e., more of the original energy in starch is retained in the ethanol fuel. Nevertheless, the switchgrass process yields higher GHG emissions. This is because most of the process energy for switchgrass process is generated from the GHG emission neutral biomass residue.

Lifecycle analysis of several ethanol feedstocks shows the emission displacement per tonne of feedstock is highest for corn stover and switchgrass (about 0.65 tonnes of CO_2 per tonne of feedstock) and lowest for corn (about 0.5 tonne).

Emissions due to cultivation and harvesting of corn and wheat are higher than those for lignocellulosics, and although the latter have a far higher process energy requirement (Figure 8). The GHG emissions are lower because this energy is produced from biomass residue, which is carbon neutral.

4. ENVIRONMENTAL AND SAFETY ASPECTS OF COMBUSTION TECHNOLOGY

This review is aimed to introduce historical background for the sustainability concept development. Special reference is given to the resource depletion and it is forecasted. In the assessment of global energy, water and environment resources attention is focused in on the resource consumption and its relevancy to the future demand. In the review of the sustainability concept development special emphasise is devoted to the definition of sustainability and its relevancy to the historical background of the sustainability idea. The recent assessment of sustainability is reflecting the normative and strategic dimension of sustainability.

Special attention is devoted to the most recent development of the concept of sustainability science. A new field of sustainability science emerging that seeks to understand the fundamental character of interactions between nature and society. Such an understanding must encompass the interaction of global processes with the ecological and so characteristics of particular places and sectors. With a view toward promoting research necessary to achieve such advances, it was proposed an initial set of core questions for sustainability science. The definition of sustainability concept involves an important transformation and extension of the ecologically based concept of physical sustainability to the social and economic context of development. Thus, terms of sustainability cannot exclusively be defined from an environmental point of view or basis of attitudes. Rather, the challenge is to define operational and consistent terms of sustainability from an integrated social, ecological, and economic system perspective. In this respect the weak and strong sustainability concept are discussed. In order to introduce measuring of sustainability the attention is devoted to the definition of respective criteria. There have been a number of attempts to define the criterions for the assessment of the sustainability of the market products. Having those criterions as bases, it was introduced a specific application in the energy system design. Measuring sustainability is a major issue as well as a driving force of the discussion on sustainability development. Special attention in this review is devoted to the potential sustainable development options. In this respect a following options are taken into a consideration: prevention of the energy resource depletion with scarcity index control; efficiency assessment; new and renewable energy sources; water pollution mitigation, water desalination technologies environment capacity for combustion products; and mitigation of nuclear treat to the environment. Most industrialised countries are in addition becoming more and more dependent on external supplies of conventional energy carriers, i.e., fossil fuels. Energy for heating and cooling can be replaced by new renewable energy sources.

Table 10. Representative sulphur contents of coals [13]

Source	Rank	Sulphur content (%)
Ayrshire, Scotland	Bituminous	0.6
Lancs. /Cheshire, UK	Bituminous	Up to 2.4
S. Wales, UK	Anthracite	Up to 1.5
Victoria, Australia	Lignite	Typically 0.5
Pennsylvania, USA	Anthracite	0.7
Natal, S. Africa	Bituminous	Up to 4.2
Bulgaria	Lignite	2.5

4.1. Sulphur in Fuels and its Environmental Consequences

Coal is formed from the deposition of plant material according to the peat to anthracite series:

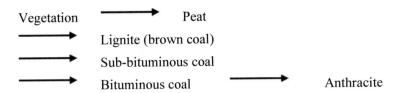

Organic sulphur is bonded within the organic structure of the coal in the same way that sulphur is bonded in simple thio-organics, e.g., thiols. Sulphur contents of coals vary widely, and Table 10 gives some examples.

4.2. Control of SO$_2$ Emissions

Emissions will also, of course, occur from petroleum-based or shale-based fuels, and in heavy consumption, such as in steam raising. There will frequently be a need to control SO$_2$ emissions. There are, broadly speaking, three ways of achieving such control:

- Pre-combustion control: involves carrying out a degree of desulphurisation of the fuel.
- Combustion control: incorporating into the combustion system something capable of trapping SO$_2$.
- Post-combustion control: removing SO$_2$ from the flue gases before they are discharged into the atmosphere.

Table 11 gives brief details of an example of each.

Throughout the energy generation process there are impacts on the environment on local, national and international levels, from opencast mining and oil exploration to emissions of the potent greenhouse gas carbon dioxide in ever increasing concentration. Recently, the world's leading climate scientists reached an agreement that human activities, such as burning fossil fuels for energy and transport, are causing the world's temperature to rise.

4.3. The Control of NO_x Release by Combustion Processes

Emission of nitrogen oxides is a major topic in fuel technology. It has to be considered even in the total absence of fuel nitrogen if the temperature is high enough for thermal NO_x, as it is in very many industrial applications. The burnt gas from the flame is recirculated in two ways:

- Internally, by baffling and restricting flow of the burnt gas away from the burner, resulting in flame re-entry of part of it.
- Externally, by diverting up to 10% of the flue gas back into the flame.
- Some of the available control procedures for particles are summarised in Table 12.

Table 11. Examples of SO_2 control procedures

Type of control	Fuel	Details
Pre-combustion	Fuels from crude oil	Alkali treatment of crude oil to convert thiols RSSR, disulphides; solvent removal of the disulphides
Post-combustion	Coal or fuel oil	Alkali scrubbing of the flue gases with $CaCO_3/CaO$
Combustion	Coal	Limestone, $MgCO_3$ and/or other metallic compounds used to fix the sulphur as sulphates

Table 12. Particle control techniques

Technique	Principle	Application
Gravity settlement	Natural deposition by gravity of particles from a horizontally flowing gas, collection in hoppers	Removal of coarse particles (>50 µm) from a gas stream, smaller particles removable in principle but require excessive flow distances
Cyclone separator	Tangential entry of a particle-laden gas into a cylindrical or conical enclosure, movement of the particles to the enclosure wall and from there to a receiver	Numerous applications, wide range of particles sizes removable, from = 5 µm to = 200 µm, poorer efficiencies of collection for the smaller particles
Fabric filters	Retention of solids by a filter, filter materials include woven cloth, felt and porous membranes	Used in dust removal for over a century
Electrostatic precipitation	Passage of particle-laden gas between electrodes, application of an electric field to the gas, resulting in acquisition of charge by the particles and attraction to an electrode where coalescence occurs, electrical resistivity of the dust an important factor in performance	Particles down to 0.01 µm removable, extensive application to the removal of flyash from pulverised fuel (pf) combustion

Figure 9 shows the variation of distribution factor with particle size.

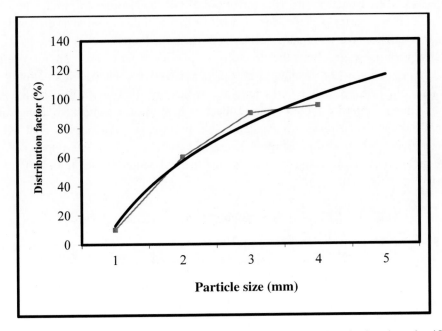

Figure 9. The variation of distribution factor against particle size for coal undersizes in a classifier. The sizes correspond to mid-point for ranges.

5. GREEN HEAT

The ground is as universal as air and solar radiation. Over the past twenty years, as the hunt for natural low-carbon energy sources has intensified, there has been an increased endeavour to investigate and develop both earth and ground water thermal energy storage and usage. Geothermal energy solutions, although well known, are another in our armoury of renewable energy sources that are within our immediate grasp to use and integrate with an overall energy policy. For high temperature heat storage with temperatures in excess of 50°C the particular concerns were:

- Clogging of wells and heat exchangers due to fines and precipitation of minerals.
- Water treatment to avoid operational problems resulting from the precipitation of minerals.
- Corrosion of components in the groundwater system.
- Automatic control of the ground water system.

As consumers in less-developed countries increase their capacity of electricity and green power, developed nations are starting to realise the benefits of using low-grade thermal energy for green heat applications that do not require high-grade electricity. This shift will not only benefit renewable energies that are designed for space conditioning, but also will contribute to the global mix of green power and green heat capacity. Earth energy (also called geothermal or ground source heat pumps or GeoExchange), which transfers absorbed solar heat from the ground into a building for space heating or water heating. The same system can be reversed to reject heat from the interior into the ground, in order to provide cooling. A typical configuration buries polyethylene pipe below the frost line to serve as the head source (or sink), or it can use lake water and aquifers as the heat medium.

An advantage is gained from the necessity to provide filtered fresh air for ventilation purposes by providing every dwelling with a heat recovery mechanical ventilation system. Incorporation of a heating/cooling coil within the air-handling unit for each of the five blocks allows for active summertime cooling (i.e., collecting heat in summer), which along with the use of roof mounted solar panels to provide domestic hot water produces as well tempered and well engineered hybrid low energy scheme at very low carbon emissions. Today, the challenge before many cities is to support large numbers of people while limiting their impact on the natural environment.

Table 13. Effects of urban density on city's energy demand

Positive effects	Negative effects
Transport: • Promote public transport and reduce the need for, and length of, trips by private cars. *Infrastructure:* • Reduce street length needed to accommodate a given number of inhabitants. • Shorten the length of infrastructure facilities such as water supply and sewage lines, reducing the energy needed for pumping. *Thermal performance:* • Multi-story, multiunit buildings could reduce the overall area of the building's envelope and heat loss from the buildings. • Shading among buildings could reduce solar exposure of buildings during the summer period. *Energy systems:* • District cooling and heating system, which is usually more energy efficiency, is more feasible as density is higher. *Ventilation:* • A desirable flow pattern around buildings may be obtained by proper arrangement of high-rise building blocks.	*Transport:* • Congestion in urban areas reduces fuel efficiency of vehicles. *Vertical transportation:* • High-rise buildings involve lifts, thus increasing the need for electricity for the vertical transportation. *Ventilation:* • A concentration of high-rise and large buildings may impede the urban ventilation conditions. *Urban heat island:* • Heat released and trapped in the urban areas may increase the need for air conditioning. • The potential for natural lighting is generally reduced in high-density areas, increasing the need for electric lighting and the load on air conditioning to remove the heat resulting from the electric lighting. *Use of solar energy:* • Roof and exposed areas for collection of solar energy are limited.

6. EFFECTS OF URBAN DENSITY

Compact development patterns can reduce infrastructure demands and the need to travel by car. As population density increases, transportation options multiply and dependence areas, per capita fuel consumption is much lower in densely populated areas because people drive so much less. Few roads and commercially viable public transport are the major merits. On the other hand, urban density is a major factor that determines the urban ventilation conditions, as well as the urban temperature. Under given circumstances, an urban area with a high density of buildings can experience poor ventilation and strong heat island effect. In warm-humid regions these features would lead to a high level of thermal stress of the inhabitants and increased use of energy in air-conditioned buildings.

However, it is also possible that a high-density urban area, obtained by a mixture of high and low buildings, could have better ventilation conditions than an area with lower density but with buildings of the same height. Closely spaced or high-rise buildings are also affected by the use of natural lighting, natural ventilation and solar energy. If not properly planned, energy for electric lighting and mechanical cooling/ventilation may be increased and application of solar energy systems will be greatly limited. Table 13 gives a summary of the positive and negative effects of urban density. All in all, denser city models require more careful design in order to maximise energy efficiency and satisfy other social and development requirements. Low energy design should not be considered in isolation, and in fact, it is a measure, which should work in harmony with other environmental objectives. Hence, building energy study provides opportunities not only for identifying energy and cost savings, but also for examining the indoor and outdoor environment.

6.1. Energy Efficiency and Architectural Expression

The focus of the world's attention on environmental issues in recent years has stimulated response in many countries, which have led to a closer examination of energy conservation strategies for conventional fossil fuels. Buildings are important consumers of energy and thus important contributors to emissions of greenhouse gases into the global atmosphere. The development and adoption of suitable renewable energy technology in buildings has an important role to play. A review of options indicates benefits and some problems [14]. There are two key elements to the fulfilling of renewable energy technology potential within the field of building design; first the installation of appropriate skills and attitudes in building design professionals and second the provision of the opportunity for such people to demonstrate their skills. This second element may only be created when the population at large and clients commissioning building design in particular, become more aware of what can be achieved and what resources are required. Terms like passive cooling or passive solar use mean that the cooling of a building or the exploitation of the energy of the sun is achieved not by machines but by the building's particular morphological organisation. Hence, the passive approach to themes of energy savings is essentially based on the morphological articulations of the constructions. Passive solar design, in particular, can realise significant energy and cost savings. For a design to be successful, it is crucial for the designer to have a good understanding of the use of the building. Few of the buildings had performed as expected by their designers. To be more precise, their performance had been compromised by a variety of influences related to their design, construction and operation. However, there is no doubt that the passive energy approach is certainly the one that, being supported by the material shape of the buildings has a direct influence on architectural language and most greatly influences architectural expressiveness [15]. Furthermore, form is a main tool in architectural expression. To give form to the material things that one produces is an ineluctable necessity. In architecture, form, in fact, summarises and gives concreteness to its every value in terms of economy, aesthetics, functionality and, consequently, energy efficiency [16]. The target is to enrich the expressive message with forms producing an advantage energy-wise. Hence, form, in its geometric and material sense, conditions the energy efficiency of a building in its interaction with the environment. It is, then, very hard to extract and separate the parameters and the elements relative to this efficiency from the expressive unit to which they belong. By analysing energy issues and strategies by means of the designs, of which they are an integral part, one will, more easily, focus the attention on the relationship between these themes, their specific context and their architectural expressiveness. Many concrete examples and a whole literature have recently grown up around these subjects and the wisdom of forms and expedients that belong to millennia-old traditions has been rediscovered. Such a revisiting, however, is only, or most especially, conceptual, since it must be filtered through today's technology and needs; both being almost irreconcilable with those of the past. Two among the historical concepts are of special importance. One is rooted in the effort to establish rational and friendly strategic relations with the physical environment, while the other recognises the interactions between the psyche and physical perceptions in the creation of the feeling of comfort. The former, which may be defined as an alliance with the environment deals with the physical parameters involving a mixture of natural and artificial ingredients such as soil and vegetation, urban fabrics and pollution [17]. The most dominant outside parameter is, of course, the sun's irradiation, our planet's primary energy source. All these elements can be measured in physical terms and are therefore the subject of science. Within the second concept, however, one considers the emotional and intellectual energies, which are the prime inexhaustible source of renewable power [18]. In this case, cultural parameters, which are not exactly measurable, are involved. However, they represent the very essence of the architectural quality. Objective scientific measurement parameters tell us very little about the emotional way of perceiving, which influences the messages of human are physical sensorial organs. The perceptual reality arises from a multitude of sensorial components; visual, thermal, acoustic, olfactory and kinaesthetics. It can, also, arise from the organisational quality of the space in which different parameters come together, like the sense of order or of serenity. Likewise, practical evaluations, such as usefulness, can be involved too. The evaluation is a wholly subjective matter, but can be shared by a set of experiencing persons [19]. Therefore, these cultural parameters could be different in different contexts in spite of the inexorable levelling on a planet- wide scale. However, the parameters change in the anthropological sense, not only with the cultural environment, but also in relation to function. The scientifically measurable parameters can, thus, have their meanings very profoundly altered by the non-measurable, but describable, and cultural parameters.

However, the low energy target also means to eliminate any excess in the quantities of material and in the manufacturing process necessary for the construction of our built environment. This claims for a more sober, elegant and essential expression, which is not jeopardising at all, but instead enhancing, the richness and preciousness of architecture, while contributing to a better environment from an aesthetic viewpoint [20]. Arguably, the most successful designs were in fact the simplest. Paying attention to orientation, plan and form can have far greater impact on energy performance than opting for elaborate solutions [21]. However, a design strategy can fail when those responsible for specifying materials for example, do not implement the passive solar strategy correctly. Similarly, cost-cutting exercises can seriously upset the effectiveness of a design strategy. Therefore, it is imperative that a designer fully informs key personnel, such as the quantity surveyor and client, about their design and be prepared to defend it. Therefore, the designer should have an adequate understanding of how the occupants or processes, such as ventilation, would function within the building. Thinking through such processes in isolation without reference to others can lead to conflicting strategies, which can have a detrimental impact upon performance. Likewise, if the design intent of the building is not communicated to its occupants, there is a risk that they will use it inappropriately, thus, compromising its performance. Hence, the designer should communicate in simple terms the actions expected of the occupant to control the building. For example, occupants should be well informed about how to guard against summer overheating. If the designer opted for a simple, seasonally adjusted control; say, insulated sliding doors were to be used between the mass wall and the internal space. The lesson here is that designers must be prepared to defend their design such that others appreciate the importance and interrelationship of each component. A strategy will only work if each individual component is considered as part of the bigger picture. Failure to implement a component or incorrect installation, for example, can lead to failure of the strategy and consequently, in some instances, the building may not liked by its occupants due to its poor performance.

6.2. Energy Efficiency

Energy efficiency is the most cost-effective way of cutting carbon dioxide emissions and improvements to households and businesses. It can also have many other additional social, economic and health benefits, such as warmer and healthier homes, lower fuel bills and company running costs and, indirectly, jobs. Britain wastes 20 per cent of its fossil fuel and electricity use. This implies that it would be cost-effective to cut £10 billion a year off the collective fuel bill and reduce CO_2 emissions by some 120 million tonnes. Yet, due to lack of good information and advice on energy saving, along with the capital to finance energy efficiency improvements, this huge potential for reducing energy demand is not being realised. Traditionally, energy utilities have been essentially fuel providers and the industry has pursued profits from increased volume of sales. Institutional and market arrangements have favoured energy consumption rather than conservation. However, energy is at the centre of the sustainable development paradigm as few activities affect the environment as much as the continually increasing use of energy. Most of the used energy depends on finite resources, such as coal, oil, gas and uranium. In addition, more than three quarters of the world's consumption of these fuels is used, often inefficiently, by only one quarter of the world's population. Without even addressing these inequities or the precious, finite nature of these resources, the scale of environmental damage will force the reduction of the usage of these fuels long before they run out.

Throughout the energy generation process there are impacts on the environment on local, national and international levels, from opencast mining and oil exploration to emissions of the potent greenhouse gas carbon dioxide in ever increasing concentration. Recently, the world's leading climate scientists reached an agreement that human activities, such as burning fossil fuels for energy and transport, are causing the world's temperature to rise. The Intergovernmental Panel on Climate Change has concluded that "the balance of evidence suggests a discernible human influence on global climate". It predicts a rate of warming greater than any one seen in the last 10,000 years, in other words, throughout human history. The exact impact of climate change is difficult to predict and will vary regionally. It could, however, include sea level rise, disrupted agriculture and food supplies and the possibility of more freak weather events such as hurricanes and droughts. Indeed, people already are waking up to the financial and social, as well as the environmental, risks of unsustainable energy generation methods that represent the costs of the impacts of climate change, acid rain and oil spills. The insurance industry, for example, concerned about the billion dollar costs of hurricanes and floods, has joined sides with environmentalists to lobby for greenhouse gas emissions reduction. Friends of the earth are campaigning for a more sustainable energy policy, guided by the principle of environmental protection and with the objectives of sound natural resource management and long-term energy security. The key priorities of such an energy policy must be to reduce fossil fuel use, move away from nuclear power, improve the efficiency with which energy is used and increase the amount of energy obtainable from sustainable, and renewable sources. Efficient energy use has never been more crucial than it is today, particularly with the prospect of the imminent introduction of the climate change levy (CCL). Establishing an energy use action plan is the essential foundation to the elimination of energy waste. A logical starting point is to carry out an energy audit that enables the assessment of the energy use and determine what actions to take. The actions are best categorised by splitting measures into the following three general groups:

(1) High priority/low cost

These are normally measures, which require minimal investment and can be implemented quickly. The followings are some examples of such measures:

- Good housekeeping, monitoring energy use and targeting waste-fuel practices.
- Adjusting controls to match requirements.
- Improved greenhouse space utilisation.
- Small capital item time switches, thermostats, etc.
- Carrying out minor maintenance and repairs.
- Staff education and training.
- Ensuring that energy is being purchased through the most suitable tariff or contract arrangements.

(2) Medium priority/medium cost

Measures, which, although involve little or no design, involve greater expenditure and can take longer to implement. Examples of such measures are listed below:

- New or replacement controls.
- Greenhouse component alteration, e.g., insulation, sealing glass joints, etc.
- Alternative equipment components, e.g., energy efficient lamps in light fittings, etc.

(3) Long term/high cost

These measures require detailed study and design. They can be best represented by the followings:

- Replacing or upgrading of plant and equipment.
- Fundamental redesign of systems, e.g., CHP installations.

This process can often be a complex experience and therefore the most cost-effective approach is to employ an energy specialist to help.

6.3. Policy Recommendations for a Sustainable Energy Future

Sustainability is regarded as a major consideration for both urban and rural development. People have been exploiting the natural resources with no consideration to the effects, both short-term (environmental) and long-term (resources crunch). It is also felt that knowledge and technology have not been used effectively in utilising energy resources. Energy is the vital input for economic and social development of any country. Its sustainability is an important factor to be considered. The urban areas depend, to a large extent, on commercial energy sources. The rural areas use non-commercial sources like firewood and agricultural wastes. With the present day trends for improving the quality of life and sustenance of mankind, environmental issues are considered highly important. In this context, the term energy loss has no significant technical meaning. Instead, the exergy loss has to be considered, as destruction of exergy is possible. Hence, exergy loss minimisation will help in sustainability. In the process of developing, there are two options to manage energy resources: (1) End use matching/demand side management, which focuses on the utilities. The mode of obtaining this is decided based on economic terms. It is, therefore, a quantitative approach. (2) Supply side management, which focuses on the renewable energy resource and methods of utilising it. This is decided based on thermodynamic consideration having the resource-user temperature or exergy destruction as the objective criteria. It is, therefore, a qualitative approach. The two options are explained schematically in Figure 10. The exergy-based energy, developed with supply side perspective is shown in Figure 11.

The following policy measures had been identified:

- Clear environmental and social objectives for energy market liberalisation, including a commitment to energy efficiency and renewables.
- Economic, institutional and regulatory frameworks, which encourage the transition to total energy services.
- Economic measures to encourage utility investment in energy efficiency (e.g., levies on fuel bills).

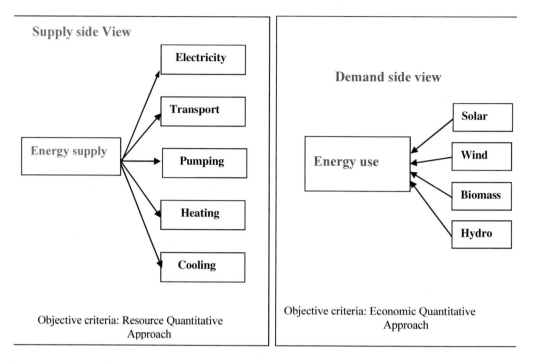

Figure 10. Supply side and demand side management approach for energy.

- Incentives for demand side management, including grants for low-income households, expert advice and training, standards for appliances and buildings and tax incentives.
- Research and development funding for renewable energy technologies not yet commercially viable.
- Continued institutional support for new renewables (such as standard cost-reflective payments and obligation on utilities to buy).
- Ecological tax reform to internalise external environmental and social costs within energy prices.
- Planning for sensitive development and public acceptability for renewable energy.

Energy resources are needed for societal development. Their sustainable development requires a supply of energy resources that are sustainably available at a reasonable cost and can cause no negative societal impacts. Energy resources such as fossil fuels are finite and lack sustainability, while renewable energy sources are sustainable over a relatively longer term. Environmental concerns are also a major factor in sustainable development, as activities, which degrade the environment, are not sustainable. Hence, as much as environmental impact is associated with energy, sustainable development requires the use of energy resources, which cause as little environmental impact as possible. One way to reduce the resource depletion associated with cycling is to reduce the losses that accompany the transfer of exergy to consume resources by increasing the efficiency of exergy transfer between resources, i.e., increasing the fraction of exergy removed from one resource that is transferred to another [22]. Buildings are significant users of energy and materials in a modern society and, hence, energy conservation in buildings plays an important role in urban environmental sustainability. The admission of daylight into buildings alone does not guarantee that the design will be energy efficient in terms of lighting. There are also a number of methods, which help reduce the lighting energy use, which, in turn, relate to the type of occupancy pattern of the building.

As explained above, exergy efficiency may be thought of as a more accurate measure of energy efficiency that accounts for quantity and quality aspects of energy flows. Improved exergy efficiency leads to reduced exergy losses. Most efficiency improvements produce direct environmental benefits in two ways. First, operating energy input requirements are reduced per unit output, and pollutants generated are correspondingly reduced. Second, consideration of the entire life cycle for energy resources and technologies suggests that improved efficiency reduces environmental impact during most stages of the life cycle. Quite often, the main concept of sustainability, which often inspires local and national authorities to incorporate environmental consideration into setting up energy programmes have different meanings in different contexts though it usually embodies a long-term perspective. Future energy systems will largely be shaped by broad and powerful trends that have their roots in basic human needs [23]. Combined with increasing world population, the need will become more apparent for successful implementation of sustainable development.

Heat has a lower exergy, or quality of energy, compared with work. Therefore, heat cannot be converted into work by 100% efficiency. Some examples of the difference between energy and exergy are shown in Table 14.

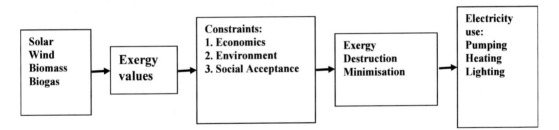

Figure 11. Exergy based optimal energy model.

Table 14. Qualities of various energy sources

Source	Energy (J)	Exergy (J)	CQF
Water at 80°C	100	16	0.16
Steam at 120°C	100	24	0.24
Natural gas	100	99	0.99
Electricity/work	100	100	1.00

The terms used in Table 14 have the following meanings:

$$\text{Carnot Quality Factor (CQF)} = (1 - T_o/T_s) \qquad (5)$$

$$\text{Exergy} = \text{Energy (transferred)} \times \text{CQF} \qquad (6)$$

where T_o is the environment temperature (K) and T_s is the temperature of the stream (K).

Various parameters are essential to achieving sustainable development in a society. Some of them are as follows:

- Public awareness.
- Information.
- Environmental education and training.
- Innovative energy strategies.
- Renewable energy sources and cleaner technologies.
- Financing.
- Monitoring and evaluation tools.

The development of a renewable energy in a country depends on many factors. Those important to success are listed below:

(1) Motivation of the Population

The population should be motivated towards awareness of high environmental issues, rational use of energy in order to reduce cost. Subsidy programme should be implemented as incentives to install renewable energy plants. In addition, image campaigns to raise awareness of renewable energy technology.

(2) Technical Product Development

To achieve technical development of renewable energy technologies the following should be addressed:

- Increasing the longevity and reliability of renewable energy technology.
- Adapting renewable energy technology to household technology (hot water supply).
- Integration of renewable energy technology in heating technology.
- Integration of renewable energy technology in architecture, e.g., in the roof or façade.
- Development of new applications, e.g., solar cooling.
- Cost reduction.

(3) Distribution and Sales

Commercialisation of renewable energy technology requires:

- Inclusion of renewable energy technology in the product range of heating trades at all levels of the distribution process (wholesale, and retail).
- Building distribution nets for renewable energy technology.
- Training of personnel in distribution and sales.
- Training of field sales force.

(4) Consumer Consultation and Installation

To encourage all sectors of the population to participate in adoption of renewable energy technologies, the following has to be realised:

- Acceptance by craftspeople, and marketing by them.
- Technical training of craftspeople, and initial and follow-up training programmes.
- Sales training for craftspeople.
- Information material to be made available to craftspeople for consumer consultation.

(5) *Projecting and Planning*
Successful application of renewable technologies also requires:

- Acceptance by decision makers in the building sector (architects, house technology planners, etc.).
- Integration of renewable energy technology in training.
- Demonstration projects/architecture competitions.
- Renewable energy project developers should prepare to participate in the carbon market by:
  - Ensuring that renewable energy projects comply with Kyoto Protocol requirements.
  - Quantifying the expected avoided emissions.
  - Registering the project with the required offices.
  - Contractually allocating the right to this revenue stream.

- Other ecological measures employed on the development include:

  - Simplified building details.
  - Reduced number of materials.
  - Materials that can be recycled or reused.
  - Materials easily maintained and repaired.
  - Materials that do not have a bad influence on the indoor climate (i.e., non-toxic).
  - Local cleaning of grey water.
  - Collecting and use of rainwater for outdoor purposes and park elements.
  - Building volumes designed to give maximum access to neighbouring park areas.
  - All apartments have visual access to both backyard and park.

(6) *Energy Saving Measures*
The following energy saving measures should also be considered:

- Building integrated solar PV system.
- Day-lighting.
- Ecological insulation materials.
- Natural/hybrid ventilation.
- Passive cooling.
- Passive solar heating.
- Solar heating of domestic hot water.
- Utilisation of rainwater for flushing.

Improving access for rural and urban low-income areas in developing countries through energy efficiency and renewable energies will be needed [24]. Sustainable energy is a prerequisite for development. Energy-based living standards in developing countries, however, are clearly below standards in developed countries. Low levels of access to affordable and environmentally sound energy in both rural and urban low-income areas are therefore a predominant issue in developing countries. In recent years many programmes for development aid or technical assistance have been focusing on improving access to sustainable energy, many of them with impressive results.

Apart from success stories, however, experience also shows that positive appraisals of many projects evaporate after completion and vanishing of the implementation expert team. Altogether, the diffusion of sustainable technologies such as energy efficiency and renewable energies for cooking, heating, lighting, electrical appliances and building insulation in developing countries has been slow.

Energy efficiency and renewable energy programmes could be more sustainable and pilot studies more effective and pulse releasing if the entire policy and implementation process was considered and redesigned from the outset. New financing and implementation processes are needed which allow reallocating financial resources and thus enabling countries themselves to achieve a sustainable energy infrastructure. The links between the energy policy framework, financing and implementation of renewable energy and energy efficiency projects have to be strengthened and capacity building efforts are required [25].

CONCLUSION

There is strong scientific evidence that the average temperature of the earth's surface is rising. This is a result of the increased concentration of carbon dioxide and other GHGs in the atmosphere as released by burning fossil fuels. This global warming will eventually lead to substantial changes in the world's climate, which will, in turn, have a major impact on human life and the built environment. Therefore, effort has to be made to reduce fossil energy use and to promote green energies, particularly in the building sector. Energy use reductions can be achieved by minimising the energy demand, by rational energy use, by recovering heat and the use of more green energies. This study was a step towards achieving that goal. The adoption of green or sustainable approaches to the way in which society is run is seen as an important strategy in finding a solution to the energy problem. The key factors to reducing and controlling CO_2, which is the major contributor to global warming, are the use of alternative approaches to energy generation and the exploration of how these alternatives are used today and may be used in the future as green energy sources. Even with modest assumptions about the availability of land, comprehensive fuel-wood farming programmes offer significant energy, economic and environmental benefits. These benefits would be dispersed in rural areas where they are greatly needed and can serve as linkages for further rural economic development. The nations as a whole would benefit from savings in foreign exchange, improved energy security, and socio-economic improvements. With a nine-fold increase in forest – plantation cover, a nation's resource base would be greatly improved. The international community would benefit from pollution reduction, climate mitigation, and the increased trading opportunities that arise from new income sources. The non-technical issues, which have recently gained attention, include: (1) Environmental and ecological factors, e.g., carbon sequestration, reforestation and revegetation. (2) Renewables as a CO_2 neutral replacement for fossil fuels. (3) Greater recognition of the importance of renewable energy, particularly modern biomass energy carriers, at the policy and planning levels. (4) Greater recognition of the difficulties of gathering good and reliable renewable energy data, and efforts to improve it. (5) Studies on the detrimental health efforts of biomass energy particularly from traditional energy users. Two of the most essential natural resources for all life on the earth and for man's survival are sunlight and water. Sunlight is the driving force behind many of the renewable energy technologies. The worldwide potential for utilising this resource, both directly by means of the solar technologies and indirectly by means of biofuels, wind and hydro technologies is vast. During the last decade interest has been refocused on renewable energy sources due to the increasing prices and fore-seeable exhaustion of presently used commercial energy sources.

REFERENCES

[1]   World Energy Outlook. International Energy Agency. OECD Publications. 2 rue Andre Pascal. Paris. France. 1995.

[2]   Energy use in offices. Energy Consumption Guide 19 (ECG019). Energy efficiency best practice programme. UK Government. 2000.

[3]   DETR. Best practice programme-introduction to energy efficiency in buildings. UK Department of the Environment, Transport and the Regions. 1994.

[4]   Bos, E; My, T; Vu, E; Bulatao R. World population projection: 1994-95. Edition, published for the World Bank by the John Hopkins University Press. Baltimore and London. 1994.

[5]   DEFRA, Energy Resources. Sustainable Development and Environment. UK. 2002.

[6]   Levine M; Hirose M. Energy efficiency improvement utilising high technology: an assessment of energy use in industry and buildings. Report and Case Studies. London: World Energy Council. 1995.

[7]   IPCC. Climate change 2001 (3 volumes). United Nations International Panel on Climate Change. Cambridge University Press. UK. 2001.

[8]   Parikn, J; Smith, K; Laxmi, V. Indoor air pollution: a reflection on gender bias. *Economic and Political Weekly*. 1999.

[9]   UNIDO. Changing courses sustainable industrial development, as a response to agenda 21. Vienna. 1997.

[10]   WRI (World Resource Institute). World Resources: A guide to the Global Environment. People and the Environment. Washington. USA. 1994.

[11]   Boulet, T. Controlling air movement: a manual for architects and builders. McGraw-Hill, pp.85-138, New York: USA. 1987.

[12]   Erreygers, G. Sustainability and stability in a classical model of production. In: Faucheux, S.; Pearce, D. and Proops J. (Eds). Models of sustainable development. Cheltenham. 1996.

[13]   Meffe, S; Perkson, A; Trass, O. Coal beneficiation and organic sulphur removal. *Fuel Cells*, 75, 25-30. 1996.

[14] BS 5454. Storage and exhibition archive documents. British Standard Institute. London. 1989.

[15] Lazzarin, RD'; Ascanio, A; Gaspaella, A. Utilisation of a green roof in reducing the cooling load of a new industrial building. In: Proceedings of the 1st International Conference on Sustainable Energy Technologies (SET), pp. 32-37, Porto: Portugal. 12-14 June 2002.

[16] David, E. Sustainable energy: choices, problems and opportunities. *The Royal Society of Chemistry*, 2003, 19, 19-47.

[17] Zuatori, A. An overview on the national strategy for improving the efficiency of energy use. *Jordanian Energy Abstracts*, 2005, 9 (1), 31-32.

[18] Anne, G; Michael, S. Building and land management. 5th edition. Oxford: UK. 2005.

[19] Randal, G; Goyal, R. Greenhouse technology. New Delhi: Narosa Publishing House. 1998.

[20] Yadav, I; Chauadhari, M. Progressive floriculture. Bangalore: The house of Sarpan, pp.1-5, 1997.

[21] EIBI (Energy in Building and Industry). Constructive thoughts on efficiency, building regulations, inside committee limited, Inside Energy: Magazine for Energy Professional. UK: KOPASS, 13-14. 1999.

[22] Erlich, P. Forward facing up to climate change, in Global Climate Change and Life on Earth. R.C. Wyman (Ed), Chapman and Hall, London. 1991.

[23] Omer, AM. Green energies and the environment. *Renewable and Sustainable Energy Reviews*, 12, 1789-1821. 2008.

[24] Omer, AM. Energy demand for heating and cooling equipment systems and technology advancements. *In: Natural Resources: Economics, Management and Policy*, 131-165. 2008.

[25] Omer, AM. Ground-source heat pumps systems and applications. *Renewable and Sustainable Energy Reviews*, 12, 344-371. 2008.

In: Advances in Energy Research. Volume 20
Editor: Morena J. Acosta

ISBN: 978-1-63463-169-3
© 2015 Nova Science Publishers, Inc.

Chapter 4

DRINKING WATER FROM SOLAR STILLS: A RENEWABLE TECHNOLOGY FOR SUDAN

Abdeen Mustafa Omer[*]

Energy Research Institute, Nottingham, UK

ABSTRACT

The harsh climate in the Red Sea area, for example the Sudan, presents unique challenges in meeting growing demands for water and power. The international demand for water increases compared to the available water resources. Many areas, especially near the Red Sea, already experience a serious shortage of potable water and this is likely to grow. These areas enjoy, however, a high intensity of solar energy. Among the renewable energy options that have received special attention are solar stills. A solar still was built based on the principle of the packed tray array for tandem distillation and heat recovery. This chapter provides a brief overview of efforts to expand such renewable technologies in Sudan in a cost-effective and sustainable way with environmental benefits associated with displacing fossil fuels.

Keywords: Red Sea area, energy consumption, solar energy, solar stills, clean water supply

1. INTRODUCTION

This section is an introduction to the energy problem and the possible savings that can be achieved through improving energy performance and the use of solar energy sources. The relevance and importance of the study is discussed in the section, which also highlights the objectives of the study, and the scope of the chapter. Energy issues affect every aspect of modern society. These issues have been of primary concern, since the second oil crisis and the Gulf War. Energy problems are associated with distribution, access and security of supply. Particularly for the energy-deficient countries and remote islands/areas, renewable

---

[*] Correponding author: E-mail: abdeenomer2@yahoo.co.uk.

energy appears to be sustainable and a clean source of energy derived from nature [12]. The utilization of available renewable energy sources like solar, wind and biomass energy is of practical importance for future socio-economic development of the country. Sudan is an agricultural country with fertile land, plenty of water resources, livestock, forestry resources and agricultural residues. Energy is one of the key factors for the development of national economies in the Sudan. Energy sources are divided into two main types; conventional energy (woody biomass, petroleum products and electricity); and non-conventional energy (solar, wind, hydro, etc.). Sudan possesses a relatively high abundance of sunshine, solar radiation, moderate wind speeds, hydro and biomass energy resources.

Application of the new and renewable sources of energy available in the Sudan is a major issue in the future strategic planning for an alternative to the conventional fossil energy used to provide part of the local energy demand. Sudan is an important case study in the context of renewable energy. It has a long history of meeting its energy needs through renewables. Sudan's renewables portfolio is broad and diverse, due in part to the country's wide range of climates and landscapes. Like many of the African leaders in renewable energy utilization, Sudan has a well-defined commitment to continue research, development and implementation of new technologies. Sustainable low-carbon energy scenarios for the new century emphasize the untapped potential of renewable resources. Rural areas of the Sudan can benefit from this transition. The increased availability of reliable and efficient energy services stimulates new development alternatives. This will also contribute to the amelioration of environmental conditions by replacing conventional fuels with renewable energy.

In the Sudan, electricity reaches only about 30% of the population, mainly in urban areas. Hence, a major problem for rural people is the inadequate supply of power for lighting, heating, cooking, cooling, water pumping, radio or TV communications and security services. Petroleum product supplies, including diesel, kerosene and liquefied petroleum gas (LPG) are irregular and often subject to sudden price increases. Because of the inadequate supply of these fuels, women trek great distances into the forest to collect fuelwood, charcoal and biomass residues from animals and agriculture, which account for more than half of total energy consumption.

Most of this is utilized for cooking and heating water in rural and semi-urban areas and by the urban poor. It is needed to provide alternative renewable energy sources to enhance women's participation, and benefit from development. Household energy was the first energy sector that paid explicit attention to women and their energy needs. The contribution of women to the environmental policy is largely ignored. Decision-making and policy formulation at all environmental levels, i.e., conservation, protection and rehabilitation and environmental management are more or less reserved for males. Women have been involved in the promotion of appropriate energy technologies, primarily for rural populations, over the past 15 years. This chapter highlights the experience of working with rural people in seeking solutions for community energy needs through renewable, environmentally friendly, energy technologies.

More than 70% of the total Sudanese population lives in rural and isolated communities characterized by extreme poverty. The unavailability and the acute shortages of conventional energy supplies (petroleum and electricity) to rural people have forced them to use alternative available energy sources like biomass [1]. This situation has caused serious environmental degradation besides the unsatisfactory services of some basic needs such as food security, water supply, healthcare and communications.

2. GEOGRAPHIC PROFILE OF THE SUDAN

This section comprises a comprehensive review of the geographical location of the Sudan, energy sources, the environment and sustainable development. It includes renewable energy technologies, efficient energy systems, energy conservation scenarios, energy savings and other mitigation measures necessary to reduce climate change. Sudan is the largest country of the African continent, with an area of approximately one million square miles (2.5 x 10^6 km^2). Sudan is a federal republic located in eastern Africa. It extends between latitudes 3°N and 23°N, and longitudes 21° 45'E and 39°E. Sudan is a relatively sparsely populated country. The total population, according to the 1999 census, was 35 x 10^6 inhabitants. The growth rate is 2.8%/y, and the population density is 14 persons per square kilometers. The country is divided into 26 states and a federal district, in which the capital, Khartoum, is located. Sudan is known as a country of plentiful water, rich in land, with the highest total and renewable supply of fresh water in the region (eastern Africa). Sudan is considered one of the least developed countries, with a per capita income of less than US $400 and a real growth rate of 0.2 % of real gross domestic product (GDP) during the last ten years. However, during the 1980s the real growth rate of GDP was negative, mainly due to drought and desertification. The backbone of Sudan's economy is its agricultural sector. The agricultural sector determines to a great extent the economic performance of the Sudanese economy. In fact the country can be rescued by proper organization and utilization of its agricultural potential. Recent development due to rehabilitation and improvement in the agricultural sector has raised the share to 41% [2].

Agriculture continues to play a pivotal role in the economy. It directly influences the level of activities in all other sectors. It provides 90% of the raw materials for local industries, accounts for 80% of export earnings and provides income and employment for more than 80% of the population. The agricultural sector is composed of three distinct modes: irrigated agriculture, mechanized rain-fed agriculture and traditional rain-fed agriculture and livestock raising. Sudan is an agricultural country with fertile land, plenty of water resources, livestock, forestry resources and agricultural residues. To ensure a better quality of life for all people, now and in the future, sustainable development initiatives are needed that promote: (1) Food and water security (2) Economic efficiency that helps to eliminate inequalities (3) Social equity for all, regardless of race, gender, disability or creed (4) Effective education for environmentally and socially responsible citizenship (5) Environmental integrity and environmental justice (6) Democracy and mutual understanding between people [13].

In a country with a high population density, there are extreme pressures on water and waste systems, which can stunt the country's economic growth. However, Sudan has recognized the potential to alleviate some of these problems by promoting renewable water and utilizing its vast and diverse climate, landscape and resources; and by coupling its solutions for waste disposal with its solutions for water production. Thus, Sudan may stand at the forefront of the global renewable water community and presents an example of how non-conventional water strategies may be implemented. In the Sudan, more than ten million people do not have adequate access to a water supply, twenty million inhabitants are without access to sanitation, and very little domestic sewage is being treated. The investment needed to fund the extension and improvement of these services is great.

3. ENERGY SITUATION IN SUDAN

Among the renewable energy sources, biomass seems to be one of the most interesting because its share of the total energy consumption of the Sudan is high at 87% and the techniques for converting it to useful energy are not necessarily sophisticated. Implementation of biomass-based energy programs will not, of course, be a definitive solution to the country's energy problem, but it will bring new insight for efficient energy use in the household sector, especially in rural areas where more than 70% of the population lives (25 million). The estimates are based on the recoverable energy potential from the main agricultural residues, livestock farming wastes, forestry and wood processing residues; and municipal wastes.

Fuelwood, animal wastes, agricultural crop residues and logging wastes have been used through direct burning in the Sudan for many years. These sources are often called non-commercial energy sources, but in the Sudan fuelwood is a tradable commodity since it is the primary fuel of rural areas and the urban poor section. Traditional fuels predominate in rural areas; almost all biomass energy is consumed in the household sector for heating, cleaning and cooking needs of rural people. Especially in the villages (households on the high plateau) the preparation of three stone fires is very attractive to the villagers. In this method, food and plant residues are put in a large boiler with water and cooked on a traditional stove, outside the house, for animal feed because cooked food and plant residues are cheaper than flour and bran. Nevertheless, this method consumes much more fuelwood than cooking on the stoves. On the other hand, wood is the most practical fuel for serving a large number of people because the size of the batch of food is only limited by the volume of the pot and not by the size of the stove's burner. Fuelwood is also convenient for cooking meat, such as a cutlet, meatball or meat roasted on a revolving vertical spit (Table 1).

Special attention should therefore be given to reviewing forest resources, plantation programs and the possibilities of substituting fuelwood for commercial fuels or for other fuels such as biogas. The main sources of fuelwood supply in the country can be broadly grouped into two main categories, i.e., forest sources (forests under the control of forest departments) and non-forest sources (private farmland and wild lands). Women, almost always assisted by children, perform the gathering of fuelwood in rural areas of developing countries. As fuelwood becomes scarce, this is the case in many parts of the world, the collection time increases. Although men do not perceive it, this has many undesirable consequences, which can be clearly seen in many rural region of the Sudan.

Women have less time for their other important functions, such as cooking, washing, water collection and child rearing which may affect the nutrition and health of the entire family. Wood energy is, for many countries, one of the few locally available sources of energy that they can afford. Its substitution by imported fossil fuels, as has often been carelessly recommended, should be carefully evaluated to avoid undesirable political, economic and social consequences. This will also contribute to the amelioration of environmental conditions by replacing conventional fuels with renewable energies that produce no air pollution or greenhouse gases. Renewable energy is needed, especially in rural areas and small communities. The role of renewables is big in solving essential life problems, especially in rural areas for people and their resource development, like availing energy for medical services for people and animals, provision of water, education, communication and small rural industries.

Table 1. Annual biomass energy consumption patterns in the Sudan (10^3 m^3) [2]

Sector	Firewood	Charcoal	Total	Percent (%)
Residential	6148	6071	12219	88.5%
Industrial	1050	12	1062	7.7%
Commercial	32	284	316	2.3%
Quranic schools	209	0	209	1.5%
Total	7439	6367	13806	
Percent (%)	54%	46%		100.0%

3.1. Problems and Difficulties in Rural Energy Development

3.1.1. Imbalance in Rural Energy Development

Due to the difference in economic conditions in different areas, the development of rural energy is considerably imbalanced. The main challenge to energy policymakers in the 21st century is how to develop and manage adequate, affordable and reliable energy services in a sustainable manner to fuel social and economic development. Generally, future rural energy will be oriented towards green energy and the future development of rural energy will concentrate on biogas, small hydropower, solar energy and wind power.

3.1.2. Insufficient Investment in Development of Rural Energy

Current rural energy relies mainly on charcoal, firewood and green energies, such as electricity and biogas. Poor economic situations lead to considerable difficulty in the development of rural energy and farmers in remote areas still prefer ''free firewood'' for their cooking due to their low income. Hence, further development of rural energy needs significant financial support from the government at various levels. Although the work of rebuilding traditional stoves has been almost finished, most of the rebuilt fuel-saving stoves have a thermal efficiency of less than 20%.

3.1.3. Excessive Dependence on Forests for Rural Energy

Currently, energy for rural household use mainly comes from burning firewood. The annual consumption of forests is 1.96×10^6 m^3, and of this 0.65×10^6 m^3 is firewood. To some extent, this pattern of energy consumption has led to environmental damage such as water and soil loss, decrease in forest cover and air pollution. The excessive use of firewood from forests for rural energy would cause damage to sightseeing resorts, make animals lose their habitats and lead to the extinction of some endangered plants. The future development of rural energy should be aimed at completely changing the current pattern of energy consumption, fully utilizing abundant resources of hydropower, biomass, solar and wind energy, promoting economic growth through the development of rural energy and integrated utilization of biomass. The National Electricity Corporation (NEC) handled a wide variety of electricity generation technologies (Table 2), including:

- Thermal (fossil, combined cycle and combustion turbines).
- Storage (pumped hydro, batteries and compressed air).
- Non-dispatchable technologies (solar, wind, cogeneration and load management).

Table 2. Comparison between different energy consumed in the Sudan (GWh)

Year	Electricity	Petroleum	Biomass	Renewable technologies
1975	800	550	3000	50
1980	900	600	3500	60
1985	1200	650	4000	100
1990	1300	700	6000	120
1995	1400	800	7000	150
2000	1500	900	8000	200
2005	1600	1000	9000	250

4. SOLAR ENERGY

This section provides a detailed literature-based review of solar energy technology. Solar radiation arriving on earth is the most fundamental renewable energy source in nature. It powers the bio-system, the ocean and atmospheric current systems and affects the global climate. Reliable radiation information is needed to provide input data in modeling solar energy devices and a good database is required for the work of energy planners, engineers and agricultural scientists [14]. In general, it is not easy to design solar energy conversion systems when they have to be installed in remote locations. Firstly, in most cases, solar radiation measurements are not available for these sites. Secondly, the radiation nature of solar radiation makes it difficult to compute the size of such systems.

The availability of data on solar radiation is a critical problem. Even in developed countries, very few weather stations have been recording detailed solar radiation data for a long enough period of time to have statistical significance and the Sudan is no exception. In various studies of solar energy systems (sizing and estimation of production), collected solar irradiation data is needed. The need for solar information is essential to the design and study of solar energy conversion devices. Other uses of such information include agricultural studies, meteorological forecasting, environmental and energy conservation.

4.1. Solar Radiation over the Sudan

Solar radiation data is not readily available in many countries. Many countries cannot afford the measurement equipment and techniques involved. The solar equipment needed for these purposes is expensive and requires maintenance as well as frequent calibration. Moreover, it is almost impossible to scan all of the country and get reliable day-by-day solar radiation data. Therefore, it is an effort to find reliable methods for prediction of solar radiation data with minimal measurements.

While solar energy data is recognized as very important, its acquisition is by no means straightforward. The measurement of solar radiation requires the use of costly equipment such as pyrheliometers and pyranometers. Consequently, adequate facilities are often not available in developing countries (Sudan is no exception) to mount viable monitoring program. This is partly due to the equipment cost and also the cost of technical manpower. Several attempts have, however, been made to estimate solar radiation through the use of meteorological and other physical parameters in order to avoid the use of an expensive network of measuring instruments [14].

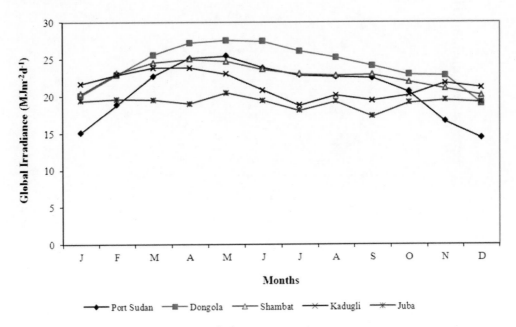

Figure 1. Measured Global irradiance $(MJm^{-2}d^{-1})$.

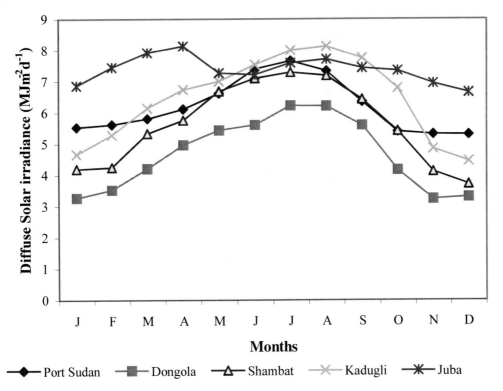

Figure 2. Estimated diffuse solar irradiance $(MJm^{-2}d^{-1})$.

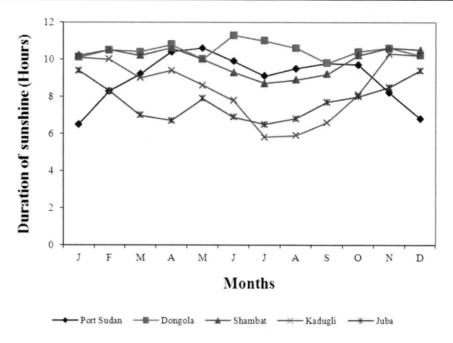

Figure 3. Duration of Sunshine per Month (Hours).

The design and estimation of the performance of all solar energy systems requires the knowledge of solar radiation data, which have been measured over a long period of time. The solar radiation measurements are very important in order to establish a complete solar map for Sudan. These data are not only useful for the country under consideration but also for many other countries. This is needed for two main reasons: (1) The possibility of plotting solar radiation maps for the whole world through the availability of the required data for all countries of the world and (2) The manufacturers of solar devices require the knowledge of solar radiation data in the different locations. This is most important in order to design such devices to suit the climate and to open new markets accordingly.

For the sizing of a solar system using total solar radiation (flat plate thermal solar collector or photovoltaic (PV) modules), or to estimate its productivity, many engineers use daily or hourly solar irradiation data. But, in many cases, such as mathematical simulation of solar energy processes, these values are not sufficient because they do not provide a precise idea of the different energy phenomena, which take place in the heart of the production system (inertia phenomenon, shadowing masks, etc.). For example, for the sizing of a stand-alone PV system, knowledge of the load is required and this load is sometimes known with a time step interior to one hour; it is then necessary to transform this load profile into hourly data, which leads to the loss of information.

Sudan has been considered as one of the best countries for exploiting solar energy. Sunshine duration ranges from 8.5 to 11 hours per day (Figure 3), with a high level of solar radiation regime at an average of 20 to 24 $(MJm^{-2}\ day^{-1})$ on the horizontal surface as shown in (Figures 1 and 2). The annual daily mean global radiation ranges from 3.05 to 7.62 $(kWhm^{-2}\ day^{-1})$. However, Sudan has an average of 7-9 $(GJm^{-2}\ year^{-1})$, equivalent to 436-639 $(Wm^{-2}\ year^{-1})$ [3]. The country strives hard to make use of technologies related to renewable sources in rural areas where it is appropriate and applicable (Table 3).

Table 3. Correlation of solar radiation with other weather parameters in the Sudan
(Yearly averages)

Station	Mean temp. (°C)	Sunshine duration (h)	Solar radiation (MJm^{-2} day^{-1})	Wind velocity (ms^{-1})	Relative humidity (%)
Port Sudan	28.4	9.0	20.87	5.1	65
Shambat	29.7	9.9	22.82	4.5	31
Wadi Medani	28.4	9.8	22.84	4.5	40
El Fasher	25.8	9.6	22.80	3.4	33
Abu Na'ama	28.2	8.8	21.90	3.1	46
Ghazala Gawazat	27.2	9.3	21.72	3.0	43
Malakal	27.9	7.8	19.90	2.8	54
Juba	27.6	7.8	19.59	1.5	66
Dongola	27.2	10.5	24.06	4.6	27
Toker	28.8	7.3	17.60	4.1	53
Hudeiba	29.3	10.0	22.37	4.0	25
Aroma	29.1	9.6	21.40	4.2	37
El Showak	26.3	9.7	22.90	4.1	39
Zalingei	24.5	8.8	22.98	2.7	39
Babanusa	28.2	8.9	21.73	2.8	48
Kadugli	27.5	8.5	21.30	2.7	48

4.2. Solar Thermal Energy

Sudan enjoys bright sunshine and dry weather most of the year. The utilization of solar energy in the Sudan can be used by:

4.2.1. Solar Cookers

The solar cookers are made from wood and glass. Different types of solar cookers (locally manufactured) have been designed and disseminated in the Sudan. Now solar cookers are commercially available in local markets [4].

4.2.2. Industrial Solar Water Heaters (SWHs)

Different system designs have been developed, tested and evaluated in the country. The best are the solar water heater on the roofs of the buildings [4]. A typical family size SWH unit consists of 1-1.44 m^2 of solar collectors' areas and a 1 m^3 hot storage tank. Due to high and reliable solar irradiance of about 5.5 kWh/m^2 day, a typical Sudanese SWH with 1.44 m^2 net area and a 25% average system efficiency over its life time, has the potential to produce around 150 l of hot water at 45°C per day for about 340 sunny days per year. Several technical and non-technical factors influence the following: (i) Selection and treatment of materials used in the manufacturing of SWH. This situation drastically reduces the economic viability and performance of SWH systems over their lifetime. (ii) Space availability on roofs especially in high-rise buildings. (iii) Lack of public awareness of the benefits of using SWH systems and of the maintenance and monitoring procedures; and (iv) The unavailability of credit schemes, especially for the low-income groups, in order to have a SWH system with easy payments.

Currently the Energy Research Institute (ERI) has a SWH laboratory for simulation of solar radiation, quality control, calibration and determination of performance behavior of SWH. This will assure the quality and reliability of SWH and protect both the consumer and the manufacturer.

4.2.3. Solar Dryers for Peanut Crops

Solar dryers have been developed, tested and proved.

4.2.4. Solar Stills

There is an important need for clean, pure drinking water in many developing countries. Often water sources are brackish (i.e., contain dissolved salts) and/or contain harmful bacteria and therefore cannot be used for drinking. In addition, there are many coastal locations where seawater is abundant but potable water is not available. Pure water is also useful for batteries and in hospitals or schools. Distillation is one of many processes that can be used for water purification. This requires an energy input, and heat and solar radiation can be the source of energy. In this process, water is evaporated, thus separating water vapor from dissolved matter, which is condensed as pure water.

Solar water distillation is a solar technology with a very long history and installations were built over 2000 years ago, although to produce salt rather than drinking water [7]. Documented use of solar stills began in the sixteenth century. An early large-scale solar still was built in 1872 to supply a mining community in Chile with drinking water. Mass production occurred for the first time during the Second World War when 200,000 inflatable plastic stills were made to be kept in life-crafts for the USA Navy [7].

There are a number of other approaches to water purification and desalination, such as photovoltaic (PV) powered reverse-osmosis, for which small-scale commercially available equipment is available. These are not considered in this study. In addition, if treatment of polluted water is required rather than desalination, slow sand filtration is a good option. The purpose of this technical brief is to provide basic information and direct the reader to other, more detailed sources.

5. ENERGY REQUIREMENTS FOR WATER DISTILLATION

The energy required to evaporate water is the latent heat of vaporization of water. This has a value of 2260 kilojoules per kilogram (kJ/kg). This means that to produce 1 liter (i.e., 1 kg since the density of water is 1 kg/liter) of pure water by distilling brackish water requires a heat input of 2260 kJ. This does not allow for the efficiency of the heating method, which will be less than 100%, or for any recovery of latent heat that is rejected when the water vapor is condensed. It should be noted that, although 2260 kJ/kg is required to evaporate water, to pump a kg of water through 20 m head requires only 0.2 (kJ/kg). Distillation is therefore normally considered only where there is no local source of fresh water that can easily be pumped or lifted.

5.1. Simple Solar Still Operation

Figure 4 shows a single-basin still. Generally, the main features of operation are the same for all solar stills. The incident solar radiation is transmitted through the glass cover and is absorbed as heat by a black surface in contact with the water to be distilled. The water is thus heated and gives off water vapor. The vapor condenses on the glass cover, which is at a lower temperature because it is in contact with the ambient air and runs down into a gutter from where it is fed to a storage tank. For high efficiency the solar still should maintain:

- A high feed (undistilled) water temperature.
- A large temperature difference between feed water and condensing surface.
- Low vapor leakage.

A high feed water temperature can be achieved if:

- A high proportion of incoming radiation is absorbed by the feed water as heat. Hence, low absorption glazing and a good radiation absorbing surface are required.
- Heat losses from the floor and walls are kept low.
- The water is shallow so there is not so much to heat.

A large temperature difference can be achieved if:

- The condensing surface absorbs little or none of the incoming radiation.
- Condensing water dissipates heat, which must be removed rapidly from the condensing surface by, for example, a second flow of water or air, or by condensing at night.

Figure 4. Solar stills in operation at Soba site, Khartoum.

5.2. Design Types and their Performance

Single-basin stills have been much studied and their behavior is well understood. Efficiencies of 25% are typical. Daily output as a function of solar irradiation is greatest in the early evening when the feed water is still hot but when outside temperatures are falling. Material selection is very important. The cover can be either glass or plastic. Glass is considered to be best for most long-term applications, whereas a plastic (such as polyethylene) can be used for short-term use [18].

Sand concrete or waterproofed concrete are considered best for the basin of a long-life still if it is to be manufactured on-site, but for factory-manufactured stills, prefabricated Ferro-concrete is a suitable material. Multiple-effect basin stills have two or more compartments. The condensing surface of the lower compartment is the floor of the upper compartment. The heat given off by the condensing vapor provides energy to vaporize the feed water above. Efficiency is therefore greater than for a single-basin, still typically being 35% or more, but the cost and complexity are correspondingly higher.

Wick stills - In a wick still, the feed water flows slowly through a porous, radiation-absorbing pad (the wick). Two advantages are claimed over basin stills. First, the wick can be tilted so that the feed water presents a better angle to the sun (reducing reflection and presenting a large effective area). Second, less feed water is in the still at any time and so the water is heated more quickly and to a higher temperature. Simple wick stills are more efficient than basin stills and some designs are claimed to cost less than a basin still of the same output.

Emergency still - To provide emergency drinking water on land, a very simple still can be made. It makes use of the moisture in the earth. All that is required is a plastic cover, a bowl or bucket and a pebble.

Hybrid designs - There are a number of ways in which solar stills can usefully be combined with another function of technology. Three examples are given:

- Rainwater collection: By adding an external gutter, the still cover can be used for rainwater collection to supplement the solar still output.
- Greenhouse-solar still. The roof of a greenhouse can be used as the cover of a still.
- Supplementary heating: Waste heat from an engine or the condenser of a refrigerator can be used as an additional energy input.

5.3. Output of a Solar Still

The basic principles of solar water distillation are simple yet effective, since distillation replicates the way nature makes rain. The sun's energy heats water to the point of evaporation. As the water evaporates, water vapor rises, condensing on the glass surface for collection. This process removes impurities such as salts and heavy metals as well as eliminating microbiological organisms. The end result is water that is cleaner than the purest rainwater. A solar still operates on the same principle as rainwater: evaporation and condensation. The water from the oceans evaporates, only to cool, condense and return to earth as rain. When the water evaporates, it removes only pure water and leaves all contaminants behind. Solar stills mimic this natural process.

An approximate method of estimating the output of a solar still is given by:

$$Q = \eta \times G \times A \tag{1}$$

Where:

Q = Daily output of distilled water (liters/day)
η = Overall efficiency (%)
G = Daily global solar irradiation (MJ/m²)
A = Aperture area of the still, i.e., the plan areas for a simple basin still (m²)

In a typical country the average, daily, global solar irradiation is typically 18.0 MJ/m² (5 kWh/m²). A simple basin still operates at an overall efficiency of about 30%. Hence, the output per square meter of area is:

$$\text{Daily output} = 0.30 \times 18.0 \times 1 = 5.4 \text{ liters (per square meter)} \tag{2}$$

The intensity of solar energy falling on the still is the single most important parameter affecting production. The daily-distilled water output (Me in kg/m² day) is the amount of energy utilized in vaporizing water in the still (Qe in J/m² day) over the latent heat of vaporization of water (L in J/kg). Solar still efficiency (η) is the amount of energy utilized in vaporizing water in the still over the amount of incident solar energy on the still (Qt in J/m² day). The yearly output of a solar still is often therefore referred to as approximately one cubic meter per square meter.

These can be expressed as:

$$\text{Solar still production: } Me = Qe / L \tag{3}$$

$$\text{Solar still efficiency: } \eta = Qe / Qt \tag{4}$$

Typical efficiencies for single basin solar stills approach 60 percent. General operation is simple and requires facing the still towards the solar noon; putting water in the still every morning to fill and flush the basin and recovering distillate from the collection reservoir (for example, glass bottles). Stills are modular and, for greater water production requirements, several stills can be connected together in series and parallel as desired. As water evaporates from the solar still basin, salts and other contaminants are left behind. Over time, these salts can build to the point of saturation if the still is not properly maintained and flushed on a regular basis. Properly operating a still requires about three times as much make-up water as the distillate produced each day. If the still produced 3 gallons of water, 9 gallons of make-up water should be added, of which 6 gallons leave the still as excess. The excess water flushes the still basin through the overflow to prevent salt build-up. If this is done on a daily basis, the flushed water is of approximately the same quality as the original feedwater that was added to the still. The excess water is of suitable quality so that it can be used for watering landscaping, washing pots and pans, etc. No sediment or sludge will build-up if the still is properly operated and flushed daily.

Solar stills have proven to be highly effective in cleaning up water supplies to provide safe drinking water. The effectiveness of distillation for producing safe drinking water is well established and recognized. Most commercial stills and water purification systems require electrical or other fossil-fueled power sources. Solar distillation technology produces the same safe quality drinking water as other distillation technologies; only the energy source is different: the sun [19].

5.4. Experience

Various versions have been constructed. Solar stills are suitable for use in laboratories, medical purposes, charging and topping batteries; and supplying drinking water to small communities in isolated sunny areas as well as local markets. Solar stills for charging and topping batteries is economically the best [4].

Despite a proliferation of novel types, the single-basin still remains the only design proven in the field. At least 40 single-basin stills with areas greater than 100 m (and up to 9000 m²) were built between 1957 and 1980 [5]. 27 had glass covers and 9 had plastic. 24 of the glass-covered stills are still operating in their original form, but only one plastic-covered unit is operational. Hundreds of smaller stills are operating, notably in Africa (Figure 5) [5].

The cost of pure water produced depends on:

- The cost of making the still.
- The cost of the land.
- The life of the still.
- Operating costs.
- Cost of the feed water.
- The discount rate adopted.
- The amount of water produced.

Table 4. Features of the solar still

• Simplicity: The still can be operated by persons who have not received training.
• Operates at sea or on land: The still incorporates a buoyancy ring enabling the still to float.
• Minimal attention: The still only requires attention each time a liter of fresh water is produced, or once a day.
• Minimum weight and bulk: Efficient design and great care over material selection provides for minimum weight and bulk.
• Conservation of impure water: There is no waste of impure water.
• Performance: Maximum output 300 mls per hour.
• Operational life: Over a long period of time in operational conditions the productivity of the still will decline due to the build up of salt on the solar collector. However, using the flushing procedure contained in the general instructions the operational life can be extended indefinitely.
Shelf life: The shelf life expectancy is set at two years.

The cost of a solar still is normally UK £50-70/m². The price of land will normally be a small proportion of this in rural areas, but may be prohibitive in towns and cities [11]. The life of a glass still is usually 20 to 30 years but operating costs can be large, especially to replace broken glass. Performance varies between tropical locations but not significantly. An average output of 2.5-1/m²/day is typical, that is, about 1m³/m²/year.

5.4.1. Solar Still Suits the Needs

Human beings need 1 or 2 liters of water a day to live. The minimum requirement for normal life in developing countries (which includes cooking, cleaning and washing clothes) is 20 liters per day (in the industrialized world 200 to 400 liters per day is typical) [10]. Yet, some functions can be performed with salty water and a typical requirement for distilled water is 5 liters per person per day. Therefore 2 m² of the still are needed for each person served (Figure 6).

Solar stills should normally only be considered for removal of dissolved salts from water. If there is a choice between brackish groundwater and polluted surface water, it will usually be cheaper to use a slow sand filter or other treatment device. If there is no fresh water then the main alternatives are desalination, transportation and rainwater collection. Unlike other techniques of desalination, solar stills are more attractive, and the required output is smaller. The initial capital cost of stills is roughly proportional to capacity [19].

The Solar Distillation-Energy Research Institute has significant economies of scale (Table 4). For the individual household, therefore, the solar still is most economic. For outputs of 1 m³/day or more, reverse osmosis or electro-dialysis should be considered as an alternative to solar stills. Much will depend on the availability and price of electrical power. For outputs of 200 (m³/day) or more, vapor compression or flash evaporation will normally have the least cost. The latter technology can have part of its energy requirement met by solar water heaters. In many parts of the world, fresh water is transported from another region or location by boat, train, truck or pipeline. The cost of water transported by vehicles is typically of the same order of magnitude as that produced by solar stills. A pipeline may be less expensive for very large quantities.

Rainwater collection is an even simpler technique than solar distillation in areas where rain is not scarce, but requires a greater area and usually a larger storage tank. If ready-made collection surfaces exist (such as house roofs) these may provide a less expensive source for obtaining clean water.

Capacity production with declining expenditures could be the main targets of any desalination facility around the world. The reverse-osmosis (RO) is a reliable and cost-effective technology, enhancement of water production by optimization of the plant operating system, capacity utilization and minimization of the production costs.

5.4.2. Solar Still Types

The single-basin still is the only design proven in the field. Multi-effect stills have the potential to be more economic but it would be helpful to gain experience first with a single-basin still.

Solar Stills have got major advantages over other conventional distillation/water purification/de-mineralization systems as follows:

1. Produces pure water.
2. No prime movers required.
3. No conventional energy required.
4. No skilled operator required.
5. Local manufacturing/repairing.
6. Low investment.
7. Can purify highly saline water (even sea water).

The solar still is a device to desalinate impure water like brackish or saline water. It a simple device to get potable/fresh distilled water from impure water, using solar energy as fuel, for its various applications in domestic, industrial and academic sectors (Figures 5, and 6).

A solar still consists of a shallow triangular basin made up of fiber reinforced plastic (FRP). The bottom of the basin is painted black so as to absorb solar heat effectively. The top of the basin is covered with transparent glass tilted so that maximum solar radiation can be transmitted into the still. The edges of the glass are sealed with the basin using tar tape so that the entire basin becomes airtight. The entire assembly is placed on a structure made of mild steel (MS) angle. The outlet is connected with a storage container. Provision has been made to fill in the still basin with water. A window is provided in the basin to clean the basin from the inside. Water is charged into the basin in a thin layer (Figure 6).

Solar stills are useful devices to get fresh / distilled water, which is required in:

Industries	For industrial processes
Hospitals and dispensaries	For sterilization
Garages and automobile workshop	For radiator and battery maintenance
Telephone exchange	For battery maintenance
Laboratory use	For analytic work
Marshy and costal area	To get fresh potable water

These devices generally imitate a part of the natural hydrologic cycle in that the sun's rays heat the saline water so that the production of water vapor (humidification) increases. The water vapor is then condensed on a cool surface and the condensate is collected as product water. An example of this type of process is the greenhouse solar still, in which the saline water is heated in a basin on the floor and the water vapor condenses on the sloping glass roof that covers the basin [6].

Variations of this type of solar still have been made in an effort to increase efficiency, but they all share the following difficulties, which restrict the use of this technique for large-scale production:

• Large solar collection area requirements.
• High capital cost.
• Vulnerability to weather-related damage.

A general rule of thumb for solar stills is that a solar collection area of about one square meter is needed to produce 4 liters of water per day (10 square feet / gallon). Thus, for a 4000 m³/d facility, a land area of 100 hectares would be needed (250 acres/mgd) [9]. This operation would take up a tremendous area and could create problems if located near a city where land was scarce and expensive. The stills themselves are expensive to construct and although the thermal energy may be free, additional energy is needed to pump the water to and from the facility. In addition, careful operation and maintenance is needed to prevent scale formation caused by the basins drying out and to repair glass or vapor leaks in the stills. An application for these types of solar humidification units has been used for desalting saline water on a small scale for a family or small village where solar energy is abundant but electricity is not.

The population increase, economic development, in addition to global warming, is creating a worldwide imbalance between supply and demand of fresh water. The task of providing adequate supplies of fresh water may indeed become the most serious problem facing the world on the onset of this new century. Sources of fresh water must be found and the most likely sources are the great oceans and seas that can be desalinated by various methods including the utilization of solar energy. Although a few techniques such as multi-effect evaporation, multistage flash distillation, thin film distillation, reverse osmosis and electro-dialysis, are energy intensive and operating costs are high, direct use of solar energy represents a promising option for eliminating the major operating cost required in each case (Figure 7).

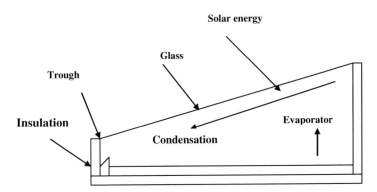

Figure 5. Principle of solar still work.

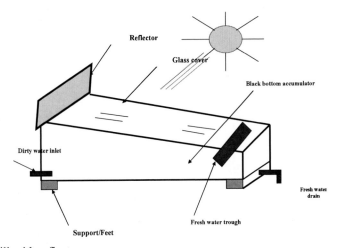

Figure 6. Solar Still with reflector.

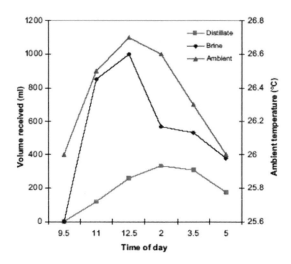

Figure 7. Hourly output of the system.

Solar distillation represents the most attractive and simple technique among other distillation processes and is especially suited to small-scale units at locations where solar energy is considerable. Accordingly, it seemed necessary to search for solar stills that are easy to construct and that could provide us with the necessary daily amount of drinking water, not forgetting the drought that has prevailed in several areas of Africa for the last two decades. Numerous attempts have been made by many investigators to produce fresh water by means of solar energy. The simple solar still of the basin type is the oldest method and improvements in its design have been made to increase its efficiency [7].

6. MATERIALS REQUIREMENTS OF SOLAR STILLS

Although local materials should be used whenever possible to lower initial costs and to facilitate any necessary repairs, keep in mind that solar stills made with cheap, unstudied materials will not last as long as those built with more costly and high-quality material. There are two possible solutions. The first is to build an inexpensive and short-lived still that needs to be replaced or repaired every few years, or build a still that is more durable with the aim of distilled water that is cheaper in the long-term. Many of the low-cost stills that have been built around the world have been abandoned. Building a more durable still that will last 20 years or more seems to be worth the additional investment. Choosing materials for the components in contact with the water represents a serious problem. Many plastics give off a substance which can be tasted or smelled in the product water, for periods of anywhere from hours to years. As a general guide, if someone is contemplating using any material other than glass or metal in contact with water, they may perform a useful screening test by boiling a sample of the material in a cup of good water for half an hour, then let the water cool and smell and taste it. This is a considerably accelerated test of what happens in the still. If there are not any differences between the test water and what they started with, the material is probably safe to use. To get some experience, try this on polyethylene tubing, PVC pipe and fiberglass resin panel.

The materials used for this type of still should have the following characteristics:

- Materials should have a long life under exposed conditions or be inexpensive enough to be replaced upon degradation.
- They should be sturdy enough to resist wind damage and slight earth movements.
- They should be non-toxic and not emit vapors or instill an unpleasant taste to the water under elevated temperatures.
- They should be able to resist corrosion from saline water and distilled water.
- They should be of a size and weight that can be conveniently packaged and carried by local transportation.
- They should be easy to handle in the field.

Ideally, the glazing material should also be strong enough to resist high winds, rain, hail, small earth movements and prevent the intrusion of insects and animals. Moreover, it must be "wettable". Wettability allows the condensing vapor to form as sheets of water on the underside of a glazing cover rather than as water droplets. If the water does form as droplets, it will reduce the performance of the still for the following reasons:

- Water droplets restrict the amount of light entering the still because they act as small mirrors and reflect it back out.
- A percentage of the distilled water that forms as droplets on the underside will fall back into the basin rather than flow down the glazing cover into the collection trough. Except for temporary conditions at start-up, such a loss of water should not be tolerated.

Other factors determining the suitability of the glazing material include the cost of the material, its weight, life expectancy, local availability, maximum temperature tolerance and impact resistance, as well as its ability to transmit solar energy and infrared light.

The acceptance of solar distillation will depend greatly on how well one understands and handles the many social issues and cultural constraints that can hamper the introduction of new technologies. Some of the more important issues that may affect the acceptance of solar distillation are outlined below:

- Stills built for village use require community cooperation that may be foreign to some cultural groups. If the distilled water is incorrectly distributed, causing a family unit not to receive its fair share of water, this could become a source of conflict. For this reason, a family-sized solar still unit, which a household has complete control over, may be more practical than a unit that serves an entire village.
- Potential users who think they will find distilled water tasteless or not in keeping with what they are accustomed to may become disappointed and possibly abandon altogether the thought of drinking the water. The problem of taste must be dealt with early on so as not to give people a reason to respond negatively to the technology as a whole.

- In some societies, conflicts may arise over whether it is the responsibility of the man or the woman of the household to operate the solar still. Not dealing with this issue early on could result in the household's total rejection of the technology.
- If solar distillation is perceived to be a threat to a community's traditional lifestyle, the community may reject the technology. Such concerns can be headed off if the technology is designed appropriately from the start and introduced at the proper time. Moreover, a community is more likely to accept the technology if it recognizes the importance of clean water and considers it a priority to the degree that it is willing to change certain aspects of its lifestyle.

7. DISCUSSIONS

There is almost no water left on Earth that is safe to drink without purification. This is a seemingly bold statement, but it is unfortunately true. Only 1% of Earth's water is in a fresh, liquid state and nearly all of this is polluted by both diseases and toxic chemicals. For this reason, purification of water supplies is extremely important. The statistics are quite shocking. According to the World Health Organization (WHO), 1.5 billion people lack access to adequately purified drinking water. About 10,000 children die from drinking contaminated water every day and 80% of all illnesses in the developing world result from waterborne diseases [8].

In the developed world, we take for granted water treatment processes that keep us safe from most diseases [16]. However, these processes are far from perfect and can cause their own problems. For instance, it is now known that the use of chlorine for purification - standard in most municipal water treatment plants - results in the contamination of drinking water with carcinogenic chemicals. Because of the challenges of dealing with the vast number of pollutants now loose in the environment, most city water systems are not even designed to remove most of them. In low levels, these chemicals are not thought to pose a high risk on an individual basis. The traditional thinking is that the added cost of purifying water of all these pollutants is not worth the public health benefits, since virtually every contaminant targeted requires another step in the purification process. However, the long-term consequence of ingesting a cocktail of many known toxic and carcinogenic substances has not been adequately studied. No one really knows how making these compromises impacts our health, but only that these compromises are economically necessary with the types of purification in widespread use. Moreover, typical purification systems are easily damaged or compromised by disasters, natural or otherwise. This results in a very challenging situation for individuals trying to prepare for such situations, and keep themselves and their families safe from the myriad diseases and toxic chemicals present in untreated water.

Fortunately there is a solution to these problems. It is a technology that is not only capable of removing a very wide variety of contaminants in just one step, but is simple, cost-effective, and environmentally friendly. This solution is solar water distillation. It is not a new process, but it has not received the attention that it deserves. Perhaps this is because it is such a low-technology and flexible solution to water problems. Nearly anyone is capable of building a still and providing themselves with completely pure water from very questionable sources. In fact, the concept is nearly as old as the Earth itself. Solar distillation is nature's way of recycling water through the ecosystem. Many know it as "nature's water cycle". The sun's energy evaporates water from the ocean, and it condenses as clouds of pure water vapor, which eventually falls as fresh rain.

Solar stills use a similar process on a much smaller scale, capturing it in a closed system. A simple but typical configuration is a sealed box with an angled glass top. Sunlight shining into the box heats contaminated water, causing it to evaporate. The moisture condenses on the relatively cool glass cover and runs down the sloped surface for collection. Because the water is purified by evaporation, the water is separated from contaminants one molecule at a time and the purified water is then collected drop by drop. This simple one-step process actually extracts pure water from the contaminants. This method is the exact opposite of traditional, expensive approaches, which attempts to remove each contaminant from the water in turn. In this way, solar distillation automatically separates virtually any pollutants from the water, no matter what they are - and this means peace of mind, since one does not always know what water might be contaminated with. In addition to being a great solution for dealing with a complex mix of pollutants, solar water distillation is also the most cost-effective and environmentally friendly means of converting seawater to fresh water. The majority of the world's population lives within 100 miles of the ocean, which could be a great source of drinking water. Unfortunately, technologies such as reverse osmosis are expensive and require a great deal of power. In contrast, solar distillation is inexpensive and utilizes clean solar energy.

Solar stills come in a great variety of sizes and types (Appendix 1). The most basic type can be made by any handy person with simple tools in their back yard. A web search will yield a variety of different plans. Other systems are more carefully engineered for greater efficiency and automation and can be purchased as complete systems. Another class of collapsible, floating stills were designed around the end of World War II specifically for use in the ocean, to help those forced into a life raft to survive at sea. Today, solar stills are helping people all over the world solve their most challenging water quality problems. The inherent simplicity, the ability to accept water polluted with many different contaminants, and the cleanse it with the environmental friendliness of solar water distillation make it a technology that is ripe for much wider use.

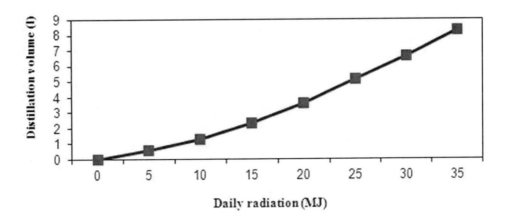

Figure 8. Daily solar radiation v output.

Table 5. Factors to be considered in economic analysis

Economic factors
• Interest on loan
• Current/future cost of alternative fuels
• Current/future cost of construction materials
• Saving of foreign currency
• Current/future labor cost
• Inflation rate
Social factors
• Employment created
• Less time consumed for fetching clean water
• Improved facilities in villages; thus less migration to cities
• Less expense for buying alternative fuels
• More time for additional income earning activities
Technical factors
• Construction, maintenance and repairs of still plants
• Availability of materials and land required
• Suitability of local materials
Ecological/health factors
• Improved health
• Environment pollution abatement
• Improvement in yields of agriculture products

8. BARRIERS TO IMPLEMENTATION

Sudan suffers from a poor technological, capital, financial and skills resource base. Despite considerable financial and human efforts, most initiatives have unfortunately been a failure. The solar still program appears to be an attractive option for the country to pursue in order to reduce the level of atmospheric carbon by enhancing carbon sequestration, which would consequently mitigate climate change. However, it is acknowledged that certain barriers need to be overcome if the objectives are to be fully achieved. These include the following:

- Low level of public awareness of the economic/environmental benefits of solar stills.
- The generally low levels of individual income.
- Poor pricing of solar stills especially in the local market.
- Weak institutional capabilities of the various Energy Research Institutes.

Renewable utilization in developing areas of the world are influenced by many inter-connected social, ecological, cultural, political and institutional factors [15]:

- A long-term commitment to their use.
- As assessment of past, present and future energy demands.
- The classification of energy demands into categories (e.g., domestic, rural, agricultural, commercial, industrial, etc.).

- An assessment of renewable energy industry potential in current utilization, R&D facilities and personnel, manufacturing capabilities and component availability.

In the Sudan, people are requested to constructed solar stills plants by themselves in order to reduce costs. In remote areas, the costs for materials increase by about 15-20% due to transportation. In an economic analysis, many factors must be considered, as outlined in Table 5. Due to the lack of knowledge and awareness, villagers cannot be expected to understand the benefits of solar stills, nutrient conservation, or health improvement. A poor rural peasant is very hesitant to enter a new venture. The negative attitude towards the use of water stills varies from place to place, but when it occurs, it is a major obstacle to the implementation of solar still technology. In designing the solar still, the following points were considered: the unit has to cost as little as possible and materials should be readily available in rural areas. Technology should be simple, within the reach of a common village man. The unit should be usable in situations of emergency, e.g., during floods and after cyclones, etc.

9. DISADVANTAGES

The following disadvantages are summarized:

- Prolonged periods of overcast weather (Figure 8) and capacity ranges are very small.
- Capital cost is high and ordinary people cannot afford to buy it and depend on pump types. If used and uncontrolled parameters are included. The vandalism or other breakages of plant components, especially glass covers of stills. Sudden significant variation in raw water. It is an intermittent technology depending on the duration of sunshine.
- Need safety equipment for handling and disposal of glass panes and broken glass pieces. Failure of the control system to stop raw water feed during the flushing cycle can lead to stills being overfilled. Raw water entering product water system via distillation collection troughs and solar still can run dry and be damaged when water feed does not initiate.
- Solar still technology is primarily aimed at small-scale household water provision and is as such not suitable for bulk water supply e.g., for sanitation and/or gardening/agriculture. Ideally, the water produced by solar stills should only be used for human intake, i.e., drinking and cooking purposes. The rest of the household water can be provided by means of a dual water supply system (e.g., where water of higher salinity can be used).

Solar distillation remains an attractive process in less developed countries. Most of the existing plants do not provide their expected output because of drawbacks in their maintenance:

- There is no built-in arrangement for basin cleaning.
- There is no provision for removal of any algae formation.

- Sealant materials used do not prevent vapor leakage through joints/corners.
- Cleaning of the glass cover is not carried out sufficiently or frequently.

As communities in developing countries seek ecologically sound, sustainable solutions to help them grow and thrive, nothing is more fundamental than securing reliable sources of clean drinking water. Today, there are over 15,000 desalination plants in the world [17]. Saudi Arabia, the United Arab Emirates and Kuwait, because of their limited water supplies and tremendous energy reserves, are the worlds' leading users of desalination technology. But desalination is also gaining popularity in the Sudan. When new desalination plants are proposed, environmental concerns are often raised, particularly surrounding disposal of the residual brine, which has twice the salinity of seawater and is typically returned to the sea. But the area's sea conditions and the local marine life's resistance to salinity are to be studied before a plant is opened. The new approaches to use renewable energy in the Sudan with desalination still have many hurdles to overcome, including maintenance needs that make them difficult to apply in remote areas. Hundreds of scientists around the world see water shortages as one of the top concerns for the new millennium. By using their expertise in desalination to dip into the nearly limitless seas, the Sudanese engineers are poised to help avert the looming water crisis by supplying clean and fresh drinking water to millions more people in Sudan.

CONCLUSION

The Red Sea area has a tremendous amount of renewable solar energy (4-6 kWh/m^2) and is surrounded by abundant volumes of renewable seawater. Coupling seawater and solar energy with the appropriate technology is the only strategic option to secure sustainable fresh water resource for generations to come. Worldwide experience in researching and marketing solar stills over three decades has provided an ample foundation for a solar still industry. The inherent technical or economic barriers have been identified. A solar still is suited to village (manufacturing) techniques and to mass production. Around the world, concerns over water quality are increasing and in special situations a solar still can provide a water supply more economically than any other method. Sudan enjoys bright sunshine and dry weather most of the year. The available solar energy can be utilized for water heating and desalination to replace fuelwood, which in turn eases pressures on forests and eliminates the associated pollution, along with the need to collect and transport the fuel. The use of solar energy for desalinization is especially appropriate since the need for potable drinking water is so great and because the areas, which lack potable water supplies, happen to have abundant solar energy. The country strives hard to make use of the technologies related to renewable sources in rural areas where it is appropriate and applicable. Sudan already has well-established solar thermal applications. The most promising solar energy technologies are related to thermal systems; industrial solar water heaters in the residential sector and in larger social institutions, such as nurseries, hospitals and schools. Solar cookers, solar dryers for peanut crops, solar stills, solar driven cold stores to store fruits and vegetables, solar collectors, solar water desalination, solar ovens and solar commercial bakers. Solar photovoltaic system (PV): solar PV for lighting, solar refrigeration to store vaccines for human and animal use, solar PV for water pumping, solar PV for battery chargers, solar PV for communication networks, microwave receiver stations, radio systems in airports, VHF and beacon radio systems in airports and educational solar posts in some villages. Sudan as an agricultural country has a good energy resources from agricultural residues, forestry resources and animal wastes.

APPENDIX 1. TAXONOMY OF SOLAR DISTILLATION SYSTEMS

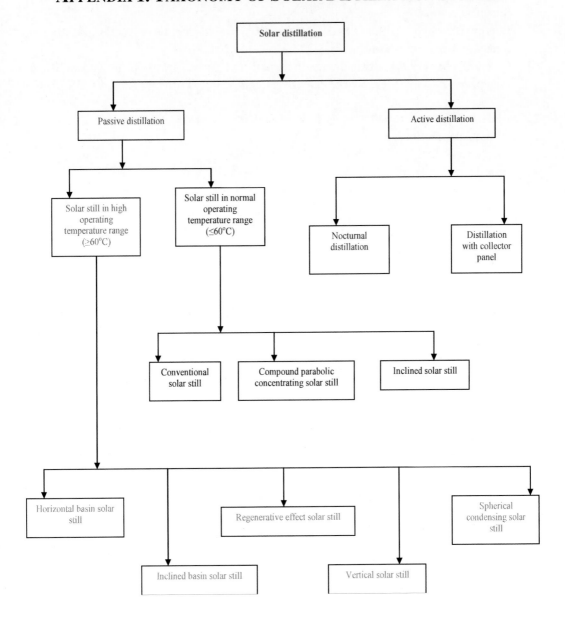

REFERENCES

[1]   Omer, A. M. (1998). 'Sudan energy background; an overview'. *Renewable Energy*, *14*(1-4), 467-72.

[2]   National Forestry Administration (NFA). (1996). 'Forestry Handbook', Khartoum: Sudan.

[3]   Omer, A. M. (1997). 'Compilation and evaluation of solar and wind energy resources in Sudan'. *Renewable Energy*, *12* (1), 39-69.

[4]   Energy Research Institute (ERI) (1997). 'Renewable energy resources potential in Sudan'. Khartoum: Sudan.

[5]   Omer, A. M. (1996). Solar energy potential and future prospects in Sudan, *World Renewable Energy Congress IV*, Part III, pp. 2002-2006, Denver, Colorado, USA, June 15-21.

[6]   Abdeen M. Omer. (2000) 'Solar stills in Sudan'. *Jordanian Energy Abstracts*, 14 (2): 39-43, Amman: Jordan.

[7]   Hirschmann, J. R. (1975). 'Solar distillation in Chile'. *Desalination,* 17: 17–30.

[8]   World Health Organisation (WHO). (2006). *'The Silent Epidemic'.* February 2006.

[9]   National Energy Administration (NEA). (1985). *'The National Energy Plan 1985-2000'*, Khartoum, Sudan, January.

[10]   Wang, X. H. & Feng, Z. M. (1996). 'Survey of rural household energy consumption in China'. *Energy*, *2*(7-8), 703-5.

[11]   Wu, J., and Boggess, W. (1999). 'The optimal allocation of conservation funds'. *Journal Environmental Economic Management,* pp.38.

[12]   Duchin, F. (1995). *'Global scenarios about lifestyle and technology, the sustainable future of the global system'.* United Nations University. Tokyo.

[13]   OECD/IEA. (2004). *'Renewables for power generation: status and prospect'.* London: UK.

[14]   Duffie J. A. & Beckman W. A. (1980). *'Solar Engineering of Thermal Processes'.* J. Wiley and Sons, New York.

[15]   John, A. & James, S. (1989). *'The power of place: bringing together geographical and sociological imaginations'.*

[16]   Sitarz D. Editor. (1992). *'Agenda 21: The Earth Summit Strategy to save our planet'.* Boulder (CO): Earth Press.

[17]   Enrique, A. (2007). Spanish companies focus on desalination technology. *Water and wastewater international*, *22*(2), 14-15.

[18]   Http://www.solaqua.com/solstilbas.htm1

[19]   http://www.solaqua.com

[20]   http://www.practicalaction.org

In: Advances in Energy Research. Volume 20
Editor: Morena J. Acosta

ISBN: 978-1-63463-169-3
© 2015 Nova Science Publishers, Inc.

Chapter 5

SOLAR ENERGY RESEARCH, SUSTAINABLE DEVELOPMENT AND APPLICATIONS

*Abdeen Mustafa Omer**

Energy Research Institute (ERI), Nottingham, UK

ABSTRACT

People rely upon oil for primary energy and this for a few more decades. Other orthodox sources may be more enduring, but are not without serious disadvantages. Power from natural resources has always had great appeal. Coal is plentiful, though there is concern about despoliation in winning it and pollution in burning it. Nuclear power has been developed with remarkable timeliness, but is not universally welcomed, construction of the plant is energy-intensive and there is concern about the disposal of its long-lived active wastes. Barrels of oil, lumps of coal, even uranium come from nature but the possibilities of almost limitless power from the atmosphere and the oceans seem to have special attraction. The wind machine provided an early way of developing motive power. The massive increases in fuel prices over the last years have however, made any scheme not requiring fuel appear to be more attractive and to be worth reinvestigation. In considering the atmosphere and the oceans as energy sources the four main contenders are wind power, wave power, tidal and power from ocean thermal gradients. The renewable energy resources are particularly suited for the provision of rural power supplies and a major advantage is that equipment such as flat plate solar driers, wind machines, etc., can be constructed using local resources and without the advantage results from the feasibility of local maintenance and the general encouragement such local manufacture gives to the build up of small-scale rural based industry. This chapter gives some examples of small-scale energy converters, nevertheless it should be noted that small conventional, i.e., engines are currently the major source of power in rural areas and will continue to be so for a long time to come. There is a need for some further development to suit local conditions, to minimise spares holdings, to maximise interchangeability both of engine parts and of the engine application. Emphasis should be placed on full local manufacture.

---

* Corresponding author: Energy Research Institute (ERI), Forest Road West, Nottingham NG7 4EU, UK.

Keywords: Renewable energy technologies, energy efficiency, sustainable development, emissions, environment

ABBREVIATIONS

a   annum
ha   hectares
l   litre

1. INTRODUCTION

The sources to alleviate the energy situation in the world are sufficient to supply all foreseeable needs. Conservation of energy and rationing in some form will however have to be practised by most countries, to reduce oil imports and redress balance of payments positions. Meanwhile development and application of nuclear power and some of the traditional solar, wind and water energy alternatives must be set in hand to supplement what remains of the fossil fuels.

The encouragement of greater energy use is an essential component of development. In the short-term it requires mechanisms to enable the rapid increase in energy/capita, and in the long-term we should be working towards a way of life, which makes use of energy efficiency and without the impairment of the environment or of causing safety problems. Such a programme should as far as possible be based on renewable energy resources.

Large-scale, conventional, power plant such as hydropower, has an important part to play in development. It does not, however, provide a complete solution. There is an important complementary role for the greater use of small scale, rural based, power plant. Such plant can be used to assist development since it can be made locally using local resources, enabling a rapid built-up in total equipment to be made without a corresponding and unacceptably large demand on central funds. Renewable resources are particularly suitable for providing the energy for such equipment and its use is also compatible with the long-term aims. It is possible with relatively simple flat plate solar collectors (Figure 1) to provide warmed water and enable some space heating for homes and offices which is particularly useful when the buildings are well insulated and thermal capacity sufficient for the carry over of energy from day to night is arranged. There is no shortage of solar-derived energy on earth and have yet to fully harness its tremendous potential to power our planet's insatiable energy demands.

In compiling energy consumption data one can categorise usage according to a number of different schemes:

- Traditional sector- industrial, transportation, etc.
- End-use- space heating, process steam, etc.
- Final demand- total energy consumption related to automobiles, to food, etc.
- Energy source- oil, coal, etc.
- Energy form at point of use- electric drive, low temperature heat, etc.

2. RENEWABLE ENERGY

The renewable energy resources are particularly suited for the provision of rural power supplies and a major advantage is that equipment such as flat plate solar driers, wind machines, etc., can be constructed using local resources and without the high capital cost of more conventional equipment. Further advantage results from the feasibility of local maintenance and the general encouragement such local manufacture gives to the build up of small scale rural based industry. Table 1 lists the energy sources available.

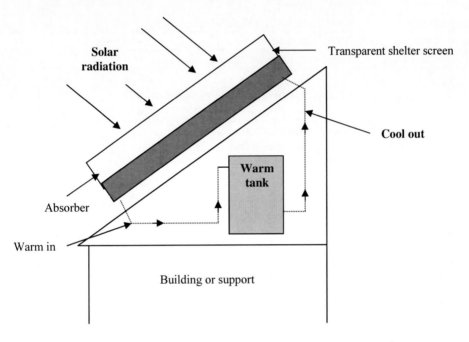

Figure 1. Solar water warmer.

Table 1. Sources of energy

Energy source	Energy carrier	Energy end-use
Vegetation	Fuel-wood	Cooking Water heating Building materials Animal fodder preparation
Oil	Kerosene	Lighting Ignition fires
Dry cells	Dry cell batteries	Lighting Small appliances
Muscle power	Animal power	Transport Land preparation for farming Food preparation (threshing)
Muscle power	Human power	Transport Land preparation for farming Food preparation (threshing)

Table 2. Renewable applications

Systems	Applications
Water supply	Rain collection, purification, storage and recycling
Wastes disposal	Anaerobic digestion (CH_4)
Cooking	Methane
Food	Cultivate the 1 hectare plot and greenhouse for four people
Electrical demands	Wind generator
Space heating	Solar collectors
Water heating	Solar collectors and excess wind energy
Control system	Ultimately hardware
Building fabric	Integration of subsystems to cut costs

Table 3. Energy needs in rural areas

Transport, e.g., small vehicles and boats
Agricultural machinery, e.g., two-wheeled tractors
Crop processing, e.g., milling
Water pumping
Small industries, e.g., workshop equipment
Electricity generation, e.g., hospitals and schools
Domestic, e.g., cooking, heating, and lighting
Water supply, e.g., rain collection, purification, storage and recycling
Building fabric, e.g., integration of subsystems to cut costs
Wastes disposal, e.g., anaerobic digestion (CH_4)

Currently the 'non-commercial' fuels wood, crop residues and animal dung are used in large amounts in the rural areas of developing countries, principally for heating and cooking; the method of use is highly inefficient. Table 2 presented some renewable applications. Renewable sources of energy are an essential part of an overall strategy of sustainable development. They help reduce dependence of energy imports, thereby ensuring a sustainable supply. Furthermore renewable energy sources can help improve the competitiveness of industries over the long run and have a positive impact on regional development and employment. Renewable energy technologies are suitable for off-grid services, serving those in remote areas of the world without requiring expensive and complicated grid infrastructure. Eventually renewable energies will dominate the world's energy supply system.

Table 3 lists the most important of energy needs.

Considerations when selecting power plant include the following:

- Power level- whether continuous or discontinuous.
- Cost- initial cost, total running cost including fuel, maintenance and capital amortised over life.
- Complexity of operation.
- Maintenance and availability of spares.
- Life.
- Suitability for local manufacture.

Table 4. Methods of energy conversion

Muscle power	Man, and animals
Internal combustion engines	
Reciprocating	Petrol- spark ignition Diesel- compression ignition Humphrey water piston
Rotating	Gas turbines
Heat engines	
Vapour (Rankine)	
Reciprocating	Steam engine
Rotating	Steam turbine
Gas Stirling (Reciprocating)	Steam engine
Gas Brayton (Rotating)	Steam turbine
Electron gas	Thermionic, thermoelectric
Electromagnetic radiation	Photo devices
Hydraulic engines	Wheels, screws, buckets, turbines
Wind engines (wind machines)	Vertical axis, horizontal axis
Electrical/mechanical	Dynamo/alternator, motor

Table 4 listed methods of energy conversion.

There is no real alternative. Mankind cannot indefinitely continue to base its life on the consumption of finite energy resources. Today, the world's energy supply is largely based on fossil fuels and nuclear power. These sources of energy will not last forever and have proven to be contributors to our environmental problems. The environmental impacts of energy use are not new but they are increasingly well known; they range from deforestation to local and global pollution. The predicted effects of global warming for the environment and for human life are numerous and varied.

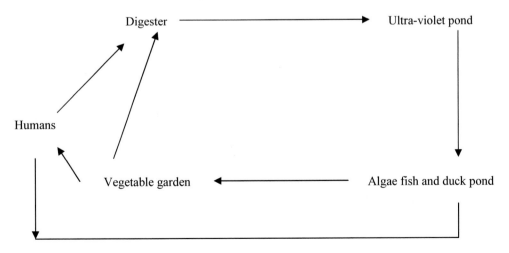

Figure 2. Biomass energy utilisation cycle.

The human wastes (four people) would provide about 280 kWh/a of methane, but with the addition of vegetable wastes from 0.2 ha or wastes from 1 ha growing a complete diet, about 1500 kWh/a may be obtained by anaerobic digestion. The sludge from the digester may be returned to the land. In hotter climates, this efficient could be used to set up a more productive cycle (Figure 2). There is a need for greater attention to be devoted to this field in the development of new designs, the dissemination of information and the encouragement of its use. International and government bodies and independent organisations all have a role to play in renewable energy technologies.

Society and industry in Europe and elsewhere are increasingly dependent on the availability of electricity supply and on the efficient operation of electricity systems. In the European Union (EU), the average rate of growth of electricity demand has been about 1.8% per year since 1990 and is projected to be at least 1.5% yearly up to 2030. Currently, distribution networks generally differ greatly from transmission networks, mainly in terms of role, structure (radial against meshed) and consequent planning and operation philosophies. The use of a heat engine or a power station to simultaneously generate both electricity and useful heat is known as combined heat and power (CHP), or cogeneration. Generally, a conventional power plant emits the heat created as a by-product of electricity generation into the environment through cooling towers, as flue gas, or by other means. The CHP or a bottoming cycle captures the by-product heat for domestic or industrial heating purposes, either very close to the plant, or for distribution through pipes to heat local housing. In Europe, the use of the CHP presents a substantial potential for increased energy efficiency and reduced environmental impacts. The efficient use of fuel, in simultaneous production of heat and power, can offer energy savings and avoid CO_2 emissions compared with separate production of heat and power. In addition, development in the use of fuels used in the CHP applications show a trend toward cleaner fuels. Nearly 40% of the electricity produced from cogeneration is produced for public supply purposes, often in connection with district heating (DH) networks.

3. ENERGY USE

Energy use is one of several essential components for developing countries:

- The overall situation and the implications of increased energy use in the future.
- The problem of the provision of power in rural areas, including the consideration of energy resources and energy conversion.

In addition to the drain on resources, such an increase in consumption consequences, together with the increased hazards of pollution and the safety problems associated with a large nuclear fission programmes. This is a disturbing prospect. It would be equally unacceptable to suggest that the difference in energy between the developed and developing countries and prudent for the developed countries to move towards a way of life which, whilst maintaining or even increasing quality of life, reduce significantly the energy consumption per capita. Such savings can be achieved in a number of ways:

- Improved efficiency of energy use, for example better thermal insulation, energy recovery and total energy.
- Conservation of energy resources by design for long life and recycling rather than the short life throwaway product.
- Systematic replanning of our way of life, for example in the field of transport.

Energy ratio is defined as the ratio of:

$$\text{Energy content of the food product/Energy input to produce the food} \qquad (1)$$

A review of the potential range of recyclables is presented in Table 5. Almost 60% of the electricity produced from cogeneration is generated by auto producers, normally for industrial processes. Currently the non-commercial fuels wood, crop residues and animal dung are used in large amounts in the rural areas of developing countries, principally for heating and cooking, the method of use is highly inefficient. As in the developed countries, the fossil fuels are currently of great importance in the developing countries. Geothermal and tidal energy are less important though, of course, will have local significance where conditions are suitable. Nuclear energy sources are included for completeness, but are not likely to make any effective contribution in the rural areas.

Table 5. Summary of material recycling practices in the construction sector [1]

Construction and demolition material	Recycling technology options	Recycling product
Asphalt	Cold recycling: heat generation; Minnesota process; parallel drum process; elongated drum; microwave asphalt recycling system; finfalt; surface regeneration	Recycling asphalt; asphalt aggregate
Brick	Burn to ash, crush into aggregate	Slime burn ash; filling material; hardcore
Concrete	Crush into aggregate	Recycling aggregate; cement replacement; protection of levee; backfilling; filter
Ferrous metal	Melt; reuse directly	Recycled steel scrap
Glass	Reuse directly; grind to powder; polishing; crush into aggregate; burn to ash	Recycled window unit; glass fibre; filling material; tile; paving block; asphalt; recycled aggregate; cement replacement; manmade soil
Masonry	Crush into aggregate; heat to 900°C to ash	Thermal insulating concrete; traditional clay
Non-ferrous metal	Melt	Recycled metal
Paper and cardboard	Purification	Recycled paper
Plastic	Convert to powder by cryogenic milling; clopping; crush into aggregate; burn to ash	Panel; recycled plastic; plastic lumber; recycled aggregate; landfill drainage; asphalt; manmade soil
Timber	Reuse directly; cut into aggregate; blast furnace deoxidisation; gasification or pyrolysis; chipping; moulding by pressurising timber chip under steam and water	Whole timber; furniture and kitchen utensils; lightweight recycled aggregate; source of energy; chemical production; wood-based panel; plastic lumber; geofibre; insulation board

4. BIOGAS

Biogas is a generic term for gases generated from the decomposition of organic material. As the material breaks down, methane (CH_4) is produced as shown in Figure 3. Sources that generate biogas are numerous and varied. These include landfill sites, wastewater treatment plants and anaerobic digesters. Landfills and wastewater treatment plants emit biogas from decaying waste. To date, the waste industry has focused on controlling these emissions to our environment and in some cases, tapping this potential source of fuel to power gas turbines, thus generating electricity. The primary components of landfill gas are methane (CH_4), carbon dioxide (CO_2), and nitrogen (N_2). The average concentration of methane is ~45%, CO_2 is ~36% and nitrogen is ~18% [2]. Other components in the gas are oxygen (O_2), water vapour and trace amounts of a wide range of non-methane organic compounds (NMOCs). Landfill gas-to-cogeneration projects present a win-win-win situation. Emissions of particularly damaging pollutant are avoided, electricity is generated from a free fuel and heat is available for use locally.

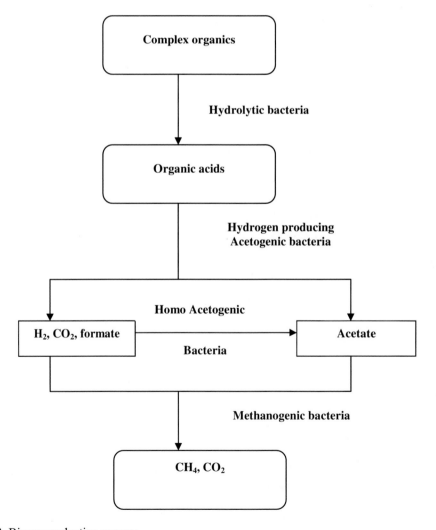

Figure 3. Biogas production process.

5. WAVE POWER CONVERSION DEVICES

The patent literature is full of devices for extracting energy from waves, i.e., floats, ramps and flaps, covering channels. Small generators driven from air trapped by the rising and falling water in the chamber of a buoy are in use around the world [3]. Wave power is one possibility that has been selected. Figure 4 shows the many other aspects that will need to be covered. A wave power programme would make a significant contribution to energy resources within a relatively short time and with existing technology.

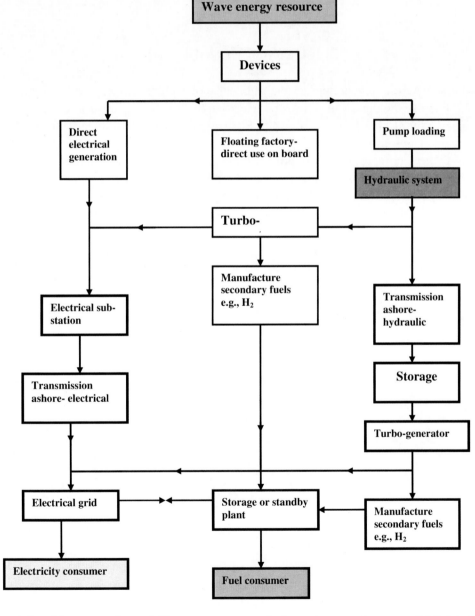

Figure 4. Possible systems for exploiting wave power, each element represents an essential link in the chain from sea waves to consumer.

Wave energy has also been in the news recently. There is about 140 megawatts per mile available round British coasts. It could make a useful contribution people needs, about twice that of the UK generating system is available provided. Although very large amounts of power are available in the waves, it is important to consider how much power can be extracted. A few years ago only a few percent efficiency had been achieved. Recently, however, several devices have been studied which have very high efficiencies. Some form of storage will be essential on a second-to-second and minute-to-minute basis to smooth the fluctuations of individual waves and wave's packets but storage from one day to the next will certainly not be economic. This is why provision must be made for adequate standby capacity.

6. ETHANOL PRODUCTION

Alternative fuels were defined as methanol, ethanol, natural gas, propane, hydrogen, coal-derived liquids, biological material and electricity. The fuel pathways currently under development for alcohol fuels are shown in Figure 5. The production of agricultural biomass and its exploitation for energy purposes can contribute to alleviate several problems, such as the dependence on import of energy products, the production of food surpluses, the pollution provoked by the use of fossil fuels, the abandonment of land by farmers and the connected urbanisation. Biomass is not at the moment competitive with mineral oil, but, taking into account also indirect costs and giving a value to the aforementioned advantages, public authorities at national and international level can spur its production and use by incentives of different nature. In order to address the problem of inefficiency, research centres around the world have investigated the viability of converting the resource to a more useful form, namely solid briquettes and fuel gas (Figure 6).

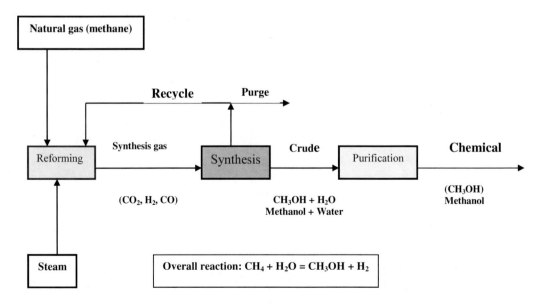

Figure 5. Schematic process flowsheet.

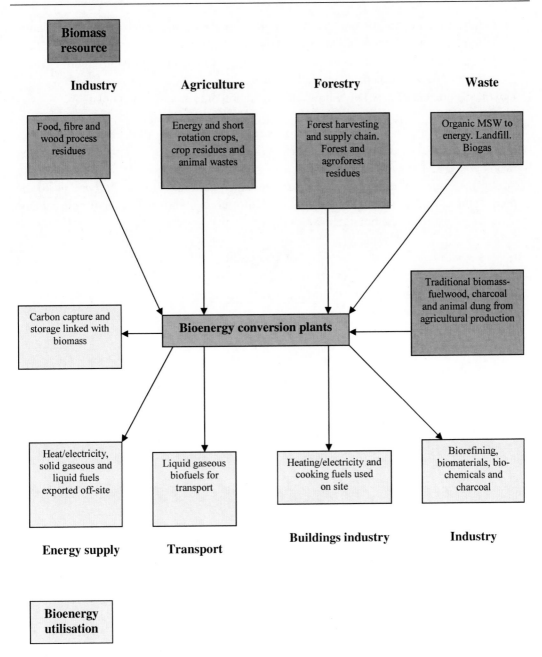

Figure 6. Biomass resources from several sources are converted into a range of products for use by transport, industry and building sectors [4].

The main advantages are related to energy, agriculture and environment problems, are foreseeable both at regional level and at worldwide level and can be summarised as follows:

- Reduction of dependence on import of energy and related products.
- Reduction of environmental impact of energy production (greenhouse effect, air pollution and waste degradation).

- Substitution of food crops and reduction of food surpluses and of related economic burdens and utilisation of marginal lands and of set aside lands.
- Reduction of related socio-economic and environmental problems (soil erosion, urbanisation, landscape deterioration, etc.).
- Development of new know-how and production of technological innovation.

Biomass resources play a significant role in energy supply in all developing countries. Biomass resources should be divided into residues or dedicated resources, the latter including firewood and charcoal can also be produced from forest residues. Ozone (O_3) is a naturally occurring molecule that consists of three oxygen atoms held together by the bonding of the oxygen atoms to each other. The effects of the chlorofluorocarbons (CFCs) molecule can last for over a century. This reaction is shown in Figure 7.

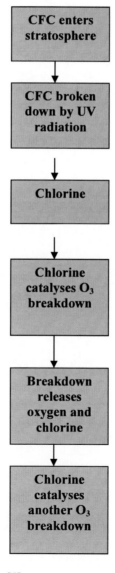

Figure 7. The process of ozone depletion [5].

It is a common misconception that the reason for recycling old fridge is to recover the liquid from the cooling circuit at the back of the unit. The insulating foams used inside some fridges act as sinks of the CFCs- the gases having been used as blowing agents to expand the foam during fridge manufacture. Although the use of ozone depleting chemicals in the foam in fridges has declined in the West, recyclers must consider which strategy to adopt to deal with the disposal problem they still present each year. It is common practice to dispose of this waste wood in landfill where it slowly degraded and takes up valuable void space. This wood is a good source of energy and is an alternative to energy crops. Agricultural wastes are abundantly available globally and can be converted to energy and useful chemicals by a number of microorganisms. The success of promoting any technology depends on careful planning, management, implementation, training and monitoring. Main features of gasification project are:

- Networking and institutional development/strengthening.
- Promotion and extension.
- Construction of demonstration projects.
- Research and development; and training and monitoring.

7. BIOMASS CHP

Combined heat and power (CHP) installations are quite common in greenhouses, which grow high-energy, input crops (e.g., salad vegetables, pot plants, etc.). Scientific assumptions for a short-term energy strategy suggest that the most economically efficient way to replace the thermal plants is to modernise existing power plants to increase their energy efficiency and to improve their environmental performance. However, utilisation of wind power and the conversion of gas-fired CHP plants to biomass would significantly reduce the dependence on imported fossil fuels. Although a lack of generating capacity is forecast in the long-term, utilisation of the existing renewable energy potential and the huge possibilities for increasing energy efficiency are sufficient to meet future energy demands in the short-term.

A total shift towards a sustainable energy system is a complex and long process, but is one that can be achieved within a period of about 20 years. Implementation will require initial investment, long-term national strategies and action plans. However, the changes will have a number of benefits including a more stable energy supply than at present and major improvement in the environmental performance of the energy sector and certain social benefits. A vision used a methodology and calculations based on computer modelling that utilised:

- Data from existing governmental programmes.
- Potential renewable energy sources and energy efficiency improvements.
- Assumptions for future economy growth.
- Information from studies and surveys on the recent situation in the energy sector.

In addition to realising the economic potential identified by the National Energy Savings Programme, a long-term effort leading to a 3% reduction in specific electricity demand per year after 2020 is proposed. This will require further improvements in building codes and continued information on energy efficiency.

The environmental Non Governmental Organisations (NGOs) are urging the government to adopt sustainable development of the energy sector by:

- Diversifying of primary energy sources to increase the contribution of renewable and local energy resources in the total energy balance.
- Implementing measures for energy efficiency increase at the demand side and in the energy transformation sector.

The price of natural gas is set by a number of market and regulatory factors that include:

Supply and demand balance and market fundamentals, weather, pipeline availability and deliverability, storage inventory, new supply sources, prices of other energy alternatives and regulatory issues and uncertainty.

Classic management approaches to risk are well documented and used in many industries. These include the following four broad approaches to risk:

- Avoidance includes not performing an activity that could carry risk. Avoidance may seem the answer to all risks, but avoiding risks also means losing out on potential gain.
- Mitigation/reduction involves methods that reduce the severity of potential loss.
- Retention/acceptance involves accepting the loss when it occurs. Risk retention is a viable strategy for small risks. All risks that are not avoided or transferred are retained by default.
- Transfer means causing another party to accept the risk, typically by contract.

Methane is a primary constituent of landfill gas (LFG) and a potent greenhouse gas (GHG) when released into the atmosphere. Globally, landfills are the third largest anthropogenic emission source, accounting for about 13% of methane emissions or over 818 million tonnes of carbon dioxide equivalent (MMTCO$_2$e) [7] as shown in Figures 8-10.

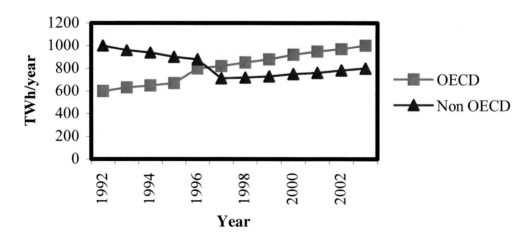

Figure 8. Global CHP trends from 1992-2003 [6].

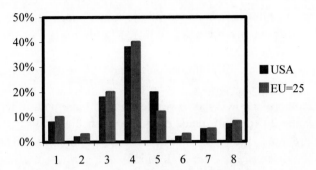

1 Food, 2 Textile, 3 Pulp & paper, 4 Chemicals, 5 Refining, 6 Minerals, 7 Primary metals, and 8 others

Figure 9. Distribution of industrial CHP capacity in the EU and USA [6].

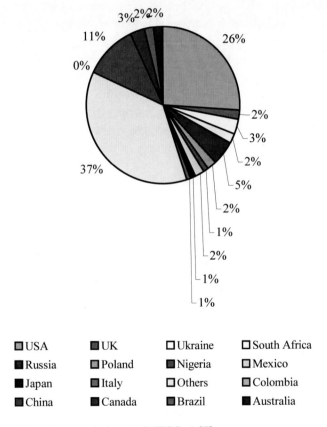

Figure 10. World landfill methane emissions ($MMTCO_2e$) [7].

8. GEOTHERMAL ENERGY

Geothermal steam has been used in volcanic regions in many countries to generate electricity. The use of geothermal energy involves the extraction of heat from rocks in the outer part of the earth. It is relatively unusual for the rocks to be sufficiently hot at shallow depth for this to be economically attractive. Virtually all the areas of present geothermal interest are concentrated along the margins of the major tectonic plates, which form the surface of the earth. Heat is conventionally extracted by the forced or natural circulation of water through permeable hot rock.

There are various practical difficulties and disadvantages associated with the use of geothermal power:

Transmission: geothermal power has to be used where it is found. In Iceland it has proved feasible to pipe hot water 20 km in insulated pipes but much shorter distances are preferred.

Environmental problems: these are somewhat variable and are usually not great. Perhaps the most serious is the disposal of warm high salinity water where it cannot be reinjected or purified. Dry steam plants tend to be very noisy and there is releases of small amounts of methane, hydrogen, nitrogen, amonia and hydrogen sulphide and of these the latter presents the main problem.

The geothermal fluid is often highly chemically corrosive or physically abrasive as the result of the entrained solid matter it carries. This may entail special plant design problems and unusually short operational lives for both the holes and the installations they serve.

Because the useful rate of heat extraction from a geothermal field is in nearly all cases much higher than the rate of conduction into the field from the underlying rocks, the mean temperatures of the field is likely to fall during exploitation. In some low rainfall areas there may also be a problem of fluid depletion. Ideally, as much as possible of the geothermal fluid should be reinjected into the field. However, this may involve the heavy capital costs of large condensation installations. Occasionally, the salinity of the fluid available for reinjection may be so high (as a result of concentration by boiling) that is unsuitable for reinjection into ground. Ocasionally, the impurities can be precipitated and used but this has not generally proved commercially attractive.

World capacity of geothermal energy is growing at a rate of 2.5% per year from a 2005 level of 28.3 GW [8]. The GSHPs account for approximately 54% of this capacity almost all of it in the North America and Europe [8]. The involvement of the UK is minimal with less than 0.04% of world capacity and yet is committed to substantial reduction in carbon emission beyond the 12.5% Kyoto obligation to be achieved by 2012. The GSHPs offer a significant potential for carbon reduction and it is therefore expected that the market for these systems will rise sharply in the UK in the immediate years ahead given to low capacity base at present.

There are numerous ways of harnessing low-grade heat from the ground for use as a heat pump source or air conditioning sink. For small applications (residences and small commercial buildings) horizontal ground loop heat exchangers buried typically at between 1 m and 1.8 m below the surface can be used provided that a significant availability of land surrounding the building can be exploited which tends to limit these applications to rural settings.

Heat generation within the earth is approximately 2700 GW, roughly an order of magnitude greater than the energy associated with the tides but about four orders less than that received by the earth from the sun [9].

Temperature distributions within the earth depend on:

- The abundance and distribution of heat producing elements within the earth.
- The mean surface temperature (which is controlled by the ocean/atmosphere system).

- The thermal properties of the earth's interior and their lateral and radial variation.
- Any movements of fluid or solid rock materials occurring at rates of more than a few millimetres per year.

Of these four factors the first two are of less importance from the point of view of geothermal energy. Mean surface temperatures range between 0-30°C and this variation has a small effect on the useable enthalpy of any flows of hot water. Although radiogenic heat production in rocks may vary by three orders of magnitude, there is much less variation from place to place in the integrated heat production with depth. The latter factors, however, are of great importance and show a wide range of variation. Their importance is clear from the relationship:

$$\beta = q/k \tag{2}$$

Where: β is the thermal gradient for a steady state (°C/km), q is the heat flux (10^{-6} cal cm^{-2} sec^{-1}) and k is the thermal conductivity (cal cm^{-1} sec^{-1} °C^{-1}).

The first requirement of any potential geothermal source region is that β being large, i.e., that high rock temperatures occur at shallow depth. Beta will be large if either q is large or k is small or both. By comparison with most everyday materials, rocks are poor conductors of heat and values of conductivity may vary from 2×10^{-3} to 10^{-2} cal cm^{-1} sec^{-1} °C^{-1}. The mean surface heat flux from the earth is about 1.5 heat flow units (1 HFU = 10^{-6} cal cm^{-2} sec^{-1}) [9]. Rocks are also very slow respond to any temperature change to which they are exposed, i.e., they have a low thermal diffusivity:

$$K = k/\rho C_p \tag{3}$$

Where: K is thermal diffusivity; ρ and C_p are density and specific heat respectively.

These values are simple intended to give a general idea of the normal range of geothermal parameters (Table 6). In volcanic regions, in particular, both q and β can vary considerably and the upper values given are somewhat nominal. It is important to determine the depth of soil cover, the type of soil or rock and the ground temperature. The depth of soil cover may determine the possible configuration of the ground coil. If bedrock is within 1.5 m of the surface or there are large boulders, it may not possible to install a horizontal ground loop. For a vertical borehole the depth of soil will influence the costs, in general, it is more expensive and time consuming to drill through overburden than rock as the borehole has to be cased. The future plan is to predict system operational performance at each observation point, based on the relationship between estimated soil thermal property and measured soil thermal conductivity.

Table 6. Values of geothermal parameters

Parameter	Lower	Average	Upper
q (HFU)	0.8	1.5	3.0 (non volcanic) ≈100 (volcanic)
k =cal cm^{-2} sec^{-1} °C^{-1}	2×10^{-3}	6×10^{-3}	12×10^{-3}
β =°C/km	8	20	60 (non volcanic) ≈300 (volcanic)

Table 7. Types of the LFG implemented recently worldwide

Landfill caps	Electricity generation	Fuel production
❑ Soil caps	❑ Reciprocating	❑ Medium BTU gas
❑ Clay caps	engines	❑ High BTU gas
❑ Geo-membrane caps	❑ Combustion turbines	❑ Liquefied methane
	❑ Micro-turbines	
LFG destruction	❑ Steam turbines	Thermal generation
❑ Flares	❑ Fuel cells	❑ Boilers
- Candlestick		❑ Kilns
- Enclosed	CHP	❑ Greenhouse heaters
	❑ Turbines	❑ Leachate evaporators
	❑ Engines	

9. LANDFILL GAS

Landfill gas (LFG) is currently extracted at over 1200 landfills worldwide for a variety of energy purposes (Table 7), such as:

- Creating pipeline quality gas or an alternative fuel for vehicles.
- Processing the LFG to make it available as an alternative fuel to local industrial or commercial customers.
- Generation of electricity with engines, turbines, micro-turbines and other emerging technologies.

In terms of solid waste management policy, many NGOs have changed drastically in the past ten years from a mass production and mass consumption society to 'material-cycle society'. In addition to national legislation, municipalities are legally obliged to develop a plan for handling the municipal solid waste (MSW) generated in administrative areas. Such plans contain:

- Estimates of future waste volume.
- Measures to reduce waste and measures to encourage source separation.
- A framework for solid waste disposal and the construction and management of solid waste management facilities.

Landfilling is in the least referred tier of the hierarchy of waste management options: Waste minimisation, reuse and recycling, incineration with energy recovery and optimised final disposal. The key elements are as follows: construction impacts, atmospheric emissions, noise, water quality, landscape, visual impacts, socio economics, ecological impacts, traffic, solid waste disposal and cultural heritage.

10. ENERGY EFFICIENCY

Energy efficiency is the most cost-effective way of cutting carbon dioxide emissions and improvements to households and businesses. It can also have many other additional social, economic and health benefits, such as warmer and healthier homes, lower fuel bills and company running costs and, indirectly, jobs. Britain wastes 20 per cent of its fossil fuel and electricity use. This implies that it would be cost-effective to cut £10 billion a year off the collective fuel bill and reduce CO_2 emissions by some 120 million tones. Yet, due to lack of good information and advice on energy saving, along with the capital to finance energy efficiency improvements, this huge potential for reducing energy demand is not being realised. Traditionally, energy utilities have been essentially fuel providers and the industry has pursued profits from increased volume of sales. Institutional and market arrangements have favoured energy consumption rather than conservation. However, energy is at the centre of the sustainable development paradigm as few activities affect the environment as much as the continually increasing use of energy. Most of the used energy depends on finite resources, such as coal, oil, gas and uranium. In addition, more than three quarters of the world's consumption of these fuels is used, often inefficiently, by only one quarter of the world's population. Without even addressing these inequities or the precious, finite nature of these resources, the scale of environmental damage will force the reduction of the usage of these fuels long before they run out.

Throughout the energy generation process there are impacts on the environment on local, national and international levels, from opencast mining and oil exploration to emissions of the potent greenhouse gas carbon dioxide in ever increasing concentration. Recently, the world's leading climate scientists reached an agreement that human activities, such as burning fossil fuels for energy and transport, are causing the world's temperature to rise. The Intergovernmental Panel on Climate Change has concluded that "the balance of evidence suggests a discernible human influence on global climate". It predicts a rate of warming greater than any one seen in the last 10,000 years, in other words, throughout human history. The exact impact of climate change is difficult to predict and will vary regionally. It could, however, include sea level rise, disrupted agriculture and food supplies and the possibility of more freak weather events such as hurricanes and droughts. Indeed, people already are waking up to the financial and social, as well as the environmental, risks of unsustainable energy generation methods that represent the costs of the impacts of climate change, acid rain and oil spills. The insurance industry, for example, concerned about the billion dollar costs of hurricanes and floods, has joined sides with environmentalists to lobby for greenhouse gas emissions reduction. Friends of the earth are campaigning for a more sustainable energy policy, guided by the principal of environmental protection and with the objectives of sound natural resource management and long-term energy security. The key priorities of such an energy policy must be to reduce fossil fuel use, move away from nuclear power, improve the efficiency with which energy is used and increase the amount of energy obtainable from sustainable, and renewable sources. Efficient energy use has never been more crucial than it is today, particularly with the prospect of the imminent introduction of the climate change levy (CCL). Establishing an energy use action plan is the essential foundation to the elimination of energy waste. A logical starting point is to carry out an energy audit that enables the assessment of the energy use and determine what actions to take. The actions are best categorised by splitting measures into the following three general groups:

1) High Priority/Low Cost

These are normally measures, which require minimal investment and can be implemented quickly. The followings are some examples of such measures:

- Good housekeeping, monitoring energy use and targeting waste-fuel practices.
- Adjusting controls to match requirements.
- Improved greenhouse space utilisation.
- Small capital item time switches, thermostats, etc.
- Carrying out minor maintenance and repairs.
- Staff education and training.
- Ensuring that energy is being purchased through the most suitable tariff or contract arrangements.

2) Medium Priority/Medium Cost

Measures, which, although involve little or no design, involve greater expenditure and can take longer to implement. Examples of such measures are listed below:

- New or replacement controls.
- Greenhouse component alteration, e.g., insulation, sealing glass joints, etc.
- Alternative equipment components, e.g., energy efficient lamps in light fittings, etc.

3) Long Term/High Cost

These measures require detailed study and design. They can be best represented by the followings:

- Replacing or upgrading of plant and equipment.
- Fundamental redesign of systems, e.g., CHP installations.

This process can often be a complex experience and therefore the most cost-effective approach is to employ an energy specialist to help.

11. POLICY RECOMMENDATIONS FOR A SUSTAINABLE ENERGY FUTURE

Sustainability is regarded as a major consideration for both urban and rural development. People have been exploiting the natural resources with no consideration to the effects, both short-term (environmental) and long-term (resources crunch). It is also felt that knowledge and technology have not been used effectively in utilising energy resources. Energy is the vital input for economic and social development of any country. Its sustainability is an important factor to be considered. The urban areas depend, to a large extent, on commercial energy sources. The rural areas use non-commercial sources like firewood and agricultural wastes. With the present day trends for improving the quality of life and sustenance of mankind, environmental issues are considered highly important. In this context, the term energy loss has no significant technical meaning. Instead, the exergy loss has to be considered, as destruction of exergy is possible. Hence, exergy loss minimisation will help in sustainability.

The development of a renewable energy in a country depends on many factors. Those important to success are listed below:

1) *Motivation of the Population*

The population should be motivated towards awareness of high environmental issues, rational use of energy in order to reduce cost. Subsidy programme should be implemented as incentives to install biomass energy plants. In addition, image campaigns to raise awareness of renewable technology.

2) *Technical Product Development*

To achieve technical development of biomass energy technologies the following should be addressed:

- Increasing the longevity and reliability of renewable energy technology.
- Adapting renewable energy technology to household technology (hot water supply).
- Integration of renewable energy technology in heating technology.
- Integration of renewable energy technology in architecture, e.g., in the roof or façade.
- Development of new applications, e.g., solar cooling.
- Cost reduction.

3) *Distribution and Sales*

Commercialisation of biomass energy technology requires:

- Inclusion of renewable technology in the product range of heating trades at all levels of the distribution process (wholesale and retail).
- Building distribution nets for renewable energy technology.
- Training of personnel in distribution and sales.
- Training of field sales force.

4) *Consumer Consultation and Installation*

To encourage all sectors of the population to participate in adoption of biomass energy technologies, the following has to be realised:

- Acceptance by craftspeople, and marketing by them.
- Technical training of craftspeople, initial and follow-up training programmes.
- Sales training for craftspeople.
- Information material to be made available to craftspeople for consumer consultation.

5) *Projecting and Planning*

Successful application of biomass technologies also require:

- Acceptance by decision makers in the building sector (architects, house technology planners, etc.).
- Integration of renewable technology in training.

- Demonstration projects/architecture competitions.
- Biomass energy project developers should prepare to participate in the carbon market by:
    - Ensuring that renewable energy projects comply with Kyoto Protocol requirements.
    - Quantifying the expected avoided emissions.
    - Registering the project with the required offices.
    - Contractually allocating the right to this revenue stream.

- Other ecological measures employed on the development include:

    - Simplified building details.
    - Reduced number of materials.
    - Materials that can be recycled or reused.
    - Materials easily maintained and repaired.
    - Materials that do not have a bad influence on the indoor climate (i.e., non-toxic).
    - Local cleaning of grey water.
    - Collecting and use of rainwater for outdoor purposes and park elements.
    - Building volumes designed to give maximum access to neighbouring park areas.
    - All apartments have visual access to both backyard and park.

6) Energy Saving Measures
The following energy saving measures should also be considered:

- Building integrated solar PV system.
- Day-lighting.
- Ecological insulation materials.
- Natural/hybrid ventilation.
- Passive cooling.
- Passive solar heating.
- Solar heating of domestic hot water.
- Utilisation of rainwater for flushing.

Improving access for rural and urban low-income areas in developing countries must be through energy efficiency and renewable energies. Sustainable energy is a prerequisite for development. Energy-based living standards in developing countries, however, are clearly below standards in developed countries. Low levels of access to affordable and environmentally sound energy in both rural and urban low-income areas are therefore a predominant issue in developing countries. In recent years many programmes for development aid or technical assistance have been focusing on improving access to sustainable energy, many of them with impressive results.

Apart from success stories, however, experience also shows that positive appraisals of many projects evaporate after completion and vanishing of the implementation expert team. Altogether, the diffusion of sustainable technologies such as energy efficiency and renewable energies for cooking, heating, lighting, electrical appliances and building insulation in developing countries has been slow.

Energy efficiency and renewable energy programmes could be more sustainable and pilot studies more effective and pulse releasing if the entire policy and implementation process was considered and redesigned from the outset. New financing and implementation processes are needed which allow reallocating financial resources and thus enabling countries themselves to achieve a sustainable energy infrastructure. The links between the energy policy framework, financing and implementation of renewable energy and energy efficiency projects have to be strengthened and capacity building efforts are required.

12. ENVIRONMENTAL ASPECTS OF ENERGY CONVERSION AND USE

Environment has no precise limits because it is in fact a part of everything. Indeed, environment is, as anyone probably already knows, not only flowers blossoming or birds singing in the spring, or a lake surrounded by beautiful mountains. It is also human settlements, the places where people live, work, rest, the quality of the food they eat, the noise or silence of the street they live in. Environment is not only the fact that our cars consume a good deal of energy and pollute the air, but also, that we often need them to go to work and for holidays.

Table 8. Annual greenhouse emissions from different sources of power plants

Primary source of energy	Emissions (x 10^3 metric tonnes)		Waste (x 10^3 metric tonnes)	Area (km^2)
	Atmosphere	Water		
Coal	380	7-41	60-3000	120
Oil	70-160	3-6	negligible	70-84
Gas	24	1	-	84
Nuclear	6	21	2600	77

Table 9. Energy consumption in different continents

Region	Population (millions)	Energy (Watt/m^2)
Africa	820	0.54
Asia	3780	2.74
Central America	180	1.44
North America	335	0.34
South America	475	0.52
Western Europe	445	2.24
Eastern Europe	130	2.57
Oceania	35	0.08
Russia	330	0.29

Obviously man uses energy just as plants, bacteria, mushrooms, bees, fish and rats do. Man largely uses solar energy- food, hydropower, wood- and thus participates harmoniously in the natural flow of energy through the environment. But man also uses oil, gas, coal and nuclear power. By using such sources of energy, man is thus modifying his environment.

The atmospheric emissions of fossil fuelled installations are mosty aldehydes, carbon monoxide, nitrogen oxides, sulpher oxides and particles (i.e., ash) as well as carbon dioxide. Table 8 shows estimates include not only the releases occuring at the power plant itself but also cover fuel extraction and treatment, as well as the storage of wastes and the area of land required for operations. Table 9 shows energy consumption in different regions of the world.

13. GREENHOUSES ENVIRONMENT

Greenhouse cultivation is one of the most absorbing and rewarding forms of gardening for anyone who enjoys growing plants. The enthusiastic gardener can adapt the greenhouse climate to suit a particular group of plants, or raise flowers, fruit and vegetables out of their natural season. The greenhouse can also be used as an essential garden tool, enabling the keen amateur to expand the scope of plants grown in the garden, as well as save money by raising their own plants and vegetables. There was a decline in large private greenhouses during the two world wars due to a shortage of materials for their construction and fuel to heat them. However, in the 1950s mass-produced, small greenhouses became widely available at affordable prices and were used mainly for raising plants [10]. Also, in recent years, the popularity of conservatories attached to the house has soared. Modern double-glazing panels can provide as much insulation as a brick wall to create a comfortable living space, as well as provide an ideal environment in which to grow and display tender plants.

The comfort in a greenhouse depends on many environmental parameters. These include temperature, relative humidity, air quality and lighting. Although greenhouse and conservatory originally both meant a place to house or conserve greens (variegated hollies, cirrus, myrtles and oleanders), a greenhouse today implies a place in which plants are raised while conservatory usually describes a glazed room where plants may or may not play a significant role. Indeed, a greenhouse can be used for so many different purposes. It is, therefore, difficult to decide how to group the information about the plants that can be grown inside it.

Throughout the world urban areas have increased in size during recent decades. About 50% of the world's population and approximately 76% in the more developed countries are urban dwellers [11]. Even though there is an evidence to suggest that in many 'advanced' industrialised countries there has been a reversal in the rural-to-urban shift of populations, virtually all population growth expected between 2000 and 2030 will be concentrated in urban areas of the world. With an expected annual growth of 1.8%, the world's urban population will double in 38 years [11]. This represents a serious contributing to the potential problem of maintaining the required food supply. Inappropriate land use and management, often driven by intensification resulting from high population pressure and market forces, is also a threat to food availability for domestic, livestock and wildlife use. Conversion to cropland and urban-industrial establishments is threatening their integrity. Improved productivity of peri-urban agriculture can, therefore, make a very large contribution to meeting food security needs of cities as well as providing income to the peri-urban farmers. Hence, greenhouses agriculture can become an engine of pro-poor 'trickle-up' growth because of the synergistic effects of agricultural growth such as [11]:

- Increased productivity increases wealth.
- Intensification by small farmers raises the demand for wage labour more than by larger farmers.
- Intensification drives rural non-farm enterprise and employment.
- Alleviation of rural and peri-urban poverty is likely to have a knock-on decrease of urban poverty.

Despite arguments for continued large-scale collective schemes there is now an increasingly compelling argument in favour of individual technologies for the development of controlled greenhouses. The main points constituting this argument are summarised by [11] as follows:

- Individual technologies enable the poorest of the poor to engage in intensified agricultural production and to reduce their vulnerability.
- Development is encouraged where it is needed most and reaches many more poor households more quickly and at a lower cost.
- Farmer-controlled greenhouses enable farmers to avoid the difficulties of joint management.

Such development brings the following challenges [11]:

- The need to provide farmers with ready access to these individual technologies, repair services and technical assistance.
- Access to markets with worthwhile commodity prices, so that sufficient profitability is realised.
- This type of technology could be a solution to food security problems. For example, in greenhouses, advances in biotechnology like the genetic engineering, tissue culture and market-aided selection have the potential to be applied for raising yields, reducing pesticide excesses and increasing the nutrient value of basic foods.

However, the overall goal is to improve the cities in accordance with the Brundtland Report [12] and the investigation into how urban green could be protected. Indeed, greenhouses can improve the urban environment in multitude of ways. They shape the character of the town and its neighbourhoods, provide places for outdoor recreation, and have important environmental functions such as mitigating the heat island effect, reduce surface water runoff and creating habitats for wildlife. Following analysis of social, cultural and ecological values of urban green, six criteria in order to evaluate the role of green urban in towns and cities were prescribed [12]. These are as follows:

- Recreation, everyday life and public health.
- Maintenance of biodiversity - preserving diversity within species, between species, ecosystems, and of landscape types in the surrounding countryside.
- City structure - as an important element of urban structure and urban life.
- Cultural identity - enhancing awareness of the history of the city and its cultural traditions.
- Environmental quality of the urban sites - improvement of the local climate, air quality and noise reduction.
- Biological solutions to technical problems in urban areas - establishing close links between technical infrastructure and green-spaces of a city.

The main reasons why it is vital for greenhouses planners and designers to develop a better understanding of greenhouses in high-density housing can be summarised as follows [12]:

- Pressures to return to a higher density form of housing.
- The requirement to provide more sustainable food.
- The urgent need to regenerate the existing and often decaying, houses built in the higher density, high-rise form, much of which is now suffering from technical problems.

The connection between technical change, economic policies and the environment is of primary importance as observed by most governments in developing countries, whose attempts to attain food self-sufficiency have led them to take the measures that provide incentives for adoption of the Green Revolution Technology [13].

Since, the Green Revolution Technologies were introduced in many countries actively supported by irrigation development, subsidised credit, fertiliser programmes, self-sufficiency was found to be not economically efficient and often adopted for political reasons creating excessive damage to natural resources. Also, many developing countries governments provided direct assistance to farmers to adopt soil conservation measures. They found that high costs of establishment and maintenance and the loss of land to hedgerows are the major constraints to adoption [13]. The soil erosion problem in developing countries reveals that a dynamic view of the problem is necessary to ensure that the important elements of the problem are understood for any remedial measures to be undertaken. The policy environment has, in the past, encouraged unsustainable use of land [13].

In many regions, government policies such as provision of credit facilities, subsidies, price support for certain crops, subsidies for erosion control and tariff protection, have exacerbated the erosion problem. This is because technological approaches to control soil erosion have often been promoted to the exclusion of other effective approaches. However, adoption of conservation measures and the return to conservation depend on the specific agro-ecological conditions, the technologies used and the prices of inputs and outputs of production.

13.1. Types of Greenhouses

Choosing a greenhouse and setting it up are important and often expensive, steps to take. Greenhouses are either freestanding or lean-to, that is, built against an existing wall. A freestanding greenhouse can be placed in the open, and, hence, take advantage of receiving the full sun throughout the day. It is, therefore, suitable for a wide range of plants. However, its main disadvantage when compared to a lean-to type is that more heat is lost through its larger surface area. This is mainly why lean-to greenhouses have long been used in the walled gardens of large country houses to grow Lapageria rosea and other plants requiring cool, constant temperature, such as half-hardly ferns. However, generally, good ventilation and shading in the spring and summer to prevent overheating are essential for any greenhouse. The high daytime temperatures will warm the back wall, which acts as a heat battery, releasing its accumulated heat at night. Therefore, plants in a greenhouse with this orientation will need the most attention, as they will dry out rapidly.

Also, greenhouses vary considerably in their shapes and internal dimensions. Traditional greenhouses have straight sides, which allow the maximum use of internal space and are ideal for climbers [13]. On the other hand, greenhouses with sloping sides have the advantage of allowing the greatest penetration of sunlight, even during winter [13]. The low winter sun strikes the glass at 90°C lets in the maximum amount of light. Where the sun strikes the glass at a greater or lesser angle, a proportion of the light is reflected away from greenhouse. Sloping sides, also, offer less wind resistance than straight sides and therefore, less likely to be damaged during windy weather. This type of greenhouse is most suitable for short winter crops, such as early spring lettuce and flowering annuals from seed, which do not require much headroom.

A typical greenhouse is shown schematically in Figure 11. However, there are several designs of greenhouses, based on dimensions, orientation and function. The following three options are the most widely used:

- A ready-made design.
- A designed, which is constructed from a number of prefabricated modules.
- A bespoke design.

Of these, the prefabricated ready-made design, which is utilised to fit the site, is the cheapest greenhouses and gives flexibility. It is, also, the most popular option [13]. The introduction of a reflecting wall at the back of a greenhouse considerably enhances the solar radiation that reaches the ground level at any particular time of the day.

Specific examples of commercially available designs are numerous. Dutch light greenhouses, for example, have large panes of glass, which cast little shade on the plants inside. They are simple to erect, consisting of frames bolted together, which are supported on a steel framework for all but the smallest models. They are easy to move and extra sections can be added on to them, a useful attraction [13]. Curvilinear greenhouses, on the other hand, are designed primarily to let in the maximum amount of light throughout the year by presenting at least one side perpendicular to the sun. This attractive style of greenhouse tends to be expensive because of the number of different angles, which require more engineering [13]. Likewise, the uneven span greenhouses are designed for maximum light transmission on one side. These are generally taller than traditional greenhouses, making them suitable for tall, early season crops, such as cucumbers [13]. Also, the polygonal greenhouses are designed more as garden features than as practical growing houses and consequently, are expensive. Their internal space is somewhat limited and on smaller models over-heading can be a problem because of their small roof ventilations. They are suitable for growing smaller pot plants, such as pelargoniums and cacti [13]. Another example is the solar greenhouses. These are designed primarily for areas with very cold winters and poor winter light. They take the form of lean-to structures facing the sun, are well insulated to conserve heat and are sometimes partially sunk into the ground. They are suitable for winter vegetable crops and early-sown bedding plants, such as begonias and pelargoniums [13]. Mini lean-to greenhouses are suitable for small gardens where space is limited. They can, also, be used to create a separate environment within larger greenhouses. The space inside is large enough to grow two tomato or melon plants in growing bags, or can install shelves to provide a multi-layered growing environment, ideal for many small potted plants and raising summer bedding plants [13].

13.2. Construction Materials

Different materials are used for the different parts. However, wood and aluminium are the two most popular materials used for small greenhouses. Steel is used for larger structures and UPVC for conservatories [14]. The introduction of a reflecting wall at the back of a greenhouse considerably enhances the solar radiation that reaches the ground level at any particular time of the day.

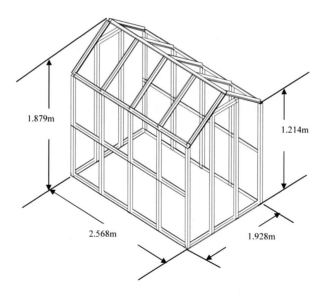

Figure 11. Greenhouse and base with horticultural glass.

The energy yield of the greenhouse with any type of reflecting wall was also significantly increased. The increase in energy efficiency was obtained by calculating the ratio between the total energy received during the day in greenhouse with a reflecting wall, compared to that in a classical greenhouse. Hence, the energy balance was significantly shifted towards conservation of classical energy for heating or lighting. The four-fold greater amount of energy that can be captured by virtue of using a reflecting wall with an adjustable inclination and louvers during winter attracts special attention. When sky (diffuse) radiation that was received by the ground in amounts shown in Figure 12, were taken into account, the values of the enhancement coefficients were reduced to some extent: this was due to the fact that they added up to the direct radiation from the sun in both new and classical greenhouses. However, this is a useful effect as further increases overall energy gain. There is also an ironing out effect expressed in terms of the ratios between peak and average insolations. Air humidity is measured as a percentage of water vapour in the air on a scale from 0% to 100%, where 0% being dry and 100% being full saturation level.

13.3. Ground Radiation

Reflection of sunrays is mostly used for concentrating them onto reactors of solar power plants. Enhancing the insolation for other purposes has, so far, scarcely been used. Several years ago, application of this principle for increasing the ground irradiance in greenhouses, glass covered extensions in buildings and for illuminating northward facing walls of buildings was proposed [15]. Application of reflection of sun's rays was motivated by the fact that ground illuminance/irradiance from direct sunlight is of very low intensity in winter months, even when skies are clear, due to the low incident angle of incoming radiation during most of the day. This is even more pronounced at greater latitudes. As can be seen in Figure 12, which depicts a sunbeam split into its vertical and horizontal components, nearly all of the radiation passes through a greenhouse during most of the day.

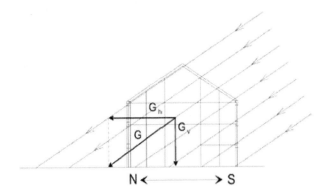

Figure 12. Relative horizontal and vertical components of solar radiation.

The comfort in a greenhouse depends on many environmental parameters. These include temperature, relative humidity, air quality and lighting. Although greenhouse and conservatory originally both meant a place to house or conserve greens (variegated hollies, cirrus, myrtles and oleanders), a greenhouse today implies a place in which plants are raised while conservatory usually describes a glazed room where plants may or may not play a significant role. Indeed, a greenhouse can be used for so many different purposes. It is, therefore, difficult to decide how to group the information about the plants that can be grown inside it. Whereas heat loss in winter a problem, it can be a positive advantage when greenhouse temperatures soar considerably above outside temperatures in summer. Indoor relative humidity control is one of the most effective long-term mite control measures. There are many ways in which the internal relative humidity can be controlled including the use of appropriate ventilation, the reduction of internal moisture production and maintenance of adequate internal temperatures through the use of efficient heating and insulation.

The main environmental control factor for dust mites is relative humidity. The followings are the practical methods of controlling measures available for reducing dust mite populations:

- Chemical control.
- Cleaning and vacuuming.
- Use of electric blankets, and
- Indoor humidity.

CONCLUSION

Two of the most essential natural resources for all life on the earth and for man's survival are sunlight and water. Sunlight is the driving force behind many of the renewable energy technologies. The worldwide potential for utilising this resource, both directly by means of the solar technologies and indirectly by means of biofuels, wind and hydro technologies is vast. During the last decade interest has been refocused on renewable energy sources due to the increasing prices and fore-seeable exhaustion of presently used commercial energy sources. Plants, like human beings, need tender loving care in the form of optimum settings of light, sunshine, nourishment and water. Hence, the control of sunlight, air humidity and temperatures in greenhouses are the key to successful greenhouse gardening. The mop fan is a simple and novel air humidifier; which is capable of removing particulate and gaseous pollutants while providing ventilation. It is a device ideally suited to greenhouse applications, which require robustness, low cost, minimum maintenance and high efficiency. A device meeting these requirements is not yet available to the farming community. Hence, implementing mop fans aides sustainable development through using a clean, environmentally friendly device that decreases load in the greenhouse and reduces energy consumption.

REFERENCES

[1]   Robinson, G. Changes in construction waste management. Waste Management World, pp. 43-49. May-June 2007.

[2]   Omer, AM; Yemen, D. Biogas an appropriate technology. *Proceedings of the 7th Arab International Solar Energy Conference*, pp.417, Sharjah, UAE, 19-22 February 2001.

[3]   Swift-Hook, DT; et al. Characteristics of a rocking wave power devices. *Nature*, 254, 504. 1975.

[4]   Sims, RH. Not too late: IPCC identifies renewable energy as a key measure to limit climate change. *Renewable Energy World*, 10 (4), 31-39. 2007.

[5]   Trevor, T. Fridge recycling: bringing agents in from the cold. *Waste Management World*, 5, 43-47. 2007.

[6]   *International Energy Agency (IEA).* Indicators for industrial Energy Efficiency and CO_2 Emissions: A Technology Perspective. 2007.

[7]   Brain, G; Mark, S. Garbage in, energy out: landfill gas opportunities for CHP projects. *Cogeneration and On-Site Power*, 8 (5), 37-45. 2007.

[8]   Rawlings, RHD. Technical Note TN 18/99 – Ground Source Heat Pumps: A Technology Review. Bracknell. The Building Services Research and Information Association. 1999.

[9]   Oxburgh, ER. Geothermal energy. *Aspects of Energy Conversion*, pp. 385-403. 1975.

[10] John, W. The glasshouse garden. The Royal Horticultural Society Collection. UK. 1993.

[11] United Nations. World Urbanisation Prospect: The 1999 Revision. New York. The United Nations Population Division. 2001.

[12] *WCED.* Our common future. New York. Oxford University Press. 1987.

[13] Herath, G. The Green Revolution in Asia: productivity, employment and the role of policies. Oxford Agrarian Studies, 14, 52-71. 1985.

[14] Jonathon, E. *Greenhouse gardening*. The Crowood Press Ltd. UK. 1991.

[15] Achard, P; Gicqquel, R. *European passive solar handbook*. Brussels: Commission of the European Communities. 1986.

In: Advances in Energy Research. Volume 20
Editor: Morena J. Acosta

ISBN: 978-1-63463-169-3
© 2015 Nova Science Publishers, Inc.

Chapter 6

STRATEGIC INTERACTIONS DURING OIL EXPLORATION IN THE GULF OF MEXICO

C.-Y. Cynthia Lin
University of California at Davis, CA, US

ABSTRACT

This chapter examines strategic interactions during oil exploration in the Gulf of Mexico. When individual petroleum-producing firms make their exploration decisions, information externalities and extraction externalities may lead them to interact strategically with their neighbors. If they do occur, strategic interactions in exploration would lead to a loss in both firm profit and government royalty revenue. Since these strategic interactions would be inefficient, changes in the government offshore leasing policy would need to be considered. The possibility of strategic interactions thus poses a concern to policy-makers and affects the optimal government policy. This chapter examines whether these inefficient strategic interactions take place in U.S. federal lands in the Gulf of Mexico. In particular, it analyzes whether a firm's exploration decisions depend on the decisions of firms owning neighboring tracts of land. Both reduced-form and structural models are employed. The results suggest that strategic interactions do not actually take place, at least not in exploration, and therefore that the current parameters of the government offshore leasing policy do not lead to inefficient petroleum exploration.

INTRODUCTION

Exploration is the first stage of petroleum production: when a firm acquires a previously unexplored tract of land, it must first decide whether and when to invest in the drilling rigs needed to begin exploratory drilling. If firms own leases to neighboring tracts of land that may be located over a common pool of reserve, there are two types of externalities that add a strategic (or non-cooperative) dimension to firms' exploration timing decisions and may render these decisions socially inefficient.

The first type of externality is an information externality: if tracts are located over a common pool or share common geological features so that their ex post values are correlated, then firms learn information about their own tracts when other firms drill exploratory wells on neighboring tracts (Hendricks & Porter, 1996). The information externality is socially inefficient because it may cause firms to play a non-cooperative timing game that leads them to inefficiently delay production, since the possibility of acquiring information from other firms may further enhance the option value to waiting. If firms are subject to a lease term by the end of which they must begin exploratory drilling, or else relinquish their lease, then the information externality would result in too little exploration at the beginning of the lease term and duplicative drilling in the final period of the lease (Hendricks & Porter, 1996; Porter, 1995). In contrast, the optimal coordinated plan would entail a sequential search in which one tract would be drilled in the first period and, if productive, a neighboring tract is drilled in the next (Porter, 1995).

A second type of externality is an extraction externality: when firms have competing rights to a common-pool resource, strategic considerations may lead them to extract at an inefficiently high rate (Libecap & Smith, 1999a; Libecap & Wiggins, 1985). When oil is extracted too quickly, it may cause a collapse in the formation being extracted from, thus collapsing the pipe and decreasing the total amount of oil extracted (Kenny McMinn, Offshore District Production Manager, Apache Corporation, personal communication, 22 January 2004).

Owing to both information and extraction externalities, the dynamic decision-making problem faced by a petroleum-producing firm is not merely a single-agent problem, but rather can be viewed as a multi-agent, non-cooperative game in which firms behave strategically and base their exploration policies on those of their neighbors. Both externalities suggest that firms will be more likely to drill when its neighbors are drilling as well. The information externality leads firms to drill when neighbors drill because a neighbor's drilling reveals to the firm that the neighbor thinks its tract is worth exploring, therefore suggesting that the firm's own tract may be worth exploring as well. The extraction externality leads firms to drill when neighbors drill because a firm wants to be able to extract from the common pool resource before its neighbor does.

Both externalities lead to strategic interactions that are socially inefficient. The information externality leads to an inefficient delay in exploration. The extraction externality leads to excessively high extraction rates and less total oil extracted. Both types of strategic behavior lead to lower profits for the petroleum-producing firms and lower royalty revenue for the federal government. It is therefore important to analyze whether these strategic interactions place, and therefore whether policies that can mitigate the strategic interactions should be implemented.

Since 1954, the U.S. government has leased tracts from its federal lands in the Gulf of Mexico to firms interested in offshore petroleum production by means of a succession of lease sales. A lease sale is initiated when the government announces that an area is available for exploration, and nominations are invited from firms as to which tracts should be offered for sale. In a typical lease sale, over a hundred tracts are sold simultaneously in separate first-price, sealed-bid auctions. Many more tracts are nominated than are sold, and the nomination process probably conveys little or no information (Porter, 1995). A tract is typically a block of 5000 acres or 5760 acres (Marshall Rose, Minerals Management Service, personal communication, 9 November 2005). The size of a tract is often less than the acreage required to ensure exclusive ownership of any deposits that may be present (Hendricks & Kovenock, 1989), and tracts within the same area may be located over a common pool (Hendricks &

Porter, 1993). To date, the largest petroleum field spanned 23 tracts. Depending on water depth, 57-67 percent of the fields spanned more than one tract and 70-79 percent spanned three or fewer tracts (Marshall Rose, Minerals Management Service, personal communication, 31 March 2005). Because neighboring tracts of land may share a common pool of petroleum reserve, information and extraction externalities that lead firms to interact strategically may be present. As a consequence, petroleum production on the federal leases may be inefficient.

This paper analyzes whether firms' exploration timing decisions on U.S. federal lands in the Gulf of Mexico depend on the exploration timing decisions of firms owning neighboring tracts of land. To answer this question, this paper synthesizes the results of Lin (2009), which estimates a discrete response model of a firm's exploration investment decision using variables based on the timing of a neighbor's lease term as instruments for the neighbor's decision, and Lin (2013), which estimates a structural econometric model of the investment timing game in exploration and development.

The research presented in this paper is important for several reasons. First, an empirical analysis of investment timing decisions enables one to examine whether the strategic interactions that are predicted in theory actually occur in practice. Second, the estimation of strategic interactions, especially those that arise in a spatial context, is of methodological interest. Third, my results have implications for leasing policy: if the strategic effects and externalities turn out to be large, then the program by which the U.S. government leases tracts to firms may be inefficient, and possible modifications should be considered.

The exploration timing game in offshore petroleum production in the Gulf of Mexico has been examined in a seminal series of papers by Kenneth Hendricks, Robert Porter and their co-authors (see e.g., Hendricks & Kovenock, 1989; Hendricks & Porter, 1993; Hendricks & Porter, 1996). These papers focus on the information externality associated with exploratory drilling. They analyze this externality and the learning and strategic delay that it causes by developing theoretical models of the exploration timing game. In addition, Hendricks and Porter (1993, 1996) calculate the empirical drilling hazard functions for cohorts in specific areas, and study the determinants of the exploration timing decision and of drilling outcomes. According to their results, equilibrium predictions of plausible non-cooperative models are reasonably accurate and more descriptive than those of cooperative models of drilling timing.

The reduced-form discrete response model of firms' exploration timing decision presented in Lin (2009) improves upon that of Hendricks and Porter (1996) in two ways. First, Hendricks and Porter do not instrument for the variables they use to capture local drilling experience, and therefore do not address the endogeneity problems that arise when measuring neighbors' effects. In contrast, Lin (2009) instruments for the neighbors' decisions. Second, Hendricks and Porter define a "neighborhood" as one of the 51 "areas" into which the U.S. government has divided the federal lands in the Gulf of Mexico offshore of Louisiana and Texas. Using their definition, any two adjacent tracts that are located along either side of an area boundary belong to two different neighborhoods, even though they are right next to each other and may be located over a common pool of petroleum reserve. To address this problem, Lin (2009) defines neighbors based on geographic distances, not on the arbitrary area boundaries drawn by the federal government.

The structural model in Lin (2013) improves upon the reduced-form approaches in several ways. First, a structural model enables the estimation of all the structural parameters of the underlying dynamic game. These parameters include not only those governing the relationship between various state variables and the profits of firms, but also parameters governing the distribution of tract-specific private information. Second, the structural model addresses the endogeneity problems without the need for instruments. Measuring neighbors' effects is difficult owing to two sources of endogeneity. One source is the simultaneity of the strategic interaction: if tract i is affected by its neighbor j, then tract j is affected by its neighbor i. The other arises from spatially correlated unobservable variables (Manski, 1993; Manski, 1995; Robalino & Pfaff, 2012). Because the structural model is based on the equilibrium of the underlying dynamic game, however, it addresses the simultaneity problem directly by explicitly modeling the firms' strategies. Moreover, the problem of spatially correlated unobservables can be addressed by interpreting the profits in the model as expected profits conditional on observables. A third advantage to a structural model is that it enables one to estimate how a firm's profits are affected by the decisions of its neighbors; the sign of the effect indicates the net sign of the information and extraction externalities. One is therefore able to quantify the net effects of the externalities. Fourth, the structural model enables one to explicitly model each of the stages of the multi-stage dynamic decision-making problem faced by petroleum-producing firms.

The results do not indicate that a firm's exploratory drilling decision depends on those of its neighbors. Information and extraction externalities do not appear to induce firms to interact strategically on net during exploration because these externalities do not become important until later stages of production.

DATA

The data set used is a data set on federal lease sales in the Gulf of Mexico between 1954 and 1990 compiled by Kenneth Hendricks and Robert Porter from U.S. Department of Interior data. There are three types of tracts that can be offered in an oil and gas lease sale: wildcat, drainage, and developmental. Wildcat tracts are located in regions where no exploratory drilling has occurred previously and therefore where the geology is not well known. Exploration on wildcat tracts entails searching for a new deposit. In contrast, both drainage and developmental tracts are adjacent to tracts on which deposits have already been discovered; developmental tracts, in addition, are tracts that have been previously offered in an earlier lease sale but either whose previous bids were rejected as inadequate or whose leases were relinquished because no exploratory drilling was done (Porter, 1995).

This paper focuses on wildcat tracts offshore of Louisiana and Texas that were auctioned between 1954 and 1979, inclusive. It does so for several reasons. First, these restrictions are similar to those made by Hendricks and Porter (1996), thus enabling a comparison of results. Second, since wildcat tracts are tracts on which no exploratory drilling has occurred previously, information externalities are likely to be most acute. Third, because the data set only contains production data up until 1990, the restriction to tracts sold before 1980 eliminates any censoring of either drilling or production.

Additional restrictions imposed for a tract to be included in the data set are that it must be a tract for which location data is available, for which the first exploration occurred neither before the sale date nor after the lease term, and for which production did not occur before exploration.

In total, there are 2404 tracts in the data set satisfying the above criteria, from 26 different lease sales. The maximum tract size, as stipulated by a provision in section 8(b) of the Outer Continental Shelf Lands Act (OCSLA), 43 U.S.C. 1337(b)(1), is 5760 acres, or 3 miles by 3 miles (Marshall Rose, Minerals Management Service, personal communication, 17 April 2003). Most tracts are either 2500 acres, 5000 acres or 5760 acres in size. The average tract size is 4790 acres (s.d. = 1100) and the median tract size is 5000 acres. The average real pre-sale value (in 1982 $) of these tracts, as estimated by the U.S. Department of Interior Minerals Management Service, is $360 per acre, while the average winning bid is $2520 per acre. Exploratory drilling eventually occurred on 1721 of the tracts. The U.S. government divides the federal lands in the Gulf of Mexico offshore of Louisiana and Texas into 51 areas; the data includes tracts from 26 of these areas.

For the panel data set, each time observation is a year. Tracts enter the panel when they are sold. Tracts that were eventually explored exit the panel after the first drilling occurs. Tracts that were never explored exit the panel after five years, which is the length of the lease term a firm is given to begin exploration, or else relinquish its lease. Tracts have on average 2.03 time observations in the panel. The panel spans the years 1954 to 1983.

Although the set of possible tracts is limited to wildcat tracts sold before 1980 for which exploration did not occur after the lease term, the set of possible neighbors for these tracts is larger. In particular, any tract sold between 1954 and 1983, inclusive, for which location data is available, for which the first exploration did not occur before the sale date and for which production did not occur before exploration is eligible as a potential neighbor for a tract i.

To be considered an actual neighbor for a given tract i at time t, a potential neighbor must also satisfy the following conditions: that (i) it is located within a certain distance of tract i, (ii) its lease began before time t, (iii) it has not been explored before time $t-1$, and (iv) it is owned by a different firm from the firm owning tract i, and, in most cases, (v) all of tract i's neighbors at time t must be sold on a different date from tract i. In the base case, the distance used to define neighbors was 5 miles; for robustness, the analyses were also run using 4 miles, 6 miles and 10 miles. The base case cutoff of 5 miles was chosen so that a neighborhood would be at least as large as the size of most petroleum fields. To date, 79% and 70% of the fields spanned 3 or fewer leases for blocks with maximum water depth of 0-199 meters and 200-399 meters, respectively (Marshall Rose, Minerals Management Service, personal communication, 31 March 2005).

There are 1139 observations in the base case. In the base case, a tract has on average 1.74 (s.d. = 1.00) neighbors at any time t. Of its neighbors, on average 43% of them began exploration in the previous period. Moreover, during the previous period an average of 36% and 15% of a tract's neighbors were in the first and last years of their lease term, respectively.

MODEL

Let t denote the time since the lease sale. At the beginning of each period t, the owner of each tract i must decide whether to invest in exploration at time t. For each period t, all firms make their time-t investment decisions simultaneously. The payoff to exploring is the expected revenue from exploring the tract minus the cost of exploration. The firm's expected revenue depends on the firm's time-t estimate of the quantity of reserves on its tract that it can extract, and therefore depends exogenous covariates such as the estimated pre-sale value of the tract and the winning bid of the tract, both of which measure the expected value of the tract prior to the neighbors' exploration, and on the fraction of neighbors j who explored at time t-1. The firm uses the fraction of neighbors who explore to update its prior on the expected value of exploration.

As formalized in Lin's (2013) structural model of the firm's dynamic decision-making problem, a firm will invest in the drilling rigs needed to begin exploratory drilling at time t if its profits from exploration exceed the continuation value from waiting. The continuation value to waiting is the expected value of next period's value function, conditional on the current information set and on not exploring this period. Because a firm must begin exploration before the end of the five-year lease term, or else relinquish its lease, this is a finite horizon problem.

In the absence of strategic considerations, the firm owning tract i would base its exploration investment timing decision on only the exogenous variables, which include: estimated pre-sale value per acre, winning bid per acre, the number of years since the lease sale, a dummy for being in the last year of the lease term, the size of the tract, the year the lease was sold, firm fixed effects, area fixed effects, and year effects. To derive its dynamically optimal investment policy, it would solve a single-agent dynamic programming problem. The estimated pre-sale value and winning bid measure the firm's initial prior on the amount of reserves on the tract. The number of years since the lease sale and the dummy for being in the last year of the lease term affect a firm's decision because they measure how much longer a firm can wait to explore before it must give up its lease. The expected amount of reserves increases with tract size. The year the lease was sold controls for time-specific factors. Firm fixed effects measure firm-specific factors that affect revenues and cost. Area fixed effects measure region-specific factors such as common geological features. Year effects measure factors such as the oil price or drilling costs that may change over time.

If information and extraction externalities were present, however, then strategic considerations would become important. A firm's exploration investment decision depends on the firm's time-t estimate of the quantity of reserves on its tract that it can extract, which in the presence of externalities is affected by whether or not the firm's neighbors drilled in the previous period and also by the outcome of the neighbors' drilling. A firm may be more likely to explore following a positive outcome from its neighbor, but less likely to explore following a neighbor's dry hole. As a consequence, the exploration investment decisions of the firm owning tract i would depend on the exploration investment decisions of the firms owning neighboring tracts of land. In other words, the firm owning tract i would base its investment timing decisions not only on the exogenous variables, but also on the fraction of neighbors j who explored at time t-1. Each firm would then no longer solve merely a single-agent dynamic programming problem, but rather a multi-agent dynamic game.

Measuring neighbors' effects is difficult owing to two sources of endogeneity. One source is the simultaneity of the strategic interaction: if tract i is affected by its neighbor j, then tract j is affected by its neighbor i. The other arises from spatially correlated unobservable variables (Manski, 1993; Manski, 1995; Robalino & Pfaff, 2012).

To address these endogeneity problems, Lin (2009) exploits a unique feature of the federal lease sales. When a tract is won, a firm must begin exploration before the end of the five-year lease term, or else relinquish the lease. As a consequence, the hazard rate of exploratory drilling has a U-shaped pattern, with high rates both at the beginning of the lease and at the end of the lease term (Hendricks & Porter, 1996; Lin, 2009). Instruments for the fraction of neighbors who explore are therefore the fraction of neighbors in the first year of their respective leases and the fraction of neighbors in the last year of their respective lease terms. The timing of a neighbor's lease term, which is related to the exogenous timing of the neighbor's sale date, is exogenous to a firm's exploratory drilling decision, as it is unlikely to have an effect except through its effect on the neighbor's exploratory drilling. Moreover, it is unlikely to be correlated with spatially correlated unobservables. The timing of lease sales is exogenous, especially for wildcat tracts, because the federal government chooses only a small subset of nominated tracts to be sold in any given lease sale (Porter, 1995); firms therefore have little influence over the timing of the lease sales. Thus, the government's choice of tracts for each sale and each tract's lease sale date are arguably random and uncertain.

To assess how a firm's exploratory drilling decision depends on the exploratory drilling decisions of its neighbors, a discrete response model is estimated by regressing the probability of exploration on tract i at time t on the fraction of neighbors j who explored at time t-1 and on other covariates. Both a linear probability model and a probit model are estimated. The coefficient of interest is the coefficient on the fraction of neighbors who explored at time t-1. Both externalities suggest that firms will be more likely to drill when its neighbors are drilling as well. The information externality leads firms to drill when neighbors drill because a neighbor's drilling reveals to the firm that the neighbor thinks its tract is worth exploring, therefore suggesting that the firm's own tract may be worth exploring as well. The extraction externality leads firms to drill when neighbors drill because a firm wants to be able to extract from the common pool resource before its neighbor does. Thus, if externalities are present, we would expect the coefficient to be positive.

The instrumental variables analogs of the two models are two-stage least squares and Amemiya generalized least squares, respectively. The Amemiya generalized least squares estimator is formed by first estimating reduced-form parameters and then solving for the structural parameters; this estimator is asymptotically more efficient than a two-stage estimator (Newey, 1987).

RESULTS

As a benchmark, the discrete response models are run without the use of instruments, when neighbors must be located within 5 miles of a tract. The coefficient of interest is that on the fraction of neighbors who drilled at time t-1. For all four specifications used, neighbors do not have a significant effect. However, the other covariates have coefficients of the expected sign: the probability of exploring increases with the estimated pre-sale value, the winning bid and the size (acreage) of the tract. Also as expected, the probability of exploring often decreases with the number of years since the lease sale, with the coefficient being either significantly negative or insignificant at a 5% level, and increases at the last year of the lease term.

To test for the endogeneity of the neighbors' drilling, a Durbin-Wu-Hausman test is used for the linear probability model and a Smith-Blundell test is used for the probit model. Both are tests of whether the residual from a regression of the variable in question on all the exogenous variables has a significant coefficient when added to the original model.

According to these tests, neighbors' decisions are not significantly endogenous at a 5% level in any of the specifications. Although the tests fail to reject an exogeneity assumption, it still seems plausible, at least in theory, that neighbors' decisions are endogenous owing to simultaneity and/or spatially correlated unobservables.

To guard against any potential endogeneity of the neighbors' decisions, fraction of neighbors who drill is instrumented with the fraction of neighbors in the first year of the lease and the fraction of neighbors at the last year of the lease term. The first-stage F-statistic from a joint test of the two instruments is over 10 in all specifications, so weak instruments should not be a concern (Stock & Watson, 2003). The instruments are thus correlated with the neighbors' decisions.

According to the results from running the discrete response analysis with the use of instruments, when neighbors must be located within 5 miles of a tract, irrespective of the probability model (linear or probit), the time period (year or quarter) and whether or not the restriction (v) that all of tract i's neighbors at time t must be sold on a different date from tract i is imposed, the effect of neighbors' decisions is statistically insignificant and small: according to the results from the base case specification, a change in the percent of neighbors who explored in the previous period from 0 percent to 100 percent would only increase a firm's probability of exploration by a statistically insignificant 0.14. Negative effects greater than 0.15 and positive effects greater than 0.43 on a firm's probability of exploration can be rejected at a 5% level.

As with the uninstrumented regressions, the signs of the coefficients on the other covariates are as expected. According to the results from the base case specification, an increase in the real pre-sale value of a tract of $10,000 per acre would increase the probability of exploration by 0.66. Thus, pre-sale values, which vary greatly from $0 to $18,230 per acre, have a very large and statistically significant effect on exploration decisions. Similarly, an increase in the winning bid of $10,000 per acre would increase the probability of exploration by 0.34. Thus, winning bids, which vary from $450 to $60,800 per acre, have a large and statistically significant effect as well. The coefficients on the pre-sale value and on the winning bid indicate that, all else equal, tracts are more likely to be explored if their ex ante estimated values are high.

The coefficient on acreage indicates that an increase in tract size of 100 acres increases the probability of exploration by 0.40. Thus, larger tracts are more likely to be explored. One likely explanation is that because larger tracts cover more surface area, the probability that oil and gas reserves are present is higher.

The coefficient on the dummy for being in the last year of the lease term indicates that, all else equal, a tract's probability of being explored is higher by 0.13 when it is in the last year of its lease term. This is because the option value to waiting goes to zero at the end of the lease term.

In addition to being robust to the probability model, the time period and whether or not the restriction (v) that all of tract i's neighbors at time t must be sold on a different date from tract i is imposed, the discrete response results are also robust to the distance used to delineate neighbors.

Externalities are likely to become more acute on smaller tracts, which are more likely to be located over a common pool of oil reserve. To examine whether strategic interactions have a larger effect on smaller tracts, where externalities arising from common-pool considerations are likely to be more prevalent, the sample is also stratified by tract size (in acres). The coefficient on the fraction of neighbors who drilled at time t-1 and the coefficient on the interaction term are both statistically insignificant. The result that neighbors do not have a significant effect on a firm's probability of exploratory drilling is therefore robust to tract size.

Thus, regardless of whether instruments are used or not, the results of the discrete response analysis by Lin (2009) do not indicate that a firm's exploratory drilling decision depends on those of its neighbors.

Test results rejecting the endogeneity of neighbors' decisions to a firm's own decision provide further evidence that neighbors do not base their decisions on each other. These results of Lin (2009) are consistent with the weak results of Hendricks and Porter (1996): in their regressions of the probability of initial exploration, the coefficients on the variables they use to capture the neighborhood exploratory drilling experience are, for the most part, not significant. Thus, even though one may expect information externalities to be particularly acute on wildcat tracts, information and extraction externalities do not appear to induce firms to interact strategically on net.

One possible explanation why the results reject strategic, non-cooperative behavior during exploration is that firms owning neighboring tracts cooperate to jointly internalize the inefficient externalities they impose on each other, for example by forming joint ventures in exploration. Joint ventures in exploration occur less frequently than one might expect, however, because negotiations are contentious, because firms fear allegations of pre-sale anti-trust violations (Marshall Rose, Minerals Management Service, personal communication, 3 May 2005), and because prospective partners have an incentive to free ride on a firm's information gathering expenditures (Hendricks and Porter, 1992). In their theoretical model of the persuasion game, Hendricks and Kovenock (1989) find that, even with well-defined property rights, bargaining does not eliminate all the inefficiencies of decentralized drilling decisions. As a consequence, the information externality may not be fully internalized.

Following exploration, firms can cooperate by consolidating their production rights through purchase or unitization. Under a unitization agreement, a single firm is designated as the unit operator to develop the entire reservoir, while the other firms share in the profits according to negotiated formulas (Libecap & Smith, 1999b). Unitization may reduce the extraction externality. There are many obstacles to consolidation, however, including contentious negotiations, the need to determine relative or absolute tract values, information costs, and oil migration problems (Libecap & Wiggins, 1984). In addition, another free rider problem that impedes coordination is that firms may fear that if they reveal to other firms their information or expertise, for example about how to interpret seismic data, then they may lose their advantage in future auctions (Hendricks & Porter, 1996). Thus, despite various means of coordination, firms may still behave strategically and non-cooperatively, and information and extraction externalities may not be fully internalized.

A second, more likely, explanation why the results reject strategic, non-cooperative behavior during exploration is that the externalities are insignificant or even nonexistent during exploration, and do not become important until later stages of production. Using a structural econometric model of the multi-stage investment timing game in petroleum production, Lin (2013) finds that while externalities from exploration do not have any net strategic effect, externalities from subsequent development, during which firms install production platforms, do have a net strategic effect. A firm's profits increase when its neighbor installs a production platform, perhaps because this is a signal to the firm that the neighbor's exploratory efforts were successful, and therefore that there may be deposits present.

In contrast, seeing a neighbor install a drilling rig may provide little additional information about a firm's own lease, since the drilling may or may not be successful. As a consequence, the information externality may be insignificant during exploration. Similarly, the extraction externality may not become important until firms are actually extracting oil and competing for the same resource, and therefore may also be insignificant during exploration as well.

CONCLUSION

This paper examines whether strategic considerations arising from information and extraction externalities are present during petroleum exploration. In particular, it analyzes whether a firm's exploration timing decision depends on the decisions of firms owning neighboring tracts of land.

Do the positive information externalities and negative extraction externalities have any net strategic effect that may cause petroleum production to be inefficient? The results do not indicate that externalities from exploration have any net strategic effect. A firm's exploration decision does not depend significantly on the exploration decisions of its neighbors. This is true even on smaller tracts, where strategic interactions are more likely, since smaller tracts are more likely to be located over a common pool of oil reserve. A firm's exploration decision instead depends on exogenous factors such as the estimated pre-sale value of the tract, the tract's winning bid in the lease sale, whether or not it is the last year of the lease term, and tract size.

A likely explanation why the results reject strategic, non-cooperative behavior during exploration is that the externalities are insignificant or even nonexistent during exploration, and do not become important until later stages of production. Seeing a neighbor install a drilling rig may provide little additional information about a firm's own lease, since the drilling may or may not be successful. As a consequence, the information externality may be insignificant during exploration. Similarly, the extraction externality may not become important until firms are actually extracting oil and competing for the same resource, and therefore may also be insignificant during exploration as well.

If they did occur, strategic interactions in exploration would lead to a loss in both firm profit and government royalty revenue. Since these strategic interactions would be inefficient, changes in the government offshore leasing policy would need to be considered. Possible changes include modifying the tract size, enacting policies to facilitate joint ventures and cooperation, and selling non-contiguous tracts of land in the lease sales. The possibility of strategic interactions thus poses a concern to policy-makers and affects the optimal government policy. However, the results of the paper suggest that strategic interactions do not actually take place, at least not in exploration, and therefore that the current parameters of the government offshore leasing policy do not lead to inefficient petroleum exploration.

REFERENCES

Hendricks, K., Kovenock, D. (1989). Asymmetric information, information externalities, and efficiency: The case of oil exploration. RAND *Journal of Economics*, 20(2), 164-182.

Hendricks, K., Porter, R. (1992). Joint bidding in federal OCS auctions. *American Economic Review Papers and Proceedings*, 82(2), 506-511.

Hendricks, K., Porter, R. (1993). Determinants of the timing and incidence of exploratory drilling on offshore wildcat tracts. *NBER Working Paper Series* (Working Paper No. 4605). Cambridge, MA.

Hendricks, K., Porter, R. (1996). The timing and incidence of exploratory drilling on offshore wildcat tracts. *The American Economic Review*, 86(3), 388-407.

Libecap, G., Smith, J. (1999a). *Regulatory remedies to the common pool: The limits to oil field unitization.* Working paper. University of Arizona and Southern Methodist University.

Libecap, G., Smith, J. (1999b). The self-enforcing provisions of oil and gas unit operating agreements: Theory and evidence. *The Journal of Law, Economics, and Organizations,* 15(2), 526-548.

Libecap, G., Wiggins, S. (1984). Contractual responses to the common pool: Prorationing of crude oil production. *The American Economic Review*, 74(1), 87-98.

Libecap, G., Wiggins, S. (1985). The influence of private contractual failure on regulation: The case of oil field unitization. *The Journal of Political Economy*, 93(4), 690-714.

Lin, C.-Y.C. (2009). Estimating strategic interactions in petroleum exploration. *Energy Economics*, 31 (4), 586-594.

Lin, C.-Y.C. (2013). Strategic decision-making with information and extraction externalities: A structural model of the multi-stage investment timing game in offshore petroleum production. *Review of Economics and Statistics*, 95(5), 1601-1621.

Manski, C. (1993). Identification of endogenous social effects: The reflection problem. *Review of Economic Studies*, 60(3), 531-542.

Manski, C. (1995). *Identification Problems in the Social Sciences*. Harvard University Press, Cambridge, MA.

Newey, W. (1987). Efficient estimation of limited dependent variable models with endogenous explanatory variables. *Journal of Econometrics*, 36, 231-250.

Porter, R. (1995). The role of information in U.S. offshore oil and gas lease auctions. *Econometrica,* 63(1), 1-27.

Robalino, J., Pfaff, A. (2012). Contagious development: Neighbor interactions in deforestation. *Journal of Development Economics* 97, 2, 427-436.

Stock, J., Watson, M. (2003). *Introduction to Econometrics*. Addison-Wesley, Boston.

In: Advances in Energy Research. Volume 20
Editor: Morena J. Acosta

Chapter 7

OWNERSHIP AND REGIONAL ECONOMIC IMPACT: WIND DEVELOPMENT IN THE STATE OF MINNESOTA

Arne Kildegaard[*†]

Economics and Management,
University of Minnesota, Morris, MN, US

ABSTRACT

This study investigates the regional economic impact consequences of local vs. external ownership in the developing wind industry in the state of Minnesota (U.S.A.). We employ a realistic *pro forma* model of a financial "flip" structure, whereby a local equity group pairs with an outside, tax-motivated equity partner. The present value of residuals as well as the other O&M expenditures are annuitized and entered into a state-level input-output model. In order to bracket the range of possible outcomes, we run two sets of parameter assumptions ("pessimistic" and "optimistic") through the local equity group's *pro forma,* and subsequently the state-wide input-output model. According to these two scenarios we find that the impact on state-level value added is 3.1 and 4.5 times larger, respectively, compared with the impacts from the external ownership model. The impact on employment is respectively 2.5 and 3.5 times larger.

I. INTRODUCTION

With RES legislation growing in popularity across the U.S., current economics favor an immense build-out of wind over the course of the next decade.[1] A great deal of analysis has

[*] Research support provided by The Otto Bremer Foundation and The West Central (Minnesota) Sustainable Development Partnership. The author thanks John Ihle, Dan Juhl, and Lowell Rasmussen for generously sharing data and experience. Research assistance was provided by Dugan Flanders and Thompson Clifford.

[†] kildegac@morris.umn.edu.

[1] Twenty-eight states and the District of Columbia have adopted Renewable Electricity Standards, while five more have adopted voluntary targets. (http://apps1.eere.energy.gov/states /maps/renewable_portfolio_states.cfm, last accessed June 21, 2010). See the [California] Renewable Electricity Transmission Initiative (2008) for a relative ranking of levelized renewable generation costs. NREL researchers recently estimated that in order to

focused on the location of best wind resources as well as on the technology and infrastructure that will be necessary to incorporate significant quantities of wind power into the generation mix.[2]

Public policy in the U.S. has been an influential if not decisive factor in shaping both the volume of wind development and also the specific business ownership structures under which development takes place.[3] Current policy, for example, strongly favors firms with sufficiently large tax liabilities and an established capital market presence.[4] Smaller pools of local capital, organized as partnerships, cooperatives, municipals, non-profits, or LLCs, have a more difficult time taking advantage of the full range of existing public policy incentives. A recent survey found that only 4% of U.S. wind capacity is locally owned, in stark contrast, for example, to the northern European figures of 83% and 45% in Denmark and Germany, respectively.[5]

This study investigates the regional economic impact consequences of local vs. external ownership in the developing wind industry. Specifically, we conduct our analysis at the level of the state of Minnesota.[6] A few prior non peer-reviewed studies have posed similar questions.[7] Our study includes some important enhancements that are not found in the previous literature: i) the cost data are actual and up-to-date, vendor-certified costs as of late 2009; ii) the power prices are consistent with power purchase agreements recently approved by the Minnesota Public Utilities Commission; iii) a fully-articulated financing model is included, complete with a tax equity partner and with supplementary bank financing; iv) the local ownership residuals (as well as the various O&M expenses) are inserted into a state-level input-output model to capture the effects of the project on the regional economy.

II. OWNERSHIP STRUCTURES

Capturing the federal tax incentives is a key element of project design, comprising as these do somewhere in the range of 30-40% of a project's overall revenue stream.[8] Bolinger and Wiser (2006) and Kildegaard and Myers-Kuykindall (2006) describe various ownership structures for local capital to participate in wind development, the most successful of which in fact capture the majority of the federal incentives.

---

reach a national goal of 20% of electricity production from wind power by the year 2030, annual installations of new capacity will have to grow by 2018 to over 16 gigawatts per year, which was roughly the entire installed capacity in the U.S., as of 2008 (Laxon, Hand, & Blair, 2008).

[2] One comprehensive example is the U.S. Department of Energy report 20% Windpower by 2030 (U.S. D.O.E., 2008)

[3] Kildegaard (2007). Bolinger and Wiser (2006).

[4] Bolinger and Wiser (2006), *inter alia.*

[5] Windustry: http://www.windustry.com/communitywind (last accessed June 21, 2012).

[6] "Community wind" is a recognized concept in Minnesota energy legislation. Policy developments relating to grid connections and tariffs are reasonably far along in the state.

[7] Galluzzo (2005), Grover (2005), Kildegaard and Myers-Kuykindall (2006), Lantz and Tegen (2008), Northwest Economic Associates (2003).

[8]The production tax credit (PTC) currently stands at $21/MWH, while the double declining depreciation allowance allows full write-down of the project's capital costs in just five years.

Harper et al. (2007) survey and evaluate a variety of financing structures for larger projects, again with the capture of federal incentives being a principal objective.

One common structure involves a tax equity partner with sufficient tax appetite to consume the entire federal incentive. Frequently an ownership "flip" is arranged at a pre-determined moment, for example upon the expiration of the production tax credit (after 10 years), or after the tax equity partner has achieved a pre-negotiated after-tax internal rate of return on its original investment. After the flip takes place, majority ownership rights to the remaining cash flow devolve back to the local equity group. Some variant of "flip" financing has been determined to be the most profitable business structure for wind development, under most circumstances.[9]

In the analysis that follows we formally model an ownership structure in which an equity partner captures most (99%) of the tax incentives (depreciation, production tax credits, interest deductions) over the first 10 years of the project. For years 11-20 the ownership shares flip to 5% for the tax equity investor and 95% for the local investor.[10]

The project's total debt financing is calibrated to enable the tax-motivated equity partner to achieve a targeted after-tax internal rate of return (IRR) on its 99% equity stake. The term on the debt is chosen to maintain debt service coverage requirements at acceptable levels. Since the flow of benefits to the local equity group is extremely uneven (see below) over the project's 20-year lifespan, we calculate and annuitize the net present value of these benefits.[11] The local ownership residuals of the project are subsequently entered into a state-wide input-output model, wherein the ultimate economic impacts are estimated and compared with projects employing exclusively non-local equity

III. PRO FORMA MODELING

A 20-year *pro forma* model was created for a 9.9 MW project (6 x 1.65), incorporating the actual capital, development, and O&M costs from a current project at the University of Minnesota. These costs are presented in Tables 1-2.

We construct two scenarios (*optimistic* and *pessimistic*), with parameters reported in Table 3. The key differences include, respectively:

1) interest rates on bank debt;
2) requisite after-tax internal rates of return;
3) discount rates applied to the ultimate net cash flows.

These differences in free parameters lead to some key differences in endogenous variables, including: 1) levels of overall debt financing in the project; 2) capital contributions

---

[9] Bolinger & Wiser (2006); Harper et al. (2007).

[10] 5% is the minimum IRS requirement for the tax partner's continued participation. See Harper et al. (2007), esp. pp.69-70.

[11] For example: if the after-tax net present value comes to $5 million, at a discount rate of 5%, this is equivalent to an 20-year annuity stream of $401,212.94 annually. In this case, we would use the annuity payment as a key input to the state-level input-output model.

on the part of the tax equity partner; 3) debt maturities.[12] A screen-shot of the *pro forma* cash flow sheet (years 1-7) is presented as Table 4.

Table 1. Upfront costs

Capital		Per Turbine	9.9 MW Project
	Turbines and towers [a]	-x-	-x-
	Land Transport [a]	-x-	-x-
	Capitalized warranty [a]	-x-	-x-
	Total Capital Costs	**$2,739,000**	**$16,436,000**
Construction			
	Gen. conditions mob/demob.	$37,000	$222,000
	Foundation, conduit & transfer pad	$153,000	$918,000
	Crane, rigging, erection labor, turbine electrical labor	$250,000	$1,500,000
	Electrical wiring from generator to transformer	$167,000	$1,002,000
	FAA obstruction light	$3,000	$18,000
	Earthwork	$15,000	$90,000
	Access road and exterior improvements	$60,000	$360,000
	Total Construction Costs	**$685,000**	**$4,110,000**
Utility Construction Costs			
	Transformer	$20,000	$120,000
	Substation/interconnection	$17,500	$105,000
	Total Utility Construction Costs	**$37,500**	**$225,000**
Misc. Development Costs			
	Engineering/Project Planning	$140,000	$840,000
	Geotechnical Exploration	$5,000	$30,000
	Permitting	$8,000	$48,000
	Independent Testing & Inspection	$7,500	$45,000
	Interconnection studies	$100,000	$600,000
	Legal & Finance	$25,000	$150,000
	Total Misc. Development Costs	**$285,500**	**$1,713,000**
Total Investment	**TOTAL**	**$3,747,000**	**$22,484,000**

[a] Itemized costs redacted to comply with vendor's contractual non-disclosure agreement.

Table 2. Operating expenses

Operating Expenses	Per Turbine	Total	Years
Land Leases	$3,500	$21,000	1-20
Service Agreement Renewal*	$25,000	$150,000	6-20
Liability & Force Majeure Insurance*	$3,000	$18,000	1-20
Equipment and Loss of Profit Insurance*	$11,000	$66,000	6-20
Power Use*	$1,250	$7,500	1-20
Accounting/Auditing*	$833	$5,000	1-20
Property Tax	$6,426	$38,557	1-20
Total Expenses, Pre-inflation (Years 1-5)	**$15,010**	**$90,057**	**1-5**
Total Expenses, Pre-inflation (years 6-20)	**$51,010**	**$306,057**	**6-20**

* 3% annual inflation rate modeled

---

[12] Debt maturities are set to ensure that the debt service coverage ratios never fall below 140%, and that the total local return never falls negative in any given year.

Table 3. Scenario assumptions

Parameter:	Scenario	
	Optimistic	*Pessimistic*
interest rate on bank debt	8%	10%
loan term (years)	12	15
after-tax IRR (tax investor)	8.5%	10%
discount rate	5%	6%
Parameter:	Scenario	
	Optimistic	*Pessimistic*
debt financing	36%	38%
equity financing	64%	62%
tax partner equity	$14.24m. (99%)	$13.89m. (99%)
local investor equity	$144k. (1%)	$140k. (1%)
	Parameter values constant across scenarios:	
project lifespan	20 years	
tax equity partner marginal tax rate[a]	40%	
local investor marginal tax rate[a]	35%	
production tax credit (PTC)	.021/kwh	
depreciation method	double declining balances (5 years)	
ownership "flip" after year	10	
pre- and post-flip shares: *tax equity partner* *local investor*	.99/.05 .01/.95	
power purchase agreement[b]	.068/kwh	
turbine efficiency[c]	39%	
turbine availability[c]	95%	
electricity sales	$2,184,924	

(a) Includes state and federal taxes.
(b) Based on power purchase agreements recently approved by the Minnesota Public Utilities Commission.
(c) Based on an average of four years of performance data for the Vestas V82 turbine installed on the campus of the University of Minnesota West Central Research and Outreach Center in Morris, Minnesota. This installation represents a class 4 wind resource, with average windspeeds at 50 meters between 7.0 and 7.5 meters per second. Much of the Great Plains, including western Minnesota, the Dakotas, Nebraska, and parts of Iowa, are categorized as class 4 or higher wind zones (U.S.D.O.E, 1986).

Figure 1 shows the annual after-tax, net profit share of the project accruing to the local ownership group. As with most flips, the local equity partner returns are much larger late than early.[13, 14] Both scenarios share a common trajectory. Year 11 the local investor is assigned

---

[13] In practice, there are various methods employed to advance the return to the local investors. These may include for example an expense item through which the tax-motivated partner pays a "management fee" to the local partners. Alternatively, an upfront development fee may be paid to the local investors. Each of these strategies

95% of the project's operating cash (and attendant profit taxes), but the remaining years of debt service (two and five years, in the *optimistic* and *pessimistic* scenarios, respectively) ensure that the corresponding *net* cash distribution is much lower. After the debt is retired (year 12 or 15), the project's net cash equals its operating cash. With the ownership shares now flipped, distributions to the local investor rise much higher for the duration of the project.

An alternative measure of the return on local equity (at various intervals of the investment horizon) is simply the internal rate of return (IRR), calculated on a rolling basis. Figure 2 illustrates the paths for each scenario, plotting the IRRs for years 2-20. The IRRs reach zero (indicating full recuperation, or "payback," of the initial outlay) after 5 and 5.5 years, for the *pessimistic* and *optimistic* scenarios, respectively. The IRRs reach the respective discount rates (6% and 5% respectively) between years 7 and 8 -- indicating a break-even after-tax net present value of zero. The IRRs grow sharply after year 10 (the flip year), and again after year 12 (*optimistic*) or 15 (*pessimistic*), at which point the debt is fully retired. At the project's conclusion, IRRs have reached 32% (*pessimistic*) and 37% (*optimistic*).

Table 4. *Pro Forma* screenshot (first seven years; optimistic scenario)

PPA Rate		$0.06800	$0.06800	$0.06800	$0.06800	$0.06800	$0.06800	$0.06800
Total Revenues		**$2,184,924**	**$2,184,924**	**$2,184,924**	**$2,184,924**	**$2,184,924**	**$2,184,924**	**$2,184,924**
Expenses								
Total Expenses		**$90,057**	**$90,972**	**$91,915**	**$92,886**	**$93,886**	**$94,915**	**$335,867**
Operating Cash		**$2,094,867**	**$2,093,952**	**$2,093,010**	**$2,092,039**	**$2,091,039**	**$2,090,009**	**$1,849,057**
Debt Service		(1,074,075)	(1,074,075)	(1,074,075)	(1,074,075)	(1,074,075)	(1,074,075)	(1,074,075)
Coverage Ratio		-1.95	-1.95	-1.95	-1.95	-1.95	-1.95	-1.72
Net Cash		$1,020,792	$1,019,877	$1,018,935	$1,017,964	$1,016,964	$1,015,934	$774,982
interest		$647,545	$613,423	$576,570	$536,770	$493,786	$447,363	$397,226
outstanding debt	8094312.72	$7,667,783	$7,207,130	$6,709,626	$6,172,321	$5,592,032	$4,965,319	$4,288,470
Taxable Income								
Operating Cash		2094866.966	2093951.966	2093009.516	2092038.792	2091038.947	2090009.106	1849057.259
Interest		-647545.018	-613422.622	-576570.435	-536770.072	-493785.681	-447362.538	-397225.544
Depreciation		-8993680.8	-5396208.48	-3237725.088	-2428293.816	-2428293.816		
TI		-7546358.852	-3915679.136	-1721286.007	-873025.096	-831040.55	1642646.568	1451831.715
Investor Return								
99% Investor		-7470895.263	-3876522.345	-1704073.147	-864294.845	-822730.145	1626220.102	1437313.398
Tax Rate		40%	40%	40%	40%	40%	40%	40%
Tax Savings		$2,988,358	$1,550,609	$681,629	$345,718	$329,092	($650,488)	($574,925)
Tax Credits		$668,009	$674,689	$681,435	$688,250	$695,132	$702,084	$709,105
Tot.taxSavings		$3,656,367	$2,225,298	$1,363,065	$1,033,968	$1,024,224	$51,596	$134,179
99% net cash		$1,010,584	$1,009,678	$1,008,745	$1,007,784	$1,006,794	$1,005,775	$767,232
Total Eq.Rtn	**$(14,245,990)**	**$4,666,951**	**$3,234,976**	**$2,371,810**	**$2,041,752**	**$2,031,019**	**$1,057,370**	**$901,412**
Local return								
1% Investor		$75,464	$39,157	$17,213	$8,730	$8,310	($16,426)	($14,518)
Tax Rate		0.35	0.35	0.35	0.35	0.35	0.35	0.35
Tax Savings		$26,412	$13,705	$6,025	$3,056	$2,909	($5,749)	($5,081)
Tax Credits		$6,748	$6,815	$6,883	$6,952	$7,022	$7,092	$7,163
Tot. TaxSavings		$33,160	$20,520	$12,908	$10,008	$9,930	$1,342	$2,081
1% Net Cash		$10,208	$10,199	$10,189	$10,180	$10,170	$10,159	$7,750
Total local Rt.	**$(143,899)**	**$43,368**	**$30,719**	**$23,097**	**$20,187**	**$20,100**	**$11,502**	**$9,831**

has specific legal and tax consequences, incorporation of which would add more heat than light to the analysis here. Presumably, financial instruments may be employed to shift the timing of cash flows in a straightforward manner.

[14] A significant portion of the early returns take the form of tax benefits, resulting from the favorable depreciation allowance ("double declining balances method"). We assume that the local investors have sufficient tax appetite to make full use of the depreciation and production tax credits accruing to their 1% of the project.

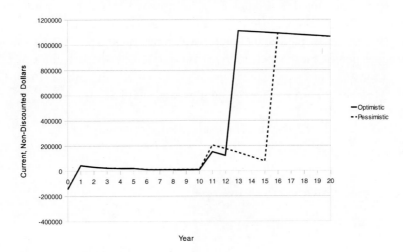

Figure 1.

In addition to the two scenarios described above, we also model a third ("*non-local*"), corresponding to the impacts of wind development under external corporate ownership. For the non-local scenario we assume identical O&M streams, however the pre-multiplier income stimulus is limited to the after-tax land-lease payments, since the project's residuals accrue externally to the region.

The next section considers the state-wide economic impact, when these direct value-added effects are added to O&M spending streams, and subsequently allowed to operate through realistic local spending multipliers.

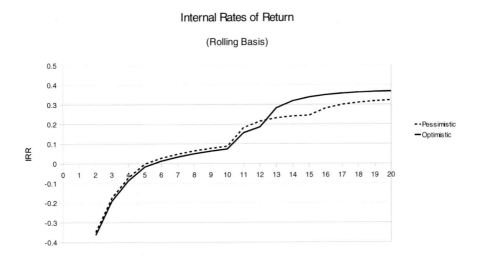

Figure 2.

In present value terms, discounting future after-tax net proceeds from the project, the two scenario yields are presented in Figure 3.[15] Under the *pessimistic* scenario, the after-tax present value of the project comes to $3.876m.; the *optimistic* scenario comes to $7.027m. For a better sense of the average annual revenue, Figure 4 annuitizes the totals from Figure 3 for a 20-year lifespan of the project, at the previously-given after-tax rates of returns. The *pessimistic* scenario produces the equivalent of a 20-year annuity payment of $338k, while the *optimistic* scenario produces a 20-year annuity payment of $563k.

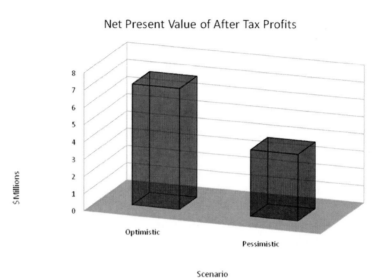

Figure 3.

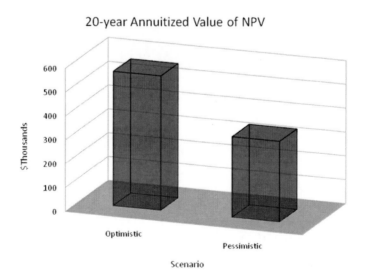

Figure 4.

---

[15] Since the annuity has a present value exactly equal to the local equity stake, subtracting the annuity payment from the gross, and then discounting the cash flow is identical to simply calculating the discounted present value of the gross cash flow, net of the initial equity investment.

IV. INPUT-OUTPUT ANALYSIS

In this section we use the outputs of the *pro forma* analysis as inputs to an economic impact analysis. Specifically, we plug the data from the *pro forma* analysis into a state-level (Minnesota) input-output analysis,[16] using data and software from the Minnesota IMPLAN Group.[17]

There are two distinct categories of impacts, having to do in the first instance with capital expenditures and construction, and in the second with on-going operational expenditures and local re-circulation of profits from the project. Our analysis is exclusively concerned with the latter, which are the lasting effects.

Since both the net revenue stream accruing to local ownership and the expenditure stream associated with on-going O&M are variable, the local economic impact will differ from year to year. In principle these streams could be smoothed over the 20-year project life-span, either through contractual terms between the partners or through financial arrangements entirely separate from the partnership. The specific timing of impacts is of less interest here than the average magnitude of these impacts, so we proceed by effectively annuitizing both the expenditure and the net revenue streams, and using these as a point of departure for the input-output model. Figure 5 presents the annuitized values of the O&M expenditure streams under each scenario,[18] including the breakdown according to expenditure category. These expenditure categories are subsequently mapped to the industry/commodity categories of the IMPLAN database, as reported in Table 5.

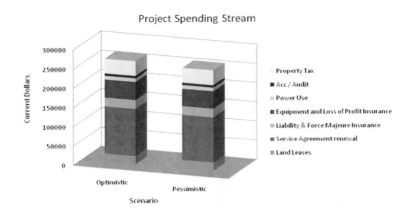

Figure 5.

---

[16] Miller and Blair (2009) is comprehensive reference for input-output modeling, including full development of social accounting matrices.

[17] IMPLAN Professional® Version 2.0. Our model uses the full social account matrix (SAM) specification, including all household institutions of final demand, along with *state and local government* (both *education* and *non-education* spending). The regional purchase coefficients are estimated econometrically by IMPLAN, and we have specified that the model choose "average" (as opposed to "max" or "first") values for the RPCs. All direct increments to household spending are assigned to the SAM institution "Households $100-$150k." As per Table 5, land leases are discounted by the tax rates from Table 3, before incrementing final demand. Project residuals, however, are already calculated after-tax, hence may be added without tax discounting to final demand.

[18] Note that the only difference between the scenarios with respect to O&M expenses is the discount rate applied to future cash flows. The pessimistic scenario models a higher discount rate, which on the expense side actually lowers the present value of future payments.

Table 5. O&M expenditures mapped to IMPLAN commodities/institutions

Pro Forma Expense	IMPLAN Commodity (Institution)
Land Leases	*Households $100-$150K [a] [disposable income]*
Service Agreement Renewal	*365 --- Commercial and Industrial Machinery Maintenance & Repair*
Liability and Force Majeure Insurance	*357 -- Insurance Carriers*
Equipment and Loss of Profit Insurance	*357 -- Insurance Carriers*
Power Use	*31 -- Electric Power*
Accounting/Auditing	*368 -- Accounting/Tax Preparation/Bookkeeping*
Property Tax	*12001 -- State & Local Government Non-Education (50%)* *12002 -- State & Local Government Education (50%)*
Net Return to Local Investors	*Households $100-$150K [b] [disposable income]*

[a] Land leases are discounted by the assumed tax rate (see Table 3) before being added as an increment to final demand.

[b] Net returns to local investors are already calculated after tax, and therefore need not be discounted before incrementing final demand.

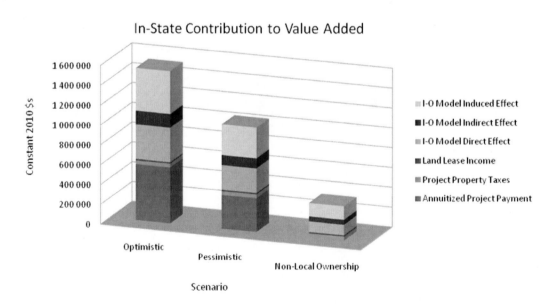

Figure 6.

Table 6. Comparative Economic Impacts

Variable:	Scenario:	Project's Direct Contribution			Input-Output Model "Multiplier" Effects				(Scenario)/ (Non-Local Scenario) Ratio
		Annuitized Disposable Income	*Project Property Tax Payments*	*Land Lease Income (After-Tax)*	*Direct*	*Indirect*	*Induced*	*Total*	
In-State Value Added	PESSIMISTIC	$338,000	$38,557	$13,650	$249,517	$101,300	$309,865	$1,050,889	3.1
...	OPTIMISTIC	$563,000	$38,557	$13,650	$348,737	$138,288	$431,328	$1,533,560	4.5
...	NON-LOCAL	$0	$38,557	$13,650	$106,092	$49,892	$135,866	$344,057	1.0
In-State Employment	PESSIMISTIC	-	-	-	3.2	1.2	4.4	8.8	2.5
...	OPTIMISTIC	-	-	-	4.7	1.6	6.1	12.4	3.5
...	NON-LOCAL	-	-	-	1.0	0.6	1.9	3.5	1.0

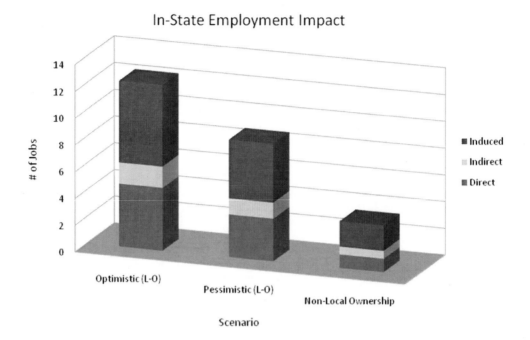

Figure 7.

Table 6 reports results from simulating the impact of each scenario on the two most obvious indicators: value added, and employment. Figures 6 and 7 present the findings graphically.[19] In terms of value added (including wages, profits, rents and taxes), the *optimistic* and *pessimistic* local ownership scenarios add an annual flow of $1.533m. and $1.05m., respectively, as compared with the outside ownership contribution of $344k. In terms of employment, the *optimistic* and *pessimistic* local ownership scenarios contributed an annual equivalent of 12.4 and 8.8 jobs, as compared with the outside ownership contribution of 3.5.

DISCUSSION

Much of the best on-shore wind resource in the U.S. is located in the central Great Plains.[20] It is an open question as to whether or not the local communities there will embrace and promote the anticipated wind development, or whether local resistance will prove too strong -- as for example it has with respect to on-shore wind development in England. In the latter case, extensive research has established that successful local resistance is strongly

---

[19] The IMPLAN model calculates three layers of effects: *direct*, *indirect*, and *induced*. The expenditure stimulus impacts the local economy *directly* through the purchase of local goods and services, and *indirectly* through the increased demand for intermediate inputs (necessary to meet this change in final demand). The re-spending of the income generated via direct and indirect effects *induces* another set of impacts, until the stimulus leaks out of the local economy via imports, taxes, and savings. For a detailed description see IMPLAN (2004).

[20] U.S. Department of Energy windmaps: http://www.windpoweringamerica.gov/wind_maps.asp (last accessed June 21, 2010).

related to an unacceptable balance between *local* costs and *local* benefits, despite a national policy that strongly promotes wind development.[21]

In the socially conservative region of the U.S. Great Plains it seems likely that political support for wind development traces more to the economic development potential that it represents than to questions of carbon emissions or other environmental considerations *per se*. Public policy provisions (such as tax depreciation allowances and production tax credits) that serve to discourage local ownership are apparently at direct cross purposes with public policy targets of greater development of wind energy.

The figures derived in the analysis above indicate that the residual stream has greater consequences for regional economic development than either the construction phase of the project or the ongoing O&M expenditures. Regional development and clean energy development are potentially important allies.

CONCLUSION

This study estimates the regional value added and employment consequences of local-versus outside-ownership of wind-powered electricity generation. We have employed a standard "flip" model for developing a modestly sized wind park in collaboration with a tax-motivated partner. In collaboration with industry participants we have modeled optimistic and pessimistic assumptions about financing terms, in an attempt to realistically bracket the range of possible outcomes. The net present value of the residuals (accruing to the local ownership group) of this model, along with the on-going O&M expenditures, were subsequently inserted into an input-output model for the State of Minnesota, in order to quantify the direct and indirect consequences of higher local incomes and spending.

The analysis concludes that local ownership yields regional value added between 3.1 times (*pessimistic*) and 4.5 times (*optimistic*) higher than a project developed by non-local ownership. The employment impacts are, respectively, 2.5 and 3.5 times greater in the two local-ownership scenarios, relative to the non-local ownership baseline.

One over-arching cautionary note must be sounded: the "flip" model of local ownership depends fundamentally on the existence of tax appetite on the part of the tax-equity partner, which in turn depends directly on corporate profits. The pool of available tax-equity financing, moving forward, will depend critically on the strength of the recovery from the 2008-2009 recession.

Publicly provided incentives are in most cases not only influential but actually decisive factors in determining the quantity and nature (including ownership structure) of wind power development. Regional policy-makers have direct influence over the tariffs for different categories of wind development as well as the non-financial terms of access to the grid. In the interest of regional development (as well as clean energy) they may wish to consider how to use those instruments to counterbalance a federal policy strongly biased against local ownership.

---

[21]Toke (2005); Devine-Wright (2005); Rogers et al. (2008); Hain et al. (2006).

REFERENCES

Bolinger, Mark, and Ryan Wiser (2006): "A Comparative Analysis of Business Structures Suitable for Farmer-Owned Wind Power Projects in the United States." *Energy Policy* V.34, No.14, 1750-1761.

Devine-Wright, P. (2005): "Beyond NIMBYism: towards an integrated framework for understanding public perceptions of wind energy." *Wind Energy* 8 (2), 125-139.

Galluzo, Teresa Welsh (2005): "Small Packages, Big Benefits: Economic Advantages of Local Wind Projects." Policy Brief, The Iowa Policy Project. http://www.iowapolicyproject.org/2005docs/050405-wind.pdf (last accessed August 3, 2009).

Grover, S. 2005. A Guidebook for Estimating the Local Economic Benefits of Small Wind Power Projects for Rural Counties in Washington State. Portland, Oregon. ECONorthwest. Retrieved from http://www.econw.com /pdf/wind_guidebook_011405.pdf

Hain, J.J., et al. (2005): "Additional renewable energy growth through small-scale community oriented energy policies." *Energy Policy* 33, 1199-1212.

Harper, John P., Matthew D. Karcher, and Mark Bolinger (2007): "Wind Project Financing Structures: A Review and Comparative Analysis." Ernest Orlando Lawrence Berkeley National Laboratory, LBNL-63434 (Sept.).

IMPLAN (2004): IMPLAN Pro Version 2, Analysis Guide. MIG, Inc. (Stillwater, MN).

Kildegaard, Arne, and Josephine Myers-Kuykindall (2006): "Community vs. Corporate Wind: Does it Matter Who Develops the Wind?" Research Report prepared in fulfillment of Institute for Renewable Energy and the Environment Grant No. SG P4c 2004.

Kildegaard (2007): "Renewable Electricity Policy in Minnesota." Chapter 13 in Perspectives on Minnesota Government and Politics, 6th ed., Pearson Custom Publishing, 2007.

Lantz, E., and S. Tegen (2008): "Variables Affecting Economic Development of Wind Energy." Conference Paper, National Renewable Energy Laboratory NREL/CP-500-43506 (July).

Laxson, A., M. Hand, and N. Blair. 2006. *High Wind Penetration Impact on U.S. Wind Manufacturing Capacity and Critical Resources.* NREL/TP-50040482. Golden, CO: NREL. http://www.nrel.gov/docs/fy07osti /40482.pdf.

Miller, Ronald E., and Peter D. Blair (2009): Input-Output Analysis: Foundations and Extensions, 2nd ed. Cambridge University Press.

Northwest Economic Associates (2003): A Methodology For Assessing The Economic Development Impacts Of Wind Power. Vancouver, Washington. Manuscript Prepared for National Wind Coordinating Committee. Retrieved from http://www.nationalwind.org/ publications /economic/econ_final_report.pdf

Renewable Electricity Transmission Initiative (2008): "Phase 1A Final Report." Prepared by Black and Veatch. http://www.energy.ca.gov/2008 publications/RETI-1000-2008-002/RETI-1000-2008-002-F.PDF (last accessed August 3rd, 2009).

Rogers, I., et al. (2008): "Public perceptions of opportunities for community-based renewable energy projects." *Energy Policy* 36, 4217-4226.

Toke, D. (2005): "Explaining wind power planning outcomes: some findings from a study in England and Wales." *Energy Policy* 33 (12), 1527-1539.

U.S. Department of Energy (1986): Wind Energy Resource Atlas of the United States. Available electronically at http://rredc.nrel.gov/wind/pubs/atlas/

U.S. Department of Energy (2008): 20% Windpower by 2030: Increasing Wind Energy's Contribution to U.S. Electricity Supply. Available electronically at http://www.osti.gov/bridge

INDEX

C

D

E

H

I

T

Y